Hard Bargains

Valerie Barwick

3P
PUBLISHING

Copyright © 3P Publishing
First published in 2019 in the UK

3P Publishing
C E C, London Road
Corby
NN17 5EU

A catalogue number for this book is available
from the British Library

ISBN 978-1-911559-75-7

Cover design: Marie-Louise O'Neill

I dedicate 'our late Mother's Memoirs' to my darling brother Robert. I thank him for leaving this manuscript to me in his will enabling me to do this publication.

Contents

The Barwick Family Tree

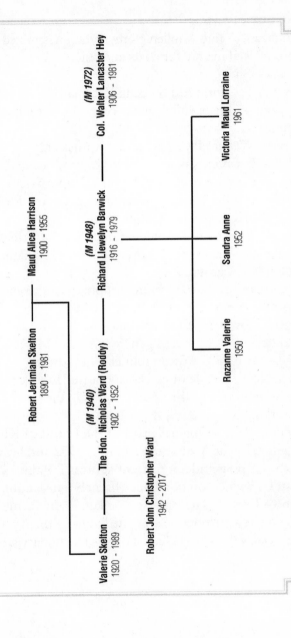

Valerie Skelton
1920 - 1989

(M 1940)
The Hon. Nicholas Ward (Roddy)
1902 - 1952

Robert John Christopher Ward
1942 - 2017

Robert Jerimiah Skelton
1890 - 1981

Maud Alice Harrison
1900 - 1955

(M 1948)
Richard Llewelyn Barwick
1916 - 1979

(M 1972)
Col. Walter Lancaster Hey
1906 - 1981

Rozanne Valerie
1950

Sandra Anne
1952

Victoria Maud Lorraine
1961

Glossary of terms:

Barathea – A fine woollen cloth, sometimes mixed with silk or cotton. Used mainly for coats and suits.

Bwana – Sir.

F.A N.Y.S. – First Aid Nursing Yeomanry's.

Fiefdom – Organization that is controlled by a dominate person or group.

Gertie – Walter Hey's pet name for Miss Hartley.

Gilgil – Town in Nakuru County, Kenya. Located between Naivasha and Nakuru. Population 18k approx.

Eddikins – Miss Hartley's (secretary) pet name for Walter Hey.

Kikuya – Kenya's largest ethnic tribe.

Kinsu – The child, the younger one (Kikuyu Tribe).

Macheria – Head servant boy, also a person's name.

Makundi – A group.

Memsahib – A married white or upper-class woman, often used as a respectful form of address by non-whites.

Msabu – (Swahili) White woman.

Munificence – Extremely generous.

Panga – A bladed African tool like a machete.

Pince Nez – A style of glasses supported without earpieces that pinch the bridge of the nose. Popular in the late 19th and 20th centuries.

Rudding Park – Originally part of the Forest of Knaresborough. Acquired by the Mackaness family in 1972 and heavily developed.

Sahib – A polite title or form of address for a man.

Salaud – Swine, son of a bitch (French translation).

Serbo – Croat – The language spoken in the former Yugoslavia.

Troglodyte – A loner – someone living by themselves or who is antisocial. Of reclusive habits or has reactionary attitudes.

INTRODUCTION

In the last days of the British Empire, there was one colony, Kenya, which gave unprecedented opportunities to people of diverse backgrounds and created a community whose overriding characteristic was confidence in their right to rule and to the possession of property.

Spanning three action-packed post-war decades of incredible glamour counterpointed with base squalor, the story is founded entirely on fact. It relates the history of a woman who must have been one of the last to regard marriage as a serious career and men as a legitimate source of income. An old-fashioned adventuress who lived on her wits, trading looks and personality for status and wealth, she struck exacting bargains. They were contracts that never worked to her genuine advantage causing her great suffering, which she endured with courage.

Her true personality remains a mystery. A maze of clues and conflicting opinions leave doubts echoing in the mind. Some said she was evil; others testify that she was the most wonderful woman they had met. The facts trace the shape of a life committed to financial survival at all costs, an appetite for luxury to rival Jackie Kennedy's and an ambition for her children, which led her to accept misery in the furtherance of their education.

In these days of Women's Liberation, the story is bound to shock. It is also guaranteed to raise questions concerning the nature of both prostitution and marriage itself, whether one loves the heroine or loathes her, it is impossible not to be awestruck by her energy and determination. One wonders too what these might have achieved had this life force been channelled into either of the two professions which were denied her.

In the end, her only triumph is to have outlived her tormentors and to learn at last that life without men is not only possible, but peaceful. She died comparatively young, burnt out by the acid of experience.

Publisher's note: Although Valerie wrote this account of her life she did work with a couple of ghost-writers, the last of which tried to turn this tale into a novel. Eventually it was decided to keep the book as a straight biography, therefore Valerie is referred to in the third person throughout.

PRIDE BEFORE THE FALL

Many families have a legend story. The one that is repeated time after time, at family gatherings from Christmas to summer barbecues. The legend of Valerie Ward began when she was very small and was told by Bobby Skelton, her father, who swears that it is true.

Barely able to walk Valerie one day disappeared from the family home. When her disappearance was discovered a major search was launched with members of the family and the servants calling Valerie's name for hour upon hour. When the first evening light fell upon the house the family feared the worst. Not for them the fears of a Western family, where panic would set in that she had been kidnapped. No, in Kenya, the fear was that Valerie had been taken by a wild animal. A sleepless night ensued and at first light the search resumed. This time further afield.

It bore no fruit and by the end of that second evening Bobby and Alice were certain that the little girl had perished. Again the search began at first light on the third day and after forty-eight hours the girl was found. This was not the end of the complication though. Far from it. They had found her with a lioness and three cubs and the rest of the pride. Valerie was dirty, but completely unharmed.

A miracle had taken place. It seemed, that because of her young age, she had been accepted by the lioness as another cub and been allowed to suckle at the teat of the mother. In this way she had been nourished and staved off dehydration. Safety with the lions had also protected her from other predators. Now they had a new dilemma. How to get Valerie away from the lions?

Guns were fired into the air and the pride dispersed leaving only the mother lion and one small cub who sat by Valerie's side. It was clear that any attempt to relieve Valerie from where she lay would

3

mean the loss of life for any would-be hero and possibly Valerie herself. The saviours were left with only one extremely sad choice and the lioness was shot dead. The magnificent beast that had protected Valerie was now sacrificed in her name.

The small cub also remained but was too traumatised to react in any other way except to yelp in a pathetic manner. Valerie was scooped up and taken back to her grateful parents. The cub was also taken home, where he stayed for a number of years. Valerie was always close to her feline brother. When the animal became a mature male lion, it was released into the wild where it thrived and found a mate.

The tale sounds too incredible to believe but Bobby repeated it often and always claimed it was true. What you will read in this tale of love and scandal will also often sound too incredible to believe. By the time you have finished you will have made up your own mind. What is true is that Valerie Ward would have an amazing life from lion to her ladyship.

PART ONE
Kenya to Rank Studios

CHAPTER ONE

After four and a half years in a Surrey boarding school, Valerie Skelton returned to her parents' Kenya home in 1938. At seventeen and a half, she was greatly changed. The Skeltons viewed her with a combination of delight and apprehension.

The stern-faced little girl with golden ringlets and a reputation for temper tantrums had emerged in the vibrant plumage of a privileged species. Her mother's friends saw nothing of the nerve-wearing childish obstinacy they remembered. A smoothly whirring engine of sexuality now powered Valerie's determination. Incandescence lit the fine fair complexion and her features had refined to an elfin loveliness. With the physical proportions of a ballerina and the same conscious grace, she captivated every eye.

It was a marvel, the matrons of Nairobi's most greenly-prestigious suburb told one another. Valerie Skelton had no right to those looks. Her mother, a valued neighbour, was pleasant enough looking, but no beauty. Mind you, they said, that's where Valerie's hyacinth eyes had come from, no mistake about that.

What Bobby Skelton's contribution can have been defied analysis. He was as plain a Yorkshire man as ever walked the streets of Bradford. A First World War Commission in the field had never obscured his simple origins. He was a solid man now, of course, as they reminded each other in the chintz-lavished drawing rooms of Muthaiga.

The General Manager of East Africa's largest timber merchant was a man of some consequence, shrewd too. The Skeltons were members of the Muthaiga Club, the acid test of social respectability.

Not to belong was to be invisible. However, never a breath of scandal had touched Valerie's family, except one, and that rebounded to their credit.

5

It was rumoured that some years ago, when thirteen-year-old Valerie was embarked at Mombasa to go to school in England, she had been placed in the care of a Kenyan policeman and his family, Adams by name. They had been going home on leave. It did not suit Alice very well that they were travelling third class, but the arrangement saved her the expense of paying Miss Ogden's passage as well. Everyone remembered Miss Ogden (Oggie), Valerie's nursery governess; it was a pity she had not spared her for this trip.

The voyage had appeared to pass without incident until Valerie was reported safely at St. Helen's School in Surrey, and then, if the story could be trusted, the Skeltons had received the most extraordinary letter from Miss Gray, the headmistress.

Apparently, those beastly Adams people had made poor little Valerie into a kind of slave. They had taken away all her lovely clothes and made her wear their own daughters' things. They had forced her to wash Mrs Adam's clothes and iron her frocks. Well, of course, Valerie, brought up in luxury as she had been, knew nothing of such work. What had not been done at home by the Kikuyu house boys had been done by the excellent Miss Ogden. Valerie had burned a garment with the iron, or so it seemed. That Adams man had taken off his belt and beaten the child quite brutally, until she bled.

It did not end there. Alice in her distress must have said one or two more things to her intimate friends than she intended. Valerie's guardians in England, it was mentioned, set the law in motion. There had been a Panel of Matrons appointed to enquire into that poor child's virginity, imagine!

Well now, it was remembered clearly, that the Adams had returned to Kenya after the expiry of their leave. Naturally, said the Muthaiga clique, they had been cold shouldered, and rightly so.

The strange thing was that the family had left again rather suddenly but Mr Adams did not go with them, nor was he heard of again.

6

Some did say, in the complete privacy of their own homes, that Bobby Skelton had lured Adams to a timber plantation in the Ngong Hills and shot him then and there. Bwana Skelton's native boys would have been extremely sympathetic in such a case, helpful too. Those pangas of theirs would make a neat job of disposing of the body, a pretty treat for the lions it stood to reason, didn't it? And so much nicer than dragging poor Valerie through the courts.

He was a fine fellow, Bob Skelton, the best. Adams had got what was coming to him, no question. And lovely little Valerie; such a tiny thing she was, had cost a life ... already.

Indeed, it was Valerie's intention to go as far as she could. Like every artist, she wished the work of her hands to be known and appreciated by as wide an audience as possible. Her raw material, which was herself, was something she continued to work on with relentless dedication.

"What is wrong?" she asked her best friend, "with wanting to be perfect? It's just stupid to make less of yourself than you could."

Ann MacMaster could not refute this icy logic. A languorous brunette, temperamentally inclined to adoration, she was the perfect foil for Valerie's scintillating, imperious blondeness. They went everywhere together. Valerie glittered and Ann softly glowed, a most elegant composition of light and tone.

Learning to type and do shorthand at Nairobi's Victory Secretarial College, and later, after war broke out in the F.A.N.Y.S., they were side by side. They joined the Nairobi Players and appeared in amateur productions together at the Theatre Royal. Ann's roles, unlike Valerie's, were always minor.

Every beauty worth their name knows the value of a good-looking friend and works hard to keep her friendly. Valerie succeeded in this and when she went off to put on a show for the troops massing in Mombasa, she wrote almost daily to Ann.

"Because," as Valerie said, "boys come and go but a girlfriend is for keeps."

7

Valerie was good at both making and keeping friends. Every relationship was developed with care and then rigorously maintained. A warmly-worded note, a telegram promptly sent, or a thoughtful invitation returned kindness for kindness with mathematical inevitability. No lady-in-waiting worked with more diligence for a Royal mistress than Valerie worked for herself. Valerie returned from school, able to conjure plaintive gaiety from the ukulele.

Valerie longed to stand on the high ground, on the snow-capped peaks of human existence. She saw what she wanted out of life. She had worked hard to deserve it and she planned to have it. Every tiny talent had been burnished. She sang, she played, she danced and acted tolerably well, her stage presence was remarkable. Valerie sensibly nipped these musings in the bud, first things must come first.

That meant marriage. As good a marriage as her looks and talent had prepared her for, or the best obtainable. It was not to be some boy and girl affair of scrimping and saving, of going to an office and hoping for promotion on the one side, of baking cakes and worrying silently on the other. Marriage was very large in Valerie's imagination as a broad, well-furnished stage. She would write the play herself, choosing the right backdrop was her serious, if unspoken business.

Her openly-avowed objective was to make life pleasant for others. Functioning in that womanly role, she acquired a sure executive touch. Parties, picnics, charades and safaris all happened memorably at her behest. Under her parents' roof, she displayed her burgeoning gifts as a hostess. Brick on brick, she built her own legend.

Perhaps her taste was not innately good, but she taught herself about beauty from the ground up. Concerning her own person, she was never wrong. She chose and wore her clothes with a passionate virtuosity. Her love of animals was sincere, in them she found a purity that art, even her own, could not imitate.

The Muthaiga Club's jaded playboys were reminded of the days when their Happy Valley had been peopled with cavorting gods and goddesses. Valerie was not touched with that divine madness, her size four feet, whilst surely not of clay took care to remain upon the earth. It was a wonder, therefore, when she married the Earl of Dudley's penniless younger brother, the Hon. Nicholas Robert Victor Gerald Ward. Roddy, to his friends.

****

An officer in the King's African Rifles, Roddy was almost eighteen years older than Valerie, divorced and even worse, tattooed. Mrs Skelton regarded him with the utmost disfavour. He was well over six foot tall, decidedly bulky and garnished with copious amounts of black hair. He would keep sending Valerie bouquets of red roses whenever she performed on stage and sometimes when she didn't. Whilst it remained the hopeless courtship of 'Beauty' by the 'Beast', there was nothing to be feared.

Roddy was romantic about small women, as big men often are. Valerie was too good for him, he thought, she would allow him to serve her but not to come too close. In his own honest opinion, he was too old, too big, too clumsy and too coarsened by the world to be fit to address the ethereal object of his dreams. Adding to that the fact that his farm at Thompson's Falls was mortgaged to the hilt, Roddy was grateful simply to count himself amongst her friends. He had nothing whatever to offer any woman, least of all the fragile Valerie. She was a woman who would need protecting.

There was a certain pathos in the way his large brown eyes would follow her around. Even the ever-watchful Alice sometimes softened when she saw the agony of unspoken love bleeding from his glance, but she hardened her heart. Not only was there no money, there were rumours of debts, it would never do.

9

Valerie saw the matter quite differently. Roddy had certain significant advantages not shared by her younger escorts. He exuded maleness like a bull elephant. She trailed her scent and flew from him … waited and ran again, in the age-old pantomime of maidenly desire. Roddy endured the teasing stolidly. He knew his duty. It was to say nothing and do nothing that might offend her exquisite delicacy. When they talked, he took care to behave as a friend should do, never once proposing himself as a lover. He was merely an admirer, Valerie was exasperated.

For her, Roddy had a hold on that higher, wider world she craved. Once he had been A.D.C. to His Royal Highness, The Prince of Wales, the one who abdicated in 1936. He was himself a man nobly born. Roddy's three thousand acres of rich, pepper-smelling red earth represented riches besides which, rupees and pounds sterling were contemptible.

Valerie did not understand about mortgages or capital borrowings. When her own parents' flax plantation at Kericho had failed, she had been only four years old. They had left because of the locusts, more than that she had not needed to know, but deep down, she had always regretted that failure to hold fast to the land. It gave a man the only irrefutable, unlosable dignity, did land. What more, Valerie asked herself, could a girl want? At least to begin with.

That Roddy should propose to her was a desirable conclusion but not essential. To yearn for the prize before it was granted would be a foolish depletion of the spirits, and a lowering of pride.

As she lay, sometimes sleepless in her muslin-frilled bedroom, Valerie considered the alternatives. There were many. As the Italian threat to Kenya's northern borders increased, the Muthaiga Club opened its exclusive portals to an ever-increasing number of officers, some were married, of course, and others were common.

The permanent members were more enticing. Joss Hay, the Earl of Erroll was free, his second wife had died of neglect and drugs and although Joss now lived in Muthaiga, the better to pursue his wartime administrative duties, his Moroccan style castle, the mysterious Djinn Palace, lay empty on the shores of Lake Naivasha.

Valerie knew she had no chance with him. Of all the men in the Muthaiga set, he had never left one of those notes in her Club pigeonhole. That fat bitch Diana Delves Broughton had got her long, painted hooks into him. Fighting a blind infatuation was work fit only for a fool.

There was Lizzie Lezard, of course, a dark, chaotic man, he had been sent to the colonies by his wife. He was fun and a frequent tennis partner, but he gambled and was broke. Lizzie liked women; he liked them altogether too much. He had no property of his own anywhere, sticking like a bur to those who had, it was not Valerie's ambition to be married to a playboy; she could do better.

Each time she turned these things over in her mind, Valerie found Roddy more and more pleasing. True, he drank too much and became uproarious in public, but anybody who was anybody, did, didn't they? It was clear that Roddy would suit her best. He must be brought swiftly to the point. All successful women married before they were twenty. Valerie did not wish to be left behind.

Roddy's proposal was knocked from him by a rabbit punch of fate.

A map reference brought Valerie's picnic guests to a picturesque hollow in the Muthaiga Hills. Nobody owned this precise spot and no house overlooked it. It was one of a very few spaces left wild in this district of suburban residences with spacious, manicured grounds. Here, you could almost believe you were up country. There was a smell of pine resin and a low, insistent buzz of insects.

It was a perfect place for a private play reading. Since the rains were due, it would also be one of the last opportunities to eat out of doors before the long, wet months set in.

The Skelton's head boy had spread oriental rugs with baskets of food and drink on the short, dry grass. "You go home now," Valerie addressed the boy when everything was to her satisfaction. "We'll wait on ourselves and bring the things back in the cars." She spoke in Swahili, in that peremptory tone for which women in the colonies were noted.

The grizzled Kikuyu nodded his assent gracefully and withdrew. Baba Valerie would be safe enough with two gentlemen, Ward Sahb and the new young magistrate.

The point of having this little rehearsal was twofold. Donal had lately arrived in Kenya and had joined the Nairobi Players. He had been given a part in *Blithe Spirit* opposite Valerie herself. His audition reading had not been lively enough; he would need a lot more work. Roddy could read the intervening lines and giving them both a picnic lunch would keep Roddy's booming voice out of earshot and away from her mother's withering glances. Alice made the poor boy nervous. Nobody, Valerie reasoned, could get themselves into the frame of mind to propose if they were nervous.

"And then you come in, Donal. Upstage left, so that means … No, Shanghai, I'll play with you in a minute." Valerie removed the damp leather ball which the Pekingese had dropped hopefully into her lap. Crossly, the little dog shook out his dark flounces and bustled away to snap at dragonflies.

"Oh yes. I'm sorry. You mean that at that point I couldn't possibly see you, so I must be talking to myself."

"Or Roddy off stage, that would work don't you think?"

Valerie went on laying the groundwork of Donal's performance with tireless attention to detail.

12

Roddy's own attention was distracted. The tones of her voice, like the middle register of a harpsichord, shivered over his nerve ends. She was beautiful. He watched her, sitting on the Bokhara rug her slim legs were tucked under her with cat-like neatness. Her polished brown arms moved in swift, emphatic gestures, the fingers of both hands spread wide and taut. It never crossed his mind that any of this could be for him.

Valerie felt his eyes on her, warm and caressing. The intense blue of her linen frock was a success she thought. It looked well against the soft, brick red tones of the rug and deepened the colour of her eyes. Valerie kept on talking to the earnestly attentive Donal while the edge of her mind was occupied with Roddy. When would he do something … or say something?

"That's it, Val, I've had it for today. You're a slave driver!" Donal threw the book onto the rug and lay back laughing. "Anyone would think we were going to get paid for this. I'll work on it, I promise."

"All right, I'll let you off for now, but the thing is, if you don't do it exactly as if you were being paid for it, it isn't worth doing at all." Valerie leaned on her elbow beside Donal. The movement succeeded in giving Roddy a stab of grief at her nearness to the other man.

"But remember, I want us to look good together by the first proper rehearsal, word perfect, no books at all. You can't practise stage craft clumping about with a book in your hand, isn't that true, Roddy?"

"Yes, ma'am," Roddy saluted bareheaded. "I'll make sure he learns the entire text by next Tuesday or fall on my sword."

"Any beer left?" Donal asked lazily. "Thank God I don't have a sword to fall on."

"There's some wine," Roddy held up the bottle questioningly. "You Val?"

Valerie waved her refusal, dropping her hand automatically to the rug beside her. She had expected to feel the Pekingese's small, silken body. Surprised by the empty space, she looked around.

Shanghai sometimes went off by himself but never very far and not for long. Now she realised she had not seen him for the past half an hour. She sat up suddenly and looked around with a sensation of rising panic.

"Shanghai! Where is he? Shanghai!"

"Over there look," Roddy gestured to a spot some thirty feet away where a mountain stream chattered innocently over its rocks and pebbles. They had forded it earlier on slippery stepping stones bringing the rugs and picnic baskets down from the cars

"He's fine," Donal confirmed cheerfully.

Instinctively, Valerie knew the dog was in some sort of distress, it was standing transfixed. As far as she could tell, its eyes were fastened on a thicket of thorn bushes, which lined the far side of the stream. The leaves moved, rattling like paper in the dry breeze. The dog was quivering, he began to whimper.

The men continued to talk indifferently.

"Shut up! Both of you."

Valerie rounded on the men fiercely. Donal had only been in the country three months but there was no excuse for Roddy. They looked at her in blank astonishment.

"Look!"

She spoke under her breath. She pointed directly ahead into the moving bushes. Shanghai was squealing in terror. A leopard's head had appeared.

"Oh my God!" Roddy's whispered expletive was almost inaudible.

Donal was silent and white faced. He just wished the dog would be quiet. His mind raced with everything he'd ever heard or read about leopards. The fastest species on land, forty miles an hour, they could jump. The stream was … what? Seven feet wide, no more, a leopard wouldn't even need to think about it.

Roddy's mind too was erupting with mixed emotions. He always kept a shotgun in the car, but he couldn't get to it. The great cat's head shone out at him, what a trophy its hide would have made. It would probably take the dog and be off.

Incredulously, he watched it happen; he should have realised and held on to her. Valerie had risen to her feet. He wanted to pull her back, but in a rational part of his brain he knew it was too late, futile, the leopard had seen her now.

Valerie went on until she reached the screaming dog. She bent down, picked it up, and then ran with it across the stepping stones only feet from where the leopard stood.

Her light, smooth-soled pumps slithered on the stones as Roddy looked away. She was dead or worse. If only he had a revolver, he could have done something.

Roddy made himself look up, he and Donal edged closer together on the rug. Their eyes cleaving to the blue figure scrambling up the farther bank, talk about courage. The dog under her right arm seemed inert, at least it was silent. The leopard's face was no longer visible, it had withdrawn the moment Valerie had seized Shanghai. It would be watching her now - gathering its huge strength - it had plenty of time. Nothing happened. Valerie reached the top of the bank; she opened the car door and got in.

"Thank God," Roddy dropped his face into his hands with relief. "At least I don't have to watch that happen."

"I don't want to appear selfish, Ward, but what about us?" Donal enquired with as much sangfroid as he could muster. "Now that the hors d'oeuvre and the entree have escaped, it might fancy moving direct to the main course."

"Look there," Roddy touched the younger man on the arm. A ripple of movement in the bushes told its own story. The leopard was moving away downstream. "Come on, quick and quiet, straight across and up the bank."

They found her sitting in the back of her mother's saloon. She was nursing the shocked Shanghai and smiling.

"Couple of slow coaches you two are. Shanghai and I have been waiting ages. Oh, I say, didn't you bring the picnic things? Mummie will be quite waxy."

Donal went back to his own car saying he would meet them for dinner at the Club. He was very badly shaken.

Roddy got into the back of the car beside Valerie, the adrenalin flowing away from him.

"I thought you'd both had it, Val. You shouldn't have."

"Leave Shanghai? You must be mad. Anyway, we're both hungry now. Aren't you going to give me dinner at the Club? The leopard was so beautiful, wasn't it? I'm glad you couldn't shoot it."

Valerie knew quite well that the creature might have ripped the face from her skull, but when danger was present, you had no time for fear.

When it was past, you did not refer to it. Good form, that was important.

In his relief and sudden, overwhelming tiredness, Roddy's speech was unguarded.

"Oh Val, darling. If only I was just ten years younger."

"Why do you have to be ten years younger?" Valerie was looking at him curiously.

Roddy found he had asked Valerie Skelton to marry him. She accepted him before he could apologise.

****

Unsurprisingly, the Skeltons forbade the engagement.

Valerie was much too young to marry Roddy; it had not been necessary to say more than that. A cigar in Bobby's study and a companionable tour around the lawns had been enough to crush the delirious lark of hope that had sprung in the big man's soul.

"It's no good, Val," he told her. "They're against me. So, unless you'll run away with me." It was only a feeble joke, but Valerie was in no mood for humour. Elopement was messy, it offended her sense of order.

"What a fool you are, darling. Just leave everything to me. We'll be married here in Nairobi very respectably before too long, you'll see." The Skeltons, however, remained adamant.

Roddy Ward, they said in a series of angry interviews with their daughter, had nothing to offer. He was an acceptable guest, just, but as a son-in-law, unthinkable. His finances were in disarray, his house was little more than a native hut, his record with women was poor and his so-called position in the world was highly questionable.

The last jibe resulted from a slip of Valerie's own. She had told her mother that Roddy's stepmother was Gertie Millar, a former music-hall artist. That clinched it. The Ward family were impossible. Countess or not, did Valerie seriously want a chorus girl for a step-mother-in-law? Valerie did, and was undeterred.

"I shall write every day," she told Roddy when he left Muthaiga to rejoin his regiment. "And you must reply at least once a week. Don't worry about my parents, they'll come around, you'll see. What kind of a girl would I be if I couldn't manage my own mother and father?"

She stood on her toes, grasping the lapels of his service-dress tunic as he leaned down to kiss her. Her fragrance, like a drift of spring flowers intoxicated him.

"Oh Val."

Roddy rarely got much further than that in the early days. Unlike Valerie, he was slow to give expression to his hopes and fears.

"Trust me. If they hold out six months, I'll be surprised."

Valerie's prediction proved correct. It took very little really.

Roddy's letters arrived with commendable regularity. They told of the progress of the campaign in Eritrea, of his plans to set up business running shooting safaris for European tourists after the war and of his undying devotion. Ann was shown the letters.

"Oh, he does love you, Val. Will you wait for him? They say the course of true love never runs smooth."

She and Valerie generally talked in clichés. Privately, Valerie had no intention of waiting for anything. The right moment would present itself and Valerie, with her unerring sense of the dramatic was confident of recognising it.

17

The expected opportunity came some weeks later. A letter arrived one day from Roddy, which described the horrific death of a young friend with whom Valerie had often built tree houses in the garden. His head had been blown off by an Italian shell. Valerie wept over the letter at breakfast with the perfect composure that belongs to those who know they cry beautifully.

Mrs Skelton sent the servants away and indicated impatiently, that her husband should also busy himself elsewhere. Roddy Ward had found somebody else. Alice felt a rush of maternal compassion combined with thankfulness. Poor little Valerie jilted by the 'Beast'. It was a good thing there had been no real or official engagement

"Show me, darling. Your father will want him horsewhipped." Valerie handed her the letter wordlessly

"Oh, poor Rob Street, how truly dreadful!" Alice scanned the closely-written sheets with horror. "I simply cannot believe it!" Reading further, Alice perceived how little she had known Roddy Ward. Clumsy and loud, he might be, abjectly and poetically in love, he most certainly was.

Mrs Skelton tapped the blade of her knife thoughtfully on the china plate. Her own husband had not seemed a very sound investment at first.

His gas-damaged lungs and shell-shocked stammer had not recommended him to her parents in that long-ago war when she had married.

Bobby Skelton was startled to find that his policy regarding Val's engagement had changed. Alice always knew best about things like that. A letter was written at once to Roddy. He was to come as soon as he could get leave to discuss his prospects.

That evening, the Skeltons dined at the Club. The mood was one of conciliation and muted celebration. Many friends greeted them. Nobody was told the news, but somehow, they all heard it. Valerie effervesced, drawing a peacock train of admiring eyes after her.

"A taking little thing," Joss Hay muttered to his companions. "Ward's done better than he'd a right to expect."

Valerie circled the room in shell pink chiffon, graciously triumphant. She would be married at nineteen.

CHAPTER TWO

When the long rains came, Roddy and Valerie were married in the District Commissioner's office in Nairobi. Lizzie Lezard was best man, which lent the occasion a fashionable, if raffish touch.

As it was wartime and there were too few brother officers available to cross their swords for the newlyweds, a quiet reception at home was followed by a sundowner at Torr's hotel the following evening. This launched the new Honourable Mrs Roddy Ward on her career as a wife.

Most of the colony's great names were represented. Delamere, Carberry and Scott. Joss Hay did not come. If Valerie was a little piqued by this neglect, she kept it to herself. No doubt Diana Delves Broughton had found some way of diverting him; she would not like to play second fiddle, even to a bride.

Valerie tossed her bouquet of yellow rosebuds to Ann who caught them fair and square. Her affair with a South African settler was progressing well enough, but slowly.

'There you are, darling!' Valerie trilled. "It will be you next didn't I say so? If only you're as happy as me.

That was Valerie all over, they said as the champagne frothed and flowed. Never too taken up with herself to think of others, that Afrikaner fellow Jan, was that his name? He'd have to marry Ann MacMaster now, darling Val had made that pretty plain.

Ann blushed miserably and smiled up at her friend forgivingly. Poor Val always meant so well.

Unable to rejoice, Alice Skelton resigned herself to dignified acceptance. At least the bridegroom had set his affairs plainly before his new father-in-law. There were some debts, it was true, but only the kind which burdened every undercapitalised farmer.

Roddy's land was fertile, and the bank borrowings would amortise slowly as time, self-denial and sustained effort began to make their mark. Roddy's absence from the farm was an unavoidable evil of the war. No bank would foreclose on an officer fighting for his country.

Bobby Skelton took a kinder view of Roddy and his circumstances than would his wife, had she been presented with the same figures. A kind of masculine fellow feeling, born of Skelton's own struggles to survive and prosper in the colony inclined him to leniency.

"See here, Ward, you'd better pay off these bits of bill, your Club subscription and so forth, no sense in having gossip about something and nothing. I'll not have my daughter embarrassed, or my wife either. If you're ever stuck, you'd best come to me."

"I know I don't deserve her, sir, but no man will work harder for Valerie than I intend to." Roddy was very well brought up; he knew exactly what to say

After that private conversation, Roddy's presents to his bride seemed extremely lavish, a large diamond solitaire and a brand new, dark blue Buick.

Unique, the only one in Kenya, Valerie's parents stilled their unease. It was hardly their affair and as for Valerie, she was entranced by these new possessions. To spoil her pleasure with meanly niggling doubts was beyond anybody's courage.

"You must set Roddy an example, darling, and not spend too much. In a couple of years, the pair of you should be better placed, so much depends on you. Your clothes should last you well enough." Alice concluded her homily complacently.

The sumptuous trousseau, her own gift had been delivered in trunks to the mud and wattle homestead at Thompson's Falls the day before. Valerie was to start married life in the proper manner. Alice had no sympathy with rusticity and an understandable cynicism when it came to agriculture.

Valerie, on the other hand was torn between the image of herself as a landowner's wife in the grand, seigneurial sense and that of a pioneer. Either interpretation of her new role was credible, although, of course, that was not the kind of thing you talked about, or even noticed yourself thinking about. Distinguished behaviour involved a degree of mannerly self-delusion.

Valerie lay awake in the crook of Roddy's arm. He slept on his back snoring intermittently. Now and again in the darkness, droplets of water splashed into buckets and empty kerosene tins distributed around the bedroom. The thatch leaked. Small creatures scurried and squeaked in the eaves. Roddy was going away tomorrow, up country, back to the regiment. There had only been a few days at the farm for a honeymoon. She would get the roof repaired while he was away. So many things needed doing.

She had got this huge, active laughing man who was somebody after all, and he had got possession of her. Valerie did not doubt the value of her self-bestowal, why should she?

She had promised to love him and stick to him. Nobody was ever too precise about what love amounted to. It was entirely natural to suppose that it meant desire in the first place followed by a determination to preserve and improve the desired object once acquired. Valerie, in the privacy of her mind, thought as honestly as she could about her contract with Roddy. Sometimes good taste must be allowed to lapse, though it was rare with her, in the interests of clarity.

Along with Roddy came co-suzerainty over a slice of paradise on the roof of Africa. Thompson's Falls was a rustic idyll. When the rain mist cleared, the mountains emerged. Glistening in their everlasting snows, they ringed the miles of rolling downland like smiling teeth, with green tongues of cedar forest snaking down to the Rift Valley below. African rollers careened in ecstasy above the house, animated sapphires spinning on the breeze. At night, the air sparkled with frost and by morning, the grass glittered with diamond drops of dew.

It was, as Valerie said, 'breath-taking'. Roddy was pleased she liked the place because it was a long way from the relative sophistication of Muthaiga. She was, he said, his 'brave, clever girl'.

Where the rich red earth was broken by the plough, its sharp, spicy smell flew up to bewitch the senses. In the uncleared forest fringes, bushbucks fled like graceful ghosts on silent hooves while monkeys gossiped overhead. Leopards, in their dark dappled cunning, prowled for most part unseen. Unfortunately, when they or any other animal of interest was seen, Roddy shot them. That was something over which they were unable to agree.

"We can't, mustn't go on like this, darling. There'll be none of these beautiful creatures left if people like us don't take a stand. You should start camera safaris after the war. All this wanton killing and cruelty."

"You're too soft-hearted, Val," Roddy would interrupt her. "You're a farmer's wife now. A lot of these beautiful creatures, as you call them, are vermin. And when they're not, they're meat. Anyway," Roddy rounded off his argument. "I have to keep the native village sweet, a carcass for the pot, when I can get it, puts a spring in their idle black feet." To Valerie, this was the wholly unacceptable face of rural life. It pained her deeply that her husband had no community of feeling with her over this, but he loved her, and she would change him.

The new life had other, social delights. It would be said later that the Kenyan white settlers would drive five miles for a cocktail. In fact, they would drive fifty. Roddy had driven Valerie the length and breadth of Aberdare Mountains seeking out friends to whom she should, as his bride be known. They were called the 'Happy Valley Crowd' and discreetly anxious to perpetuate their own myth. War or no war, there was a great deal of the old 'devil may care' attitude among them and Roddy's new wife was scrutinised closely for her potential as a neighbour.

Of course, the Olympian, orgiastic days of cocaine-powered frolics were a memory now. Wives were largely faithful these days. Very nearly sober, too. This little wife of Ward's would be faithful, they could all see that.

Detailed reactions were diverse.

"Rather pleased with herself, I'd say."

"Well, she's a right to be. She's got herself a fine big fellow and she's a pretty girl," the easy-going countered.

Veranda doors would slam before Valerie's Buick was fairly out of sight. Male contemplation continued outside as the sun sank. Valerie and her visits were not easily put aside.

"Well," snapped one wife as she watched the Buick grow smaller in the distance, "She's not half as lyrical as she thinks she is."

"I don't know," muttered that particular husband as he signed the Kikuyu boy to pour another gin. "To me she seems like the last rose of summer. All that happiness … a forecast of doom."

Valerie, quick to spot a nuance, had a fair idea of what was said about her. She snapped her fingers, there was so much jealousy.

In the morning, Roddy left. The farewell was tenderly acrimonious. The honeymoon was over, and the marriage started.

"Do try to keep your drinking down, my darling. It really isn't good for you, you know. I want you fit and healthy for the farm … and me!"

Roddy had never been so adroitly nagged. He gave his promise of sobriety somewhat confused as to whether his wife wished to promote the health of a farm labourer or her lover. He decided to rest content with the implied compliment to his prowess. He kissed her and Shanghai's fluffily frowning brow as the dog was held out to him.

"What shall I do about paying the men and the servants?"

"Nothing, my sweet, we have squatter herdsmen here you know, it doesn't work on the wage labour system. I'll attend to it when I get back, there's time enough." Roddy glossed over the subject quickly.

"You just carry on getting used to the place. I hope you won't be bored. Go back to Muthaiga if you get lonely. Kiwainu's quite used to running things. I'll get leave again as soon as I can but I'm afraid it'll be weeks and weeks. Write, won't you."

"In the meantime," Valerie informed Roddy's Kikuyu houseboy, "I shall take my ride. Later you can help me get all of these awful skins off the walls," Valerie's eyes swept the trophy-decorated living room. Those stripes, Zebra skins, so loud, she hated it. It was like a charnel house; Roddy was not a bachelor any longer. Chintz and watercolours ... she would arrange a shopping trip to Nairobi.

"Yes Msabu." The boy received his orders with outward passivity. He was not sure he wanted to interfere with Bwana's hunting trophies. Nothing had been said. He might be angry, but Msabu ... she *would* be obeyed

"And tell Makundi to pull himself together and make out some respectable menus. I have a friend visiting next week," Ann MacMaster was coming to keep her company for a day or two the following week, her first houseguest. Valerie addressed Macheria in staccato Swahili tones.

Makundi was the cook. He functioned in varying degrees of alcoholic intoxication. His work was correspondingly slipshod, and his repertoire limited. Valerie could not cook herself. It was difficult to know how to improve Makundi, but that was Macheria's business, he was the head boy.

Valerie rode every morning around the Ward domain. Three thousand acres was not a vast area by Kenya standards. The long-horned cattle, which were Roddy's principal investment, moved moodily against the hillsides, growing fat on the greening grassland. In the Kikuyu Village of round, thatched hut, the smoke billowed from cooking fires, while the women squatted in the doorways, watching the white man's bride pass by. Shaven-headed maids nudged each other and giggled as they pounded grain. Msabu Ward was very small, and Bwana Ward was very big, she had dignity. With the women, at least, Valerie had scored a point.

25

The men tended the maize fields they cultivated in part exchange for herding their master's cattle. Their greetings were desultory, their eyes full of speculation. "Will the harvest be good?" Valerie asked a pewter-haired old man in Swahili. The people here were strangely silent. The old man leaned on a staff and regarded her unsmilingly. It was Kiwainu, the man. "It will need to be," he answered finally.

Chilled, Valerie urged her pony to a canter. What was the matter with him? She'd asked a civil, friendly question and he'd been almost rude; Roddy had said that Kiwainu was always belly aching about something or other. Now she came to think of it, Roddy had kept her away from the native village, silly of him, because she was good with natives.

Valerie was fermenting plans. Why should they not clear some more land and grow pyrethrum? There was a ready sale for the crop. Insecticide manufacturers used it. Roddy, who was a cattleman, had not seemed enthusiastic at the suggestion.

But Valerie was determined to make a contribution to their future. Kiwainu would have to spare some men for the work of clearing. First, she must get him on her side. An opportunity to advance her relationship with the native village came unexpectedly.

Kiwainu paid her a visit of ceremony. He wore a cloak of blue-dyed monkey furs and approached the house with immense hauteur. Watching from a window, Valerie felt certain she was to be put to some test. Macheria opened the door to the old man but he would not enter and asked if Msabu Ward would speak with him outside. Gathering Shanghai in her arms, Valerie went onto the veranda and motioned the headman to be seated on the short grass. He sank, straight backed, into a cross-legged posture and remained motionless while Valerie settled herself on a rattan chair.

After a pause, Kiwainu began speaking. During the past seven days, he said, three goats had disappeared from the village and now, today, another was gone. Clearly, there was a leopard at work. There was a pause as the old Kikuyu allowed these facts to sink into Valerie's mind.

"Has anyone seen the leopard?"

"No, Msabu. They have not. It comes by stealth in the night."

"And you would like me to shoot it?" Valerie asked calmly. Like all white women in Kenya, she could handle both revolver and rifle. Roddy had admired her marksmanship though it was confined, so far, to shooting tin cans off a fence.

The headman inclined his head. He had though that perhaps some male friend of Bwana Ward's might be approached to take care of the leopard. It was certainly a leopard.

It was arranged that she should come after dusk had fallen. If the leopard were to attack again, the young men of the village would surround it and drive it towards Valerie's gun. A place for her to rest during the hours of waiting would be prepared.

Valerie spent two comfortless nights in a dirty hut, cleaning her rifle and attempting sleep on a pile of skins. The rains had ceased, and the dry air was sharp with frost once the sun sank below the horizon. The first night she had eaten some sort of sweet potato stew and a half-raw, half-charred chicken leg offered in a wooden bowl. The native food had made her sick and the next day Makundi made sandwiches of ham and cheese for her, they were a little better.

Towards dawn, Valerie had got up and was preparing to leave, happily convinced that if there had been a leopard it had sensed its danger and gone elsewhere, when there was a shout of anguish. Emerging from the hut, she saw the dying night-time fires glowing in the grey light and black bodies running everywhere.

"Over here, Msabu! My she-goat, which was tethered here at my door has gone!"

With the rifle broken under her arm, Valerie walked wearily towards a hut on the far side of the village. It was raised on stilts. Outside a man in a long white robe pranced frantically. A rope dangled from a stake.

There was nothing to be seen.

A rustle beneath the stilted hut attracted Valerie's flagging attention. Squatting down to discover what might have caused the stirring, she gagged.

Not at first able to believe the evidence of her own eyes, she called for a torch. A flare was lit from one of the fires. Valerie held it, as best she could, to illumine the monster's dark refuge.

A great snake, thirty feet in length lay bloated on the ground. Ten feet from its head an ugly bulge betrayed the presence of the goat. She stood up, swaying slightly. Whether from hunger or disgust, she could not have said.

"Look. Under the hut."

A crowd of Kikuyu boys and men joined her, whooping and yelling. They drove the torpid snake from its lair with sticks and long-handled tools. When it slid painfully into view, it was clear that one of the goat's horns had pierced its diamond patterned hide. Compassion for the creature's agony swept over Valerie and lent her courage. She cocked the rifle and fired two rounds between the snake's eyes at close quarters. The kikuyu fell on it, swinging sharp bladed machete's and axes. Within moments, the snake was bloodily sliced. The goat was recovered, and to Valerie's infinite relief, was found to be quite dead. A bond was sealed.

Word of her encounter with the snake spread. Valerie learned to think rather more highly of her own bravery as neighbours called to congratulate her. She was hardly to be blamed if the picture of herself as a 'remarkable young woman' was amply reinforced. As an artist, she was naturally impressionable.

The same neighbours warmly praised the new arrangement in the house.

"Delightfully fresh."

"A woman's touch ... nothing to beat it."

"Roddy will really know he's married now!"

A week's leave was granted to him a month or so later owing to the outstanding success of the campaign in Ethiopia. Roddy wrote that he was under orders to accompany an important prisoner, the Duke of Aosta, to his assigned place of detention in Gilgil.

He was a nice chap and rather poorly, who would give nobody any trouble. Roddy would see him settled, he wrote, and then come home. He added that at a later date, when the position in general was clearer, it might be possible to get a parole for the Duke to spend some time with them at the farm.

This was most exciting. A grateful Duke, even a foreign one, could be most useful to both of them. An affectionate wife thought of these things and made them happen naturally. She had a talent for that kind of thing.

Roddy's first leave since his marriage did not go smoothly. In short, as that neighbour had prophesied, he did indeed know that he was married.

After the first rapturous greeting, most competently staged by Valerie whose mind was really on the Duke, Roddy's face darkened.

"I see you've been very busy here, Val," he said dangerously. Valerie's smiles and reasonable explanations did not soon dispel his very real anger. Macheria was ordered to restore the hides and trophies to the sitting room walls. They were dragged out from under tarpaulins in the store room and the elephant tusks resumed their place.

The next thing was a pile of bills, not only for chintz and one or two other items of domestic interior decoration, including a fearsomely expensive Turkoman rug obtained from a notoriously rapacious Asian dealer, but fruit trees and printed stationery. To Valerie they seemed the bare necessities of domesticity. Her mother would have agreed with her, except perhaps in the case of the rug.

Roddy agreed to pay the bills, although with cheques that would probably bounce. He did not admit that to Valerie. There were other demands to contend with. Two mess bills for a start, a long bar bill at the club, Valerie's Buick was not yet paid for and the jeweller in London seduced by the Dudley name, still waited for settlement.

Roddy had not been quite as honest and open with Valerie's father as he might. His London creditors could be held at bay. Moreover, an ignominious cancellation of his wedding plans would have reduced his credit still further.

A man of lordly impulses, it came naturally to Roddy to pick up the bill for entertainment when in company. Roddy found it difficult to face arithmetical facts. When they were forced upon him, he drank.

The quarrel was made up, but making love to her that night, Roddy showed rather less finesse with Valerie than he had used during his honeymoon. Finally, she composed herself for sleep, lying on her back with her legs straight. Waking himself once in the night with a particularly loud snore, Roddy was much struck with this pose of angelic dignity, Val was a marvel.

There was uproar of a different kind next day. Dinner was served at one end of the living room, now restored to its former bloodthirsty gloom. Valerie and Roddy had changed, because as they said, although there was no company, a first leave was a kind of anniversary, and in any case, standards must be kept up, war or no war. Roddy bawled for Macheria.

"Wapi Soup?" he demanded inelegantly.

Macheria's eyes rolled in real despair.

"Soup too hot, Makudi try to cool," the Kikuyu improvised.

Roddy and Valerie looked at each other and laughed. Dismay replaced hilarity when an odour from the kitchen warned something was amiss. The little lean-to kitchen area was ablaze when they got there. Makundi was flapping ineffectually at the flames with a ragged cloth, taking frequent swigs from a bottle of native hooch

"Get this bloody fool out of here, Macheria," Roddy shouted in Swahili, "and you, Valerie go and get some village natives and make sure they all bring a pail of water from the well."

Valerie did as she was bid, bouncing over the rough track to the native village in the Buick. It was alarming the flames were perilously near the thatch. Suppose by the end of the evening they'd not only had no dinner but had no home either.

30

By the time she returned to the house, a Kikuyu straggled on foot behind her, Roddy had controlled the fire by smothering it with a buffalo hide he prized..

'That was bloody close." Roddy's face, hands and shirt front were blackened with smoke.

"We should have lost the house if we'd had to depend on them," Valerie gestured towards the group of natives angrily.

"We'd better go to Muthaiga. I daresay your parents will put us up for the night. There'll be no room at the Club at this short notice, but we'll get a bite to eat there and see what else is cooking."

Valerie looked forward to it with zest. After the isolation of the farm and many evenings spent quite alone, it would be agreeable to be the centre of attention again. The bride's longing for an exclusive tête-à-tête with her husband had slipped away unnoticed. She needed people.

Valerie was disappointed with her welcome. There was a rustle of greeting, of course, but no applause.

"Darling …," Valerie extended both her hands to all the friends whose eyes she caught. The flash of Roddy's diamond turned a few heads momentarily, but the heads turned back again. Every eye was riveted to Joss Hay and Diana Delves Broughton who danced enfolded in each other's arms.

Diana's ice-blue eyes aligned briefly on Valerie, then she arched her pearl-garland neck and dropped her forehead onto Joss's shoulder for an instant. Looking up again, she met Valerie's unmoving regard. They knew each other through and through. Joss only had eyes for Diana.

Valerie took the first chair she was offered sitting near to Diana's husband. He toasted his wife and her lover in full view of the room.

Roddy went away to the bar. When he came back there was talk of going onto the Claremont nightclub. It was not yet three in the morning. For Joss and Diana, the night still throbbed with possibilities; they were all spangled with the joy of each other.

"Shall we make a night of it, Val and go to the Claremont too?" Roddy suggested. He had been drinking heavily like everyone besides Valerie. The confused vibrations around him eluded him entirely.

"No," she said. "No, I shan't go." The night and its stars belonged to Diana. Why prolong it? "You go if you want." In the morning, Joss Hay was found on the Ngong road, dead in Valerie's car.

CHAPTER THREE

Waking to the news, Muthaiga residents lost no time in telephoning each other to review the facts. Those who had been present at the Club the previous night were in demand. Each word, each glance and gesture were eagerly recalled and retold for the benefit of those who had been absent.

The peace of the Skelton's breakfast table was also disturbed by a flurry of tactful enquires. Was Valerie all right? How uncanny that her car should be involved. Was there anything they could do? Bobby Skelton fielded the telephone calls robustly.

When they did appear, neither Valerie nor Roddy wanted much breakfast.

"Oh Valerie," her mother's dismayed voice greeted her at the foot of the stairs. "It's all too horrible. Superintendent Poppy's just called, he's on his way over, he wants to talk to you and Roddy. There's been an accident."

Valerie greeted Poppy at the door herself composedly. Joss Hay had been a very dear friend, she assured the policeman formally. Her concern for Diana, so deeply in love with poor Joss, and now so tragically bereft, was quite overwhelming. Valerie's summer-blue eyes were dewy with compassion.

"I feel so awful," Valerie said

"May l trouble you for a sight of your car, Mrs Ward?"

"But of course."

And there it was, parked at the rear of the house. It had all been such a silly mistake. Valerie's Buick was not, in fact, the only T-model saloon in the country. There was one other, hired by Joss from Tiny Gibb's garage in downtown Nairobi. There was one digit's difference between the registration numbers. As far as the Wards were concerned, that cleared the matter up.

Of course, Superintendent Poppy was not interested in all Valerie could tell him about the previous night's events, regarding her own movements, she was asked little.

Roddy's hangover prevented him from adding much more than the occasional corroborative grunt. Poppy didn't seem very interested in what Roddy had been doing. That was fortunate as he could not remember clearly. He had been to and from the bar a few times, Valerie knew that.

By the time it was generally known that Joss had been shot in the head, and not pierced by a metal spike protruding from the dashboard, as had at first been thought, everybody had forgotten about the affair of the Buick. A stupid error, the merest coincidence. Whatever could the whole ghastly business have to do with Valerie and her husband? Nothing, absolutely nothing. The obvious culprit was Broughton, the betrayed husband. Who else?

Once 'Jock' had been arrested, Valerie thought the time ripe to announce her pregnancy. She very much wanted a boy, she told everyone. Really, the first one ought to be a boy, an heir for Roddy.

Valerie's news brought about an upsurge of protective tenderness in her husband. Despite his years and two previous marriages, fatherhood was something Roddy had not yet achieved. His wife's person acquired an extreme sanctity in his eyes. Nothing was too good for her.

"You realise," his mother-in-law- told him, "that Valerie cannot remain at the farm in the circumstances. It simply isn't safe with you away so much she must stay here with us."

Roddy had no hesitation in agreeing, Valerie, however, rejected the idea of returning to her parents' house. It had not occurred to her that the infant would act as a brake on her own liberties.

"I can't, I won't!" Valerie stormed prettily up and down their bedroom. "How dare you agree to it? Thompson's Falls is my home. Not there! I'm needed here ... Mummie will make me come in every night at ten o'clock."

"But Val, darling," Roddy's features were perplexed. "Where else would you want to be?"

"That's not the point!"

No man worthy of the name will chop logic with a truly feminine woman, nor will any kindly man, in triumphant flush of prospective fatherhood, thwart the wishes of a pregnant spouse … assuming the child to be his own. Valerie's consciousness had been imprinted with these facts since birth. She had only to continue steadfast in her intent. Roddy owed it to her.

What Roddy finally agreed he owed was the lease on the whitewashed, furnished bungalow for Valerie in Muthaiga. Valerie chose it herself. It was sufficiently close to her parents' house, but not too close. It was within walking distance of the Club with running water, electricity, a secluded garden and adequate servants' accommodation … "it had everything," Valerie announced to friends.

"She'll be calling it her 'town residence' next," Ann MacMaster's mother sniped when told of Valerie's latest move.

Ann, an able seamstress, was soon busy with the adaptation and replacement of some of the bungalow's soft furnishings. A small fee was to be paid and Ann, hoping to marry shortly and not over-generously treated by her less-prosperous parents, needed the money. As Valerie said, "What are friends for, if not to be useful to each other?" It was just like her.

Valerie was inattentive. The baby's advent sealed the bargain between her and Roddy, and what was more to the purpose, gave her a long-lasting claim upon the Ward family … those interesting people in England, who she had never met.

According to Roddy, his family had a large acquaintance amongst theatre and film people. Perhaps, in the future, they would take an interest in her. They could hardly avoid it now. She was united to them by the ties of flesh and blood. Looks and talent in exchange for useful connections, it was a fair trade, a future insurance policy. Valerie took care never to look these thoughts fully in the face, not yet; she was happily married and often said so.

The pregnancy itself passed uneventfully. Roddy was still fully occupied in the north with his regiment.

At times, Valerie would visit Thompson's Falls making herself busy with carpenters from Gilgil, summoned to reconstruct the kitchen. She pored over account books, they meant little to her. She paid visits to the native village where she was greeted warmly enough but without much awe.

To her great relief, Valerie's early pregnancy did little to mar the neat outline of her figure. She continued to play tennis and hear the gossip at the Club. Things looked very black for 'Jock' Broughton. Of course, he and Diana were persona non grata there now. To be a cuckold on the one hand was one thing, to be an adulteress on the other, was something to be tolerated, but to be accused of murder, or to be the living, breathing motive for that murder, that was inexcusable. At least for the moment.

That was convenient to Valerie, because while she played tennis with her husband's best man, who had also been in a fair way to being Joss Hay's best friend, her own story, the one she had told to Superintendent Poppy, was undergoing a number of changes. It was not so much what she had seen on that last night of Joss's life, but where she had seen it and with whom.

Valerie now had a new and pressing concern. The entertainment of her friend, Amadeo. The captive Commander-in-Chief of the Italian forces, Roddy's Duke, as Valerie had privately dubbed him, was now an occasional weekend visitor. He was everything that might be hoped of an Italian nobleman and more.

Alighting gracefully from the staff car, he greeted Valerie. Experience and training had taught him to value pretty women at their own estimation. It came as naturally as breathing. A flashing smile would briefly illuminate the classic contours of his handsome face and then be allowed to smoulder lazily in his eyes. Its effect on Valerie was transporting.

"Amadeo! How wonderful to have you home again." She advanced from her position on the veranda, hands extended with the Shanghai bouncing at her heels. Roddy sometimes wondered if Val didn't overplay her hand a bit.

Unknown to Roddy, Valerie had often played the scene in reverse. After the war, one day, it would be Amadeo standing on the steps of some marble palace under a blue enamelled, Italian sky, waiting to receive an honoured guest, his godson, and accompanying the precious child would be his beautiful mother, with whom the Duke was so deeply and hopelessly in love.

Urged by Valerie, Roddy did indeed invite the Duke to become the godfather of his first child. He spoke with some slight reluctance, wondering if this plan of Val's wasn't just a little 'pushy'. It would however be dangerous to cross Val at a time like this. Dangerous to the baby, that was, Roddy would have a quiet word with his charge on the way back to Gilgil.

"My dear chap," Amadeo answered in his excellent English. "I am touched beyond measure that you should think of me. I hope I may survive to be of use to the little fellow."

That was the only reference Amadeo made to the alarming flecks of blood he found on his handkerchief after coughing, which unfortunately, he did with increasing frequency. It was getting harder and harder to repress the desperate gasps as his lungs fought for oxygen in the thin, highland air.

Valerie's child was born in the Carberry Nursing Home in Nairobi. It was a boy and slightly premature. The obstetrician was amused, first babies were inclined to tardiness as a rule, but this one clearly shared his mother's appetite for life. A fuzz of platinum hair blurred the pinkness of the child's scalp. He was to be called Robert after his paternal grandfather. Roddy contemplated his 'heir', as Valerie would insist on calling this pink, winkling scrap of humanity, with something like astonishment, he had not really expected it to look like a person at all, not yet. The blondeness was startling. He got it from Val, of course.

The expression on his son's face was one of good-humoured patience. His grandmother, Alice, could hardly be persuaded to put him down. To her, he seemed like some late-come child of her own. Young Robert was to have a good granny.

"Aren't you thrilled, darling?" Valerie asked the new father, lying back on her pillows. Her room was bowered with the fruit and flowers sent by well-wishers. "I know I am, I feel like a film star, and Robert is sweet, isn't he?"

Roddy found it difficult to supply her with an answer. His feelings were far too complex to be encompassed with a single word. Everything he had once felt of protectiveness towards Valerie was now transferred to his child. There was terror too, that he would, had already, failed him. Could you support a son on credit? Public schools did not take rubber cheques, not more than once, anyway.

Valerie's radiance did little to lift his spirits; he should have bought her some jewellery to mark the birth. By a stroke of good fortune, his previous wife had sent him back the diamond and sapphire cluster he had once presented to her. The jewels now shone on Valerie's lace-cuffed hand, a companion for his solitaire.

"Such a wonderful thing for her to have done, don't you think?" Valerie asked Ann MacMaster, whose rather small diamond winked modestly in response. "People are so very kind. This makes it all quite perfect."

In motherhood as in everything else, Valerie satisfied every visual requirement. She affected a decent amount of fatigue and her pastel silks, but the clasp of her hand was dry and strong. She had a new, reinforced authority.

"I shall make Roddy put Robert down for Eton right away. That's where the Wards always go, tradition," she said proudly.

Amadeo was "unable to pay his respects to his little prince," as he tactfully expressed the restraints on his movements, but in his letter, he gave notice of his intention to provide two playmates for his godson: a baby chimpanzee and a lion cub. "I know they could have no kinder or more understanding home," he added. "God bless you, my dear, and kiss my godchild for me."

38

Everyone was impressed by the letter and its melancholy grace. There was something very special about Val. She drew people to her with her vigorous, magnetising will. She was so clever, so amusing.

Amidst the cacophony of celebration, the champagne and flowers, Roddy sought an escape from the burden of responsibility in hard liquor.

When his wife and child left the nursing home a week later, the bait, which had never entirely left him, had him completely in thrall. He spent much time at the Club in male company. The cooings and flutterings of female visitors to the bungalow made it intolerable to him. At the Club, the masculine chaff about his new status was equally unwelcome.

At the expiry of his leave, Roddy returned to the regiment without once visiting the farm. Before he left, there had been a painful row. Valerie wanted funds to travel to South Africa for her friend, Ann's wedding. It was to take place in Johannesburg to enable Ann's elderly, infirm parents to attend.

"What about the baby?" Roddy raised the best objection he could think of.

"My parents would love to have Robert to themselves for a week, you know that."

"Look Val. It's awkward about money at the moment."

"But I'm not asking for much ... I'd pay for it out of my own allowance if I had an allowance." The taunt touched Roddy on the rawest of raw nerves. He had been drinking and he shoved her hard, causing her to fall backwards into a chair, she bruised her thigh on the chair's wooden arm. Roddy was instantly remorseful, what had come over him? He was not the sort of man who laid violent hands on women. Roddy went over to the other side of the room and turning his back, looked out of the window. His son was sleeping on the veranda. His son.

What was it he wondered in that moment of desperate calm, about his wife's neat featured face that had let to this sudden loss of self-control? She was so unchangeably beautiful.

The perfect, predictable ellipse of her smile, her carriage, so faultlessly erect, the crisp, clipped little voice and her eyes glittering with the greed of life. He quailed before her strength. It was an incomprehensible paradox because she depended on him. Roddy knew, as he had always known, he was not a man to be depended on.

Roddy returned once again to the regiment and Valerie made the best of things. In the weeks that followed, 'Jock' Broughton walked out of court a free man. Opinion on the rectitude of the court's decision was divided. Nobody really knew who'd killed Joss Hay, not for certain.

In the Club, she overheard a fragment of conversation in the ladies' room. "Whoever did it deserved a medal." Silently, Valerie agreed. Joss, in all his fair, patrician glory had been a source of suppurating evil, a bad man. But whenever Valerie spoke of him, and it seemed that his name would live forever, she referred to him as a 'sad loss' and a 'dear friend'.

The still sadder loss of a truer friend was in store. Amadeo was dead. Pulmonary tuberculosis, Roddy wrote of his prisoner's death himself.

"I can't say how this has shaken me up," he wrote. "I don't know why exactly, but I think it means we should make a new start. We both loved Amadeo and I'm ashamed to think what he'd have thought if he'd known we had fallen out." Valerie found she was quite angry with Amadeo for dying too. It was a cruel disappointment.

A few days later, the lion cub and the chimpanzee were delivered. Valerie held their confiding little bodies close and wept over them. The loss of their sender cut through the fog of frustrated ambition and cloying daydream. Amadeo had understood her. He played opposite her like a pro, and then touched her really with the utmost gentleness.

As soon as Robert could sit up and feed himself from a bottle, they joined him in his playpen. They played together in the mutual contentment, which exists between animals and men before the power of human speech robs the relationship of innocence. Shanghai would squirm angrily in his mistress's arms, obscurely aware of the affront to his seniority

Watching the three infants together gave Valerie hours of untroubled selfless pleasure.

"Really," Alice protested one day. "You're not fit to have a baby at all." She had arrived in time to see Robert share his ten o'clock bottle of orange juice with his companions. The bottle was passed from hand to paw and mouth to mouth in solemn rotation. Each little creature sucked and suffered the bottle to be taken from him peaceably by the next in line.

In spite of his unconventional nursery, Robert continued to thrive. His equable temperament endeared him to the servants and to his grandparents. Valerie was fond of him too. He was no trouble, and of course, he was a Ward, a thing that might be of considerable importance to his mother. A woman needed sons to secure her future.

Roddy, meanwhile, had a new task to perform as officer in charge of the bodyguard to the newly restored Emperor Haile Selassie of Ethiopia. Valerie loved his other titles. King of Kings … Lion of Judah.

"Pity she didn't think of asking the Lion of Judah to be her son's godfather, isn't it? Christian king … one up on an enemy Duke." That was one dinner-table pleasantry circulating at the time of Roddy's new appointment

"Oh, for God's sake," those with sweeter natures defended. "Val's got an ear for poetry … which is more than can be said for some … She looks a picture with that little fellow of hers … making of a good mother." Valerie's detractors would subside, snubbed.

There was, however, a deal of inescapable unpleasantness brewing. In a self-protective way that mothers have, Valerie had tried to outface the ever-growing suspicion that her husband was in deep financial trouble, but the signs were unmistakable.

One day at the Club, she was treating Ann, still fairly recently married, to luncheon. A belated celebration. When she tried to sign the chit in the usual way, the Kikuyu waiter's face was long. He took the pink slip of paper away and Valerie thought no more about it until a minute later, the lordly Ali was hovering beside the table.

Would it incommode Msabu Ward to pay in cash? The Secretary ... The Somali shrugged very slightly, disclaiming any part in this extraordinary break with custom.

Valerie glared at him haughtily. Ali, grey faced and implacable, stood his ground.

"Please Val," Ann intervened, pink with mortification for her friend's discomfiture. "Let me sign for this. It's just some silly misunderstanding ... Roddy's been away so much, maybe he's forgotten."

Valerie knew all too well what he had forgotten. The bill had been in the pigeon-hole for weeks. She had removed it and sent it to him. Then another appeared in its place, and another. When he was home on leave, she would ask him about these bills. There was always a row. Thank God Robert was still young enough to sleep undisturbed through his father's drunken bellows.

Ann did sign the chit on that occasion and Valerie was grateful to her ever afterwards. She knew Jan checked her expenditure with all the rigour that was in his frugal, Boer blood.

"I shall never forget this, you know. You can be sure of that," Valerie said grimly. "And I shall never forgive Roddy."

"It was nothing; don't be too hasty, darling. They have a lot on their minds at the moment, these men."

"I think," Valerie said slowly, "you are the nicest person I have ever met, much nicer than me." She silenced Ann's protests with a bejewelled wave of her hand.

"You may as well listen because I shall never say this again, not to you or anybody. I am not all that bothered about being nice. I want to survive, but I'm afraid for you. Is that husband of yours treating you properly?"

Ann flushed faintly and looked away. Jan was a man from a different background. A different culture. He didn't realise he was sometimes oppressive.

"Because if you ever need me, I shall come. No matter from where."

Not long afterwards, the petrol-pump attendant at a nearby garage refused to fill Valerie's Buick. The driver came back to the bungalow and announced the fact without emotion. In his hand, he held a sheaf of grubby pieces of paper. All carbon copies of unpaid bills. Valerie's heart sank, how long would it be before they were unable to buy food?

That night she discharged a round from her pistol through the window of her bedroom. It was her usual routine; a lot of white women did it. The crack of the bedtime bullet was intended to warn African robbers that the householders would defend themselves. It was also supposed, pathetically, to give the impression that there were menfolk around. A forlorn hope when all the servants gossiped incessantly to each other. They all knew when the Bwana-this or Bwana-that was away from home.

Valerie slept fitfully, tormented by the problems that confronted her. At about two in the morning, she was roused to full consciousness by the gleam of moonlight on a sinuous black form. She lay rigid for a moment, then the whites of the eyes reflected what little light there was. It was a man. A naked African in her room. He was standing in front of the dressing table. Valerie leaped from her bed and grabbed hold of his wrist, for a split second he looked at her. It was Mohammed, her driver. The African slipped from her grasp and fled. Valerie's hand was oily; the man had been covered in grease, the old housebreaker's trick.

She was in time to see him disappear noiselessly across the lawn and through the bushes. Shivering, she went back to her room. She had been in time; the rings were still there on her dressing table, hanging on the glass ring tree. There had been a few currency notes and some coins, they were gone.

After looking at Robert, sound asleep in his cot in the room next door to her own, Valerie went back to bed. Tomorrow she would have to sell the rings. Boys did not rob their own employers when they had a good place, were well treated and well paid. Evidently, her servants had not been paid.

As an earnest show of good intent, and before going to her father, Valerie sold the Buick. It realised a worthwhile sum, as good second-hand cars were difficult to come by in the colony at that date. She also sold the rings, fine as they were, they raised pitifully little.

Valerie was obliged to accept a derisory sum for both rings. But it was enough for what she had in mind. She kept the proceeds of that sale on one side.

Bobby Skelton was perturbed at what his daughter told him. He examined the bundle of unpaid bills she removed from her handbag with pursed lips. Valerie admitted that it was selling the Buick that had enabled her to pay the Club bills and one or two others, that was all.

During the next few days, Bobby made searching enquiries. As a man of influence, information that might have been denied to others was made readily available to him. Roddy was insolvent neither his domestic servants nor his squatter herdsmen had been paid for three years. There had been loan upon loan. The very cattle on his ranges had been pledged as collateral, the farm would have to go.

All the Wards' outstanding domestic debts were settled by Valerie's father. About the farm, it was not possible for him to act. Roddy was in Ethiopia, not eligible for leave just then and neither his wife nor his father-in-law held a power of attorney for him. That had been an elementary mistake, Alice was not slow to mention. She was very angry, risking little Robert's future like that.

Calling at the bungalow, she was bemused to find Valerie in the throes of packing. "What are you doing? Your father paid the rent for the next three months." Alice sank gratefully into a basket chair on the veranda near the play pen. She had been walking and was tired. A touch of angina, the doctor said.

"I can't stay here, Mummie. I simply can't, I'm leaving, leaving altogether. Will you take care of my animals for me? I expect Robert will miss them, but it can't be helped."

Valerie's words had a galvanising effect. That evening her parents listened in stunned amazement to her plans. She wanted to divorce Roddy and leave for London, England, taking Robert with her, she had it all worked out. She would go on a Nile steamer as far as Cairo and then take a ship from Port Said. The world of show business awaited her.

"With the Mediterranean full of German U-boats? Oh no you won't my girl! Not with my grandson, you won't."

Valerie had anticipated that reaction. Robert would be much better off with his grandparents, Valerie would fight to take him with her but not too hard.

"You and Roddy must try and make a go of it. You've a child and responsibilities; you can't just shrug them off when it suits you."

"I've put up with him for over two years. I've done my best. I'm twenty-one and I've got my whole life before me. I've got to get away, a clean break, now."

Her determination was unbreakable, her faith in her future career, unshakeable. The Ward family would be her passport into the 'right circles'. She had already cabled her brother-in-law, Lord Dudley.

"I shouldn't think they'd be much help," Bobby Skelton's laugh was a short bark. "You divorce Roddy and then calmly expect them to set you up with a job and all? You've a screw loose, you can't have it both ways, Val, as far as Roddy's family are concerned, you'll be an outsider."

"You seem to forget," Valerie replied with freezing dignity. "My son is a Ward." It crossed Alice's mind that her grandson's name was his most lovable feature in his mother's eyes. Neither the physical dangers of the voyage nor war-torn Europe would dissuade Valerie. Seeing that her resolve could not be broken, her parents gave her some money and the address of some modestly-situated friends in London. She could lodge with them for a week or two. Eric Dudley had offered nothing. Of course, Valerie's cable might never have reached him.

A paddle steamer was to leave Namasagali in a few days' time. Bobby undertook to drive his daughter across the Uganda border to join it. Roddy was not informed, and Robert was left behind. Valerie's spirits soared on the updraught of adventure. Come what may, she was going to be rich and famous, they would all be proud of her.

CHAPTER FOUR

Valerie watched as the two-deck steamer edged away from the crowded concrete jetty, trailing its floating shanty town of lighters with it. The stench of pigs, frightened cattle and unwashed natives gusted nauseatingly in her nostrils. Ahead, the margins of water were fringed with the jungle's supernatural degree, steaming in a hundred degrees of heat. The journey of dreams started here.

It would take a day or two for her fellow passengers to realise who she was. Fortunately, the Goddards, friends of her parents were on board, they would make it plain. Her father had gone, not much of a man for prolonged farewells or emotional speeches, only the extra tightness in his final embrace betrayed Bobby Skelton's fears he might never see her again.

"Send us a wire when you can Val. Your mother will be on hot bricks and don't you worry about Robert."

Valerie was not worried about Robert.

"And the Goddards will look after you in Cairo, you stick with them."

Valerie promised that she would. The middle-aged official and his wife were respectable of appearance and correct in manner, suitable protectors. She would attach herself to them until better things turned up.

Day followed delightful day as the steamer churned its way north through the wide waters of the river. The ukulele now came into its own. A lovely young woman immersed in her music will always command attention. A generalised curiosity among her companions was all that Valerie desired, about the decks and public saloons, there were mutterings and nudgings.

47

Bobby Skelton had not told the Goddards that Valerie's marital affairs were in disarray. On that point, Valerie had commanded silence. "The Emperor takes up so much of my husband's time, we both agreed I should have a change of scene, no fuss or luxury, just a little wander through the world."

There was always a slight, satisfying hush when she said things like that. The vague implication that the Earl of Dudley's sister-in-law normally travelled with a maid, was very nearly credible. Layer on layer, Valerie swathed herself in veils of mystery, she did not reveal her future plans, they might change, anything was possible. It was entirely a matter of what fate had in store.

Aswan was reached. There was no doubt now that the steamer must stop. The European passengers wished to rest.

The place to go in Aswan was a houseboat permanently moored on the bank. From its foredeck, there was an enchanting view of Elephant Island and inside, the appointments were such as might be expected from any decent club, better, Vera Goddard told Valerie. The houseboat's proprietress had a proper idea of what was important in life, had made a very good thing out of offering hospitality to the cream of Cairo Society.

"You will meet only nice people there, Valerie, dear, do come."

Gravely, Valerie agreed that Mrs Heslop's houseboat sounded like the sort of place where her two friends might safely escort her. Vera was bemused, she had forgotten weeks ago, that this was Bobby Skelton's little girl. Somehow or other, such was Valerie's skill, Vera had become convinced that she was a species of minor royalty. Where she went and with whom was a matter of delicacy. Valerie could only be introduced to people of impeccable reputation, people of standing, it was a responsibility.

Safely aboard the houseboat, with Valerie, demure, in floor-sweeping white lawn pleats, Mrs Goddard was greatly relieved to see Lord and Lady Sligo. Her husband had served a tour of duty in Egypt, so they knew the ambassador and his wife. Valerie would not turn up her nose at His Majesty's plenipotentiary. The Cairo residency was still regarded as a good address, surely.

Jimmy Goddard was not so bowed down with the weight of his old friend's daughter's dignity. Bluff and good natured, the Sligos were glad to see him.

"Jimmy! Vera! How nice to see you, yes," admitted the ambassador, his eyes already straying to Valerie. "We'd a few days to ourselves for once, so we thought we'd run down here for a breath of fresh air not to mention a taste of Nile Perch Facon de Heslop, aren't you going to introduce us?" Lord Sligo fingered the edge of his bow tie in the way that so many men did when they first met Valerie. She was not slow to notice an opportunity.

"Well of course, this is Mrs Roddy Ward ... the Honourable Mrs ..." Jimmy could not resist the solecism. He'd put up with a lot on that steamer and had borne it pretty well. Valerie's airs and graces were becoming just a little oppressive.

"Oh! We know who you are exactly," Lady Sligo broke in with professional suavity. The glint in her husband's eye did not excuse her from duty. "At least, I should say, we know who your husband is."

Moonlight on the Nile, a waterside table gleaming with damask and silver and Valerie's lovely, piquant face in candlelight. The ambassador was entranced. Truth to tell, her ladyship warmed to the girl as well. Ignorant, certainly, but vivacious and appreciative, such a pretty laugh.

"Do you know how they fuel the trains here, Mrs Ward?"

"Please, do call me Valerie," she interjected sweetly.

The ambassador assured her that he would and thanked her for the privilege. He did not offer his own name, however. There was seniority to be considered. A step at a time.

"Yes, well, as I was saying, about the trains. They burn mummies."

This always caused a sensation and had a most gratifying effect on young Mrs Ward. She positively gagged behind her napkin. Polly Sligo smiled. Any girl really up to snug would have allowed her jaw to sag unveiled. Mrs Ward was very clever, but she still had a few things to learn. Still, she was a charming child and giving poor dear Miles such a lot of fun.

"I assure you Valerie, it's the truth. The Egyptians have been mummifying their dead since pre-pharaonic times, the hills round here are just riddled with caves stuffed full of them, you might say they're a natural resource."

Valerie's hyacinth eyes were as round as ping-pong balls. Before the Goddards could give him away, Miles Sligo did admit that the supply of mummies was running down. Inexorably, Egypt was joining the modern world.

Three weeks was the intended length of stay. A boat was leaving for Port Said for Gravesend then. Berths had been reserved on the *SS Karachi*, though goodness knew what they would be like in wartime, everyone had to rough it these days.

"But that's splendid," the ambassador beamed. "Now what do you say, Mrs Ward – Valerie? I've some very pleasant young people in my embassy who'd be delighted to show a ravishing, and if I may say so, very intelligent young woman the local sights. Don't you think we should draw up a programme of instruction for you?"

He was a practised flatterer. Lord Sligo caught his wife's eye; they had had the same thought. Valerie was invited to spend the whole of her sojourn in Cairo at the Residency. There was so much for her to see and not a moment to waste. Valerie accepted, her interest in tombs and temples was suddenly profound.

The Goddards, on the other hand would adhere to their original plan. They were booked into the Shepheard's Hotel. Privately, and in their different ways, they were glad of the opportunity to transfer Valerie to the protection of somebody who would know how to value her.

For the visitor to Cairo, there could be only one address better than Shepheard's Hotel: the British Embassy. The ambassador's residence, with its soaring ceilings, shining parquet floors, lacy iron work, balconies and gilded French furniture, was the most beautiful house Valerie had yet seen, let alone occupied, even as a guest.

Unaccustomed to imperial splendour, Valerie was quick to acclimatise. How right she had been to leave Roddy, it was in places such as this, agelessly elegant, immutably serene, that she was destined to live.

Lady Sligo's maid unpacked Valerie's suitcases, whisking away items for laundering and pressing. Like all her kind, she examined the things with a detective's perspicacity. Her ladyship's maid found it difficult to place Valerie. Mrs Ward's nightgowns, cami-knickers and crêpe-de-Chine blouses were of good quality, but not new. But then, as she remarked to his Lordship's valet, the war could account for that.

"She's never had a maid of her own, though, I'm certain of that … for all she'd like you to think so."

"A real lady would have her things mended, even if she did it herself. Oh, she's very smart on top I'll give you that, but it's what's underneath that counts. It's nothing very much, you know, just a thread or two loose. I'd never let her ladyship go out with so much as a scrap of frayed lace to her petticoat."

With Cairo thronged with allied troops of every nationality, there was no shortage of new faces at Polly Sligo's dinner table. Novelties of the masculine sex were hardly a difficulty, but unattached, attractive women to whom to introduce them were in rather shorter supply, and then there was the perennial problem of poor King Farouk. He did like pretty ladies so, and he would go wherever one corresponding to that description was to be found. Better he should find her under British protection than in French or American hands.

Paramount in Lady Sligo's mind was the business of enhancing her husband's career. Keeping Egypt's dissolute puppet king sweet was a priority. In that way, British interests were best served. Valerie Ward would have a part to play in that, a sweet little dish of peaches and cream to set before the King and when he tired of the taste, then the dish should be removed. Polly Sligo hoped she would have found another to put in its place by that time.

Unaware of these patriotic plans, Valerie enjoyed every day to the full. Each morning, a housemaid brought her breakfast and ran her bath. Another was deputed to lay out her clothes. Valerie appreciated these services; she never had to open a cupboard door or drawer for herself.

Lady Sligo's hopes were amply fulfilled. Seated at dinner beside Egypt's mountainous King that night, Valerie's capacity to charm and be charmed exceeded every expectation. Valerie glittered; she was in the right company.

There were only twenty people ranged on either side of the long table. The party was officially categorised as 'informal'. That did away with any problem of precedence and allowed Lady Sligo to place her guests without reference to their rank. The King, of course, occupied the place of honour at her right hand and Val, sat on his right.

Farouk talked and Valerie listened, leaving each dish as it was served, virtually untouched. She looked impressed; she was impressed. A King no matter how unlovely, can never really be dull and this one with his cosy, playful manner, was charming. His pudgy hand rested on the edge of the table and more than once, it closed over Valerie's in the friendliest way. Valerie's blue eyes shone up into his face confidently. He liked her.

Behind the dark sunglasses he habitually wore, Farouk's bulging brown eyes drank in the sight, fresh, pretty, English and unsullied, well, almost. She was married, but that was a safeguard, no embarrassments. Farouk noticed something else, Valerie wore a wedding ring but there were none of the customary gems given as betrothal tokens on her finger. Poor? Even better, she would be grateful.

"Should you like to have supper with me at my house in Heliopolis tomorrow evening, Mrs Ward? A few friends only; quite informal. It would be so pleasant if you could come."

"Of course, you must go, Val darling, we will spare her to you for the evening, sir, precious though she is."

What could be more delightful? To be desired as a guest by a King in his own country and treasured by her own King's ambassadorial couple. Graciously, Valerie acceded to Farouk's request. She did feel rather important.

Farouk took her to the races and placed her bets. Naturally, she was allowed to keep her winnings. He took her to the Champagne Club at Mena House to watch the stars wheel over the desert's immensity. For a time, she was his constant and preferred companion and if the sight of her tiny, elegant figure beside Farouk's obscene bulk aroused any derogatory comment, Valerie did not hear of it. Lady Sligo made certain of that.

It was very exciting. Messages came by hand to the Embassy. There were flowers too. The marble tops of the commodes in Valerie's room were lavished with lilies, hibiscus and lotus blossom. At the heart of every bouquet, a handsome cheque drawn on a London bank was secreted. About these, Valerie said nothing. If a gentleman, albeit a King, wanted to give a lady a nice present then that surely, was their private affair.

The time for Valerie to rejoin the Goddards and catch the boat leaving with a convoy from Port Said came and went.

"Oh, you can't leave us now, dearest. Miles and I would miss you so. We've only just got to know you ... And the King monopolising your time so much lately." Lady Sligo was sincere in her efforts to hold on to her guest.

The influence proved short-lived. The King had waited patiently, but he was not accustomed to waiting long for his wishes to be fulfilled. Mrs Ward, he was beginning to find, was obtuse. Flowers, cars, meals and lavish gifts of money did not come for nothing. Mrs Ward did not understand. A stupid woman? Or merely virtuous. It made no difference. Enough was enough.

Valerie remained in the residency for a full seven weeks. When, finally, she left for Port Said to embark on *SS Matiana*, the ambassador provided an armed escort as far as Cairo railway station.

"You do spoil me so," she said extending both her hands in farewell. "Darling Polly, darling Miles, how can I ever thank you?"

She was whisked away in the Embassy limousine through Cairo's palm-lined boulevards, the Sligos watched, waving and smiling until she was out of sight. A cavalcade fit for a princess, no less.

The *SS Matiana*, a grey-painted troop ship of the British India service, was not comfortable. Valerie stood amid her cabin luggage on 'A' Deck, bewildered. It was crowded with people milling around waving their tickets. The distracted purser moved among them with a mill board in his hand.

"Now, Mrs Ward, isn't it?" The purser consulted his list, "I've put you on 'B' Deck in a second-class berth. I'm afraid it's the best I can do. You're sharing with …" The purser stopped in mid flow and looked down at Valerie, a smasher and no mistake. "Look, if I've anything better when I get this lot settled, I'll try and … just stand by."

"Don't worry," she replied gamely. "There's a war on isn't there? I'll manage."

And Valerie did manage quite splendidly. It was clearly no time for striking attitudes, nobody would notice. All around her, a twitter and boom of discontented voices swirled, masking fear with complaints about trivia. A ship had gone down the week before, torpedoed, lost with all hands. It was a very long way from the well-upholstered certainties she had left behind. What was needed now, Valerie decided shrewdly, was a show of courage and gaiety. She was nothing if not adaptable.

The news came three days out of Port Said. The convoy ahead had been attacked by German U-boats, lives had been lost. On the *Matiaga*, upper lips were stiff, but faces were pale. By contrast, Valerie's glowed. Walking the thronged, wind whipped decks, she felt the nerve pinging thrill of acute danger, it was better than champagne.

Valerie played her ukulele and sang until the last exhausted passengers stumbled clumsily away to their cabins. After three weeks at sea, sing-songs and cocktails brought them safely to Gravesend.

Before disembarkation, Valerie was cheered to the echo. Deck officers and crew, military officers and men, even the few women passengers were grateful.

Britain in wartime was a monochrome world. It began on the quayside. There was a porters' strike, passengers would have to handle their baggage both hold and cabin, as best they could. At first, Valerie was almost immobile with shock. How could she? She couldn't remember a time when she'd been required to lift more than her own handbag. There was nobody to meet her; she would have to get up to London on the train.

Valerie's heart sank. This was not what she had expected. To be of so little account was depressing, even frightening. A sandwich! She would feel better after some food.

"Cheese and pickle or beef, dearie?" The woman in the terminal café advertised her flyblown wares indifferently. She leaned back, hands on hips and eyed Valerie appraisingly. She knew the type, Colonial. Thought they were the cat's pyjamas, just because they'd had a few natives to boss. This little madam would find things very different here. "Cheese and pickle or beef, dearie?" The woman repeated impatiently. There were others in the queue.

"Oh," Valerie still hesitated, neither sounded very appetising. "Well, cheese and pickle, then. How much do I owe you? Sixpence?" She handed the unfamiliar feeling coins across.

"Oi! That's no good. Not without yer ration book! Where's your ration book? There's a war on, don't you know nothing?"

Valerie did not have a ration book. She had not known it was necessary. Turning away from the counter with tears in her eyes for the second time that day, she didn't know if she had done the right thing after all. She did know there was a war on; people never stopped telling her, it was all so hateful.

The Smiths' small flat was no more inspiring. Valerie was shown into a cupboard of a room at the back, next to the kitchen. It looked down into the well of the building, zigzagged with fire escapes and washing lines. The basement window had a metal frame, it was rusty with condensation. If she craned her neck upwards, she could see a square grey sky. There was neither leaf nor tree to be seen anywhere.

"I expect you'll be quite comfortable in here," Edna Smith remarked complacently. "It was the maid's when we had one. Went off to work in a munitions' factory, like they all do. Piece of luck for you, eh? Anyway," she added after a pause in which Valerie was not able to bring herself to say anything, "you're welcome to stay till you find work. Bobby, your pa, was always a good friend to my hubby. Grew up together, they did, in Yorkshire. You're part of the family, in a manner of speaking."

"You're very kind," Valerie said glacially.

"Well, I'll leave you to get unpacked then," Edna replied. Obscurely, she felt annoyed. Valerie might have looked more cheerful, they could have got five bob a week for that room if they'd let it.

Valerie shuddered in distaste as her hostess closed the door. It would not do she must find a way out and quickly.

Later, when the blackout was in position and a supper of macaroni cheese followed by blancmange and tea had been served. Valerie asked if she might use the telephone.

"My husband's family are expecting me, but I couldn't give any idea exactly when I would arrive, you see."

"I'll get t'number, lovey," Bill Smith offered kindly. "What is it?"

"I'm afraid I don't know my mother-in-law's number," (no need to mention the 'step' faction in the relationship). "It'll be a Mayfair number ... Gertie, Dowager Countess of Dudley."

"My, my," Edna observed sourly as she cleared the dishes. "Toffs, are they?"

56

"Hallo!" A peremptory voice answered after an interval. "Who did you say you were? M'parlourmaid's deaf, y'know ... Ward y'say? Roddy Ward's wife. Well, what of it?"

The terrible, stomach churning sound of the air raid siren started. At the other end, the telephone went dead.

CHAPTER FIVE

Gertie Millar, in her youth a legendary Gaiety Girl, had become the second wife and later widow of the second Earl of Dudley. To Valerie, she came as a shock.

Valerie waited for her as instructed in the foyer of the Mayfair Hotel at half-past twelve on Tuesday. Nervously, she watched revolving doors, this meeting was so important.

"Thought I'd look you over," a voice trumpeted. Valerie became conscious of a substantial presence bearing down on her. "M'stepson said he'd had a wire from you, Roddy's wife, eh? More fool you, that's what I say."

Gertie, as she preferred to be called inserted her corpulent frame into the small armchair opposite Valerie.

Valerie sprang to her feet.

"Oh! How do you do, Lady Dudley."

"You needn't bother with all that palaver," the Countess asserted, shaking the hand Valerie proffered perfunctorily. "May as well get down to brass tacks. No, can't concern m'self on an empty stomach." She held up a plump, beringed hand. "Get some scoff organised first, you can get a smidgen of Dover Sole here if you're lucky. Well, I daresay it's no more than lemon sole."

"Get a move on then," Gertie concluded her business with the head waiter. "The lass looks as though she could do with a square meal inside her."

Valerie was grateful, she was very hungry. Even the acquisitions of her own ration book had brought little improvement in the quantity and none at all in the quality of the food served at the Smiths' flat.

"What you going to do then? Divorcing Roddy, ain't you? Don't suppose you've got two halfpennies to rub together." Valerie began at the beginning and came swiftly to her point.

"And I did think you might introduce me to some of the right people. Film people, you must know everyone in show business worth knowing ... Won't you help me, please?" Valerie smiled adorably.

Gertie chased the last shred of chicken around her soup bowl while she meditated her answer.

"No. Bluntly, my dear no, I won't."

Valerie was taken aback.

"But surely ..."

"Look here, what's y'name ... Valerie ... I came up the hard way. And that's what I am, hard, you'll have to do it on your own."

"Look at you, little lady, aren't you? Hold an audience? Sell yourself? Don't make me laugh. Couldn't sell a pork chop to a starving millionaire, you. No good, you know, unless you can sell one in a synagogue. What else can you do? Type?"

Valerie admitted that she could. The machine gun fire of statements and questions had scattered her thoughts, destroyed her plans.

"Type then, no shortage of work of that sort, type and then marry the boss. That's what you're cut out for. Don't think because you can manage a battalion or so of sex-starved soldiers or a bunch of gentlemen and lady friends, that you can handle yourself when the rotten tomatoes start flying. You need backbone for that, backbone and background, I've got the background, you haven't."

Valerie argued in vain. All her experience was set at naught. The E.N.S.A. concert in Mombasa, the Theatre Royal in Nairobi, chicken feed, Gertie said. Her courage went unrecognised. The passengers on the *SS Matiaga* ... They'd have cheered a deaf and dumb dwarf, they were so glad to find themselves alive.

"Tell you what though," the Countess confided smacking her lips over a cabinet pudding. "You've done right about Roddy. Never could get a bloody thing right. I'd divorce him sharpish while you've still got those looks. Marriage, that's your game."

Inwardly, Valerie fumed. The rotten, vulgar, selfish old woman wasn't going to help. Outwardly, she smiled and introduced some talk of her son.

The photographs of little Robert, Gertie's step-grandson were taken out. They were brushed aside with only conventional remarks and barely a glance. Gertie Millar had no children of her own. Valerie's arsenal was exhausted.

"Thank you for my lunch, Lady Dudley ... and for your advice."

The Countess tapped her arm kindly. Gertie treated her step-daughter-in-law to a twinkling smile and left as abruptly as she had appeared.

Uncharacteristically, Valerie havered for days over her next move. To approach, Roddy's older brother, the third Earl of Dudley direct, seemed the only option left. But he had not answered her wire, or the second message she had sent in the Diplomatic Bag from Cairo. Her tactic of first engaging Gertie's support and opening an oblique avenue of approach to Eric, had failed. There could be no more mistakes. The Ward connection was too precious.

There had been air raids every night since Valerie arrived in London. The Smiths belonged to that fatalistic class of Londoner who did not believe in air raid shelters.

"Nothing you can do if it's got your number on it," Edna would say as the sirens went. "Making for the East End anyway. Make a cup of tea, Val, there's a duck."

'Duck' was the operative word. But Valerie was not a coward and she fought the impulse to get under the kitchen table, or better still, join the troglodyte population in the tube stations underground. It would be sensible, yes, but the prospect of having Edna Smith jeer at her was intolerable.

One evening she was in luck. Returning from Wardour Street after an afternoon spent in humiliating attempts to get interviews with film companies, the air-raid siren went just as she alighted from a bus at Oxford Circus. It was a dark, autumn afternoon and the blackout reigned. Deafened and momentarily disorientated, Valerie stood still, clutching her ukulele case whilst the crowd, a grey tide of humanity, swept past her. What should she do? The sky was criss-crossed with moving lights. Where should she go?

"C'mon lovely," a Brylcreemed corporal in battledress jostled her elbow. "What you bleedin' waiting for? Cinderella's bleedin' coach? Hang onto me, nearest's down here!"

She was swept down the crowded steps and into Oxford Street tube station. Safety ... and a smell. Smoke and human bodies, warm and draughty.

"Oh, thank you! I've never been out in an air raid before, I don't know what I'd have done without you, how can I thank you?"

"Give us a kiss, Princess, and we'll call it quits."

Valerie was kissed soundly on the mouth. It was the beginning of a long night of discovery. The bottom layer of human existence. Somebody pressed a cup of soup on her, another, a slug of Scotch. The fiery spirit burned her throat, but it put heart into her. In extremes, the Londoners were both generous and pleasant.

After a while, there were 'turns' on mouth organs, then there were sing-songs, Valerie joined in, she played her ukulele, harmonising with an accordion player. Requests came thick and fast. 'Lili Marlene', crude soldier's songs about Hitler, 'Ten Green Bottles' and all the rest. It was fun, at first. But the 'all clear' did not sound.

"Ere, Princess!" Valerie's corporal came over to her. "Better turn in. Bloke'll let you have this coat. It looks lousy to me, but better than nothing, inn'it? Tell y'what. You have me greatcoat and I'll have this 'ere. Can't have a lady like you ending up wi'nits, can we?"

It was only a few hours, from the early hours until dawn, but they were some of the longest that Valerie was to live through. Far above, the crump of explosions. In the tube station, the cries of hungry, sleepless children, the insane ramblings of disturbed dreams and the raucous song of drunks ... and the stink.

In the morning, the 'all clear' sounded at last. Crumpled and cold, Valerie walked up into the November sunshine towards Colebourne Street. She could think no further ahead than a bath and eating her single, treasured egg. This was the time for an egg.

Turning into Colebourne Street, the way was blocked by fire engines and ambulances. Men in uniforms trotted past with blanket-covered stretchers.

"What's happened, please?" Valerie asked a policeman.

"Doodlebug, Madam. Direct hit on a block of flats. Digging survivors out now. Not many of 'em, I'm sorry to say."

Valerie walked a little further up the street. Colebourne Court had been torn apart. Half of the building lay in smoking rubble, the rest stuck up into the sky like a broken tooth. She stared fascinated for a moment. Floral wallpaper flapped in the breeze, fireplaces still clung to chimney breasts. Ludicrously, a set of brass fire irons, all polished and prim, sat in one of the hearths, waiting. Pictures hung crooked on the naked walls. Cats stalked over the rubble, inquisitive and calm, broken glass glittered on the ground.

Bombed out. The egg and the Smiths were forgotten. This was the perfect excuse.

The Wards swung into action. With no home, job or clothes Valerie was destitute and could no longer be ignored. The comforting little bank balance of a thousand pounds she kept to herself. Why pay for lodgings when you could get them for free?

From the moment when Gertie's elderly, suspicious parlour maid opened her mistress's Brook Street door, Valerie was gathered into a cocoon of practical kindness.

62

"Turned up again, have you?" The warm pressure of the Dowager Countess's hand on Valerie's arm belied her customary asperity. "Sit ye down. You look like a scarecrow. Don't suppose a bath would go amiss, then we've cold pheasant to put you on till lunchtime … What happened to your friends? The ones you lodged with."

"I'm afraid I've no ideas. Terribly selfish of me, but …"

"Stuff and nonsense. Got to look after number one first. I've got a pal at Scotland Yard. Pull a few strings. Find out what happened. Leave it to me."

A few telephone calls were all it took to transform her life. Eric was contacted at his Whitehall offices. His sister-in-law was in a pickle. Harassed, as he was, he came directly to his stepmother's house.

"You'd best go down to my wife at Dudley. Place is a hospital now, but at least you'll be safe. Gather you're looking for work in films."

Eric ran his eye over Valerie. A good face, a good figure, presence, too. Gertie's old negligee would be a test of anybody's self-confidence. What a fool Roddy was to have let her get away.

"We've some friends in the business, might be able to give you a hand. Anyway, first things first. Laura's expecting you tonight, she'll be glad of your company."

Valerie's thanks were just sufficiently effusive. She had a claim on these people after all; they should have done something about her before.

Dudley Hall was in Staffordshire. A rambling pile of masonry. The size of her brother-in-law's country residence was very reassuring. So, also, was the car sent for her as far as the station at Smearbourough Stack. In every sense, this was home ground, the fiefdom of the Wards.

Nothing could have been warmer than Laura's greeting. What an intelligent woman, Valerie wrote that night.

Her room, with its spindly Regency furniture, glistening damasks and testered bed was in satisfactory contract to the mean little apartment in Colebourne Court. Here, there were no shortages. Cows for milk, cream and butter, chicken for eggs. There was even coal. A bright fire burned in the polished steel grate, a convalescent hospital had to be kept warm.

Before she slept, Valerie vowed never to be cold or hungry again. Never to live among ugly things, in spaces that were too small, or with people who were not, well, there wasn't a word for that sort of thing. It was just the thing that mattered most. The morning brought an introduction to the hospital's formidable matron and new duties.

"Keep the men amused if you can," that a lady directed. "And keep out of my nurses' way."

"She's awfully nice really," Laura comforted. "Just terribly efficient and absolutely devoted to the men."

Valerie too devoted herself to the men. Far from keeping out of the nurses' way, she learned from them or rather, she learned from the patients themselves. It seemed silly to call for a nurse when all that was needed was a pillow plumping or a urine bottle passing. They were all such good friends.

"Might make a nurse if you trained," Matron observed critically. "Something to be said for a pretty face on the ward, bit of a kick start for the boys. Course wouldn't wash in a female ward, that kind of thing."

For several weeks, this peaceful, useful life was undisturbed. Talking and reading to the patients in the morning. Valerie spent the afternoons walking with them or wheeling them briefly in the wintry grounds. Sometimes, in the evening, she would give a one-woman concert with her ukulele. The favourites were 'We'll Meet Again' and 'Bluebirds Over the White Cliffs of a Dover'. Valerie sang them again and again in her strong unwavering voice. She gave pleasure and she was never tired of pleasing. Valerie was content. Instinct told her to rest. Her heart's desire would come to her.

Laura telephoned her husband in London. There was to be a small house party at Dudley over Christmas. Sam Goldwyn had been invited. Could he come? Yes, he had accepted.

"This is your chance, Val! Sam's a chum of Eric's. If he can do anything, I know he will."

She shivered with excitement. This was the small, crucial window of opportunity. The greatest film mogul of them all, and she would have him all to herself. Everything which had gone before had been leading to this moment.

For the next week she affected a sore throat. She must rest her voice for the Christmas concert. Every one of Laura's hand-me-down frocks was tried on. Valerie twisted and turned before the cheval mirror in her room. No, none of them would quite do. There was just time to go up to London and buy something with the hoard of clothing coupons she had received as gifts from Laura and her friends. Something white, innocent and pure.

It worked. Sam Goldwyn saw no reason why not. Valerie was 'kinda droll' and 'Could really belt those ditties out'. She had sex appeal, more self-confidence than ability, he remarked privately to Eric, but a little talent went a long way in the film industry. Push went even further.

"She's got plenty of that," Eric conceded. "More in common with Gertie than either of them like to think." He paused to put more chalk on his billiard cue. "Is she er, moral, would you say?"

Sam blew two surprised smoke rings from his cigar.

"I dunno, feller. She's a commodity. That's all I know. I guess she knows it too."

The task of giving Valerie a screen test was sub-contracted to Gainsborough Pictures Ltd at Shepherd's Bush.

"Just walk down that staircase nice and natural, babe. No, take the fur off. I don't like the fur. For Christ's sake loose that bloody handbag."

Valerie walked and ran up and down the studio staircase which led from nowhere to nowhere a score of times.

"No, don't act, just natural. I want to see how your body moves, how the camera likes your face. No! Cut the fussy movement with your hand. Natural, like I said, don't you broads ever listen!"

It wasn't easy. Executing a natural movement without motive, real or imagined, freezes the muscles of the face and stiffens the limbs.

Maurice Ostrer, or Oscar Lewin if going by his substitute name, pushed her to the edge, searching out the limits of her endurance. If Valerie were world class, which Lewin doubted, it would show sooner or later. He didn't give a damn who she was. Right now, she was meat on the slab. For the moment, all that was required was a great face on top of a good body all wrapped up in a thick skin. Chicks with temperament and a little talent were two a penny.

Lewin talked the international dialect of film people, even in his head. The harsh language of money showed on his face.

Valerie's smile never slipped. She'd get over this hurdle and show them all what she was made of. For her, this was just a formality. With the Wards and Sam Goldwyn behind her, how could she fail? But she knew things had to be made to look fair. The world of films was riddled with jealousy. She'd go through the mill like everyone else and make them respect her. Gertie Millar would eat her words.

Finally, Lewin was satisfied. He hardly needed to look at the reel. Experience told him that this was the kind of face beloved by the camera lens. A Vivien Leigh type. Mean? Well, maybe, you had to be mean to go places.

"You wanna read?"

She read one of Helena's speeches from *A Midsummer Night's Dream*. She read it well. No pause or hesitation, and not a smack of individuality either. Proficient but no poetry.

"Yeah," Lewin interrupted before Valerie had uttered the last ringing syllable. "Reckon you'll do, you're on the payroll. Twelve pounds a week."

Lewin knew Sam wanted to do Eric Dudley a favour. And Lewin wanted to have something in credit with Sam. Putting this chick on ice was no problem, there was always a walk-on part for a tasty piece like her.

"You want lunch? I got a table at the Ritz, some people coming, show you around."

"Oh, how kind you are to me. Of course, I'd absolutely love to!"

On the crest of a wave, the Ritz was the only place to go for lunch. The greyest of days is brilliant there. The light from the vast windows reflects in the arch-head looking glasses, shimmering the chandeliers and blazing the silver. And to those who knew, champagne fizzed faster at the Ritz than in other places.

She and Lewin were joined at a large round table in the window by a half a dozen people. Valerie's eyes devoured their faces, her memory caressed their names. Could they really be real? Stars from the giddiest heights of the film business. They were so handsome, intelligent and articulate. Even Alex Korda, with his plain face and round spectacles, was invested with the dazzlement of power. He'd got into bed with J. Arthur Rank, that's the way he put it.

"You ever fall out with these guys," he threw Lewin a challenging look. "Come to me for a film test, Mrs Ward." And he handed her a card right across the table. A Belgravia address, nothing now could go wrong.

As Lewin saw her into a taxi, Valerie wound down the window to speak to him.

"We forgot! When do I report to you for work? Remember, I still have to find myself a flat." She was terribly excited.

"No need, you're going straight down to Worthing. Great little repertory company they've got there. Solid experience, that's what you need, start at the bottom, live in theatrical digs, feel your way into the business."

"Worthing?"

"Yeah, seaside town on the south coast, very bracing, put the roses in your cheeks. See you later."

With her usual resilience, Valerie soon came to terms with the idea of Worthing. She would be a person of some significance there. It would be a sort of holiday, away from the demands of her more testing, natural background, a new adventure.

Theatrical digs, however, were rejected. The memory of Edna Smith and Colebourne Court was too fresh in her mind. She would take a flat of her own. Out of season, they should be cheap. With twelve pounds a week, she could afford the best address in town. She had promised herself, hadn't she, that she would never settle for anything less?

"But Val," Laura urged, "Wouldn't it be fun? You read such hilarious things about theatrical landladies. If I were you, I wouldn't miss it for the world!" Eric added his voice to that of his Countess.

"I think you're making a mistake, Val. Muck in with the rest, that's what Gertie would say, study the opposition and learn from it."

Worthing was not a success.

The pressure on accommodation was higher than Valerie had expected. The best flats were already taken by middle-class families from London escaping the bombing. Letting agents shook their heads at Valerie. All they could offer was single rooms with shared baths, it was not good enough.

Thoughtfully, the leading lady of the repertory company, a brassy blond trooper of some forty summers and a motherly soul at heart, had negotiated with her landlady to squeeze the new girl in. She was to have a camp bed in her own room, quite a compliment.

The landlady affected some gentility, but she had a cigarette permanently attached to the corner of her carmine-stained mouth. The ash grew in a long drooping curve and dropped off of its own accord, onto the floor, into the food. She kept the key of the bathroom around her neck. Baths were extra.

After a couple of nights of Carolyn Cockermouth's snores, the tickle of coarse blankets, not too frequently washed, suppers of ersatz sausage and chips fried in dirty fat, Valerie resumed her search.

That didn't please the producer. His horn-rimmed spectacles flashed with exasperation.

"You're supposed to be here at the Theatre, learning something. Not pounding the pavements looking for some non-existent penthouse."

"But I haven't even got a part."

"And until you show some commitment, young lady, you won't get one. Who do you think you are? Merle Oberon? Clark Gable? What's good enough for Carolyn is certainly good enough for you."

A small cheer from the wings confirmed the producer's view. Carolyn, centre-stage at that moment, wriggled her body from shoulder to hip with pleasure.

They were jealous, Valerie thought. It was very hurtful, it wasn't her fault they were all nobodies, but open hostility was something to which Valerie was unaccustomed. She did not like it.

"Well come on then, have you learned Loretta's lines?"

"Yes, of course I have," Valerie always learned her lines. In that respect she was rigorously professional, never needed a prompt.

The play was a domestic farce and it suited both Valerie's experience and talent. She had a neat sense of timing and no small gift for slapstick comedy. Loretta, the tall girl she was understudying, came back from her foraging errand in time to see Valerie enact some brisk, confusing stage business with beds and wardrobe doors. It was slick, gracefully done and with not a foot out of place. A complicated sequence. When she had finished, there was scattered, if grudging applause.

"Upper class bitch!" Loretta hissed between her teeth.

"I'd watch my mouth, if I were you, darling," Carolyn cooed in response as she screwed a Woodbine into her long cigarette holder.

"It doesn't do to make enemies in this business. The girl's got contacts." Her own eyes narrowed as she drew the smoke deep into her lungs.

Although Valerie found a bedsit on the sea front with a bath of its own and a tiny, curtained off kitchenette, her attempts to entertain the company there were disappointing.

It was not her fault; every question her colleagues asked was answered truthfully. They wanted to know who she was. The facts did not make her any better loved.

"All right for some."

"If you believe a word she says."

"Never short of the telling detail, though is she?"

"Funny. That's just what she is short of to my mind. She tells you the names with all their boring titles, and the places, how big they are and how grand, but it doesn't live. Stone cold."

Those were the women's complaints. The men fantasised aloud about coarse remedies.

"Nothing a good spanking wouldn't cure," Carolyn Cockermouth's leading man firmly believed. He said so nearly every night for three months in the cockroach-infested intimacy of the green-room bar.

"Screw her up to her neck, I would," said the juvenile male lead, over his half pint of mild.

"Get away! Never get the chance, mate," scorned the gnarled party who'd done everything from Alfred Doolittle to rear half of the horse in most pantomimes.

"I know the frigging type. Only puts it about where it'll be useful."

Valerie went back to Gainsborough Pictures. Her six-month sentence was only half over.

Lewin sighed. He might have known. Still, the producer down there said she had the makings; there was plenty she could learn in London.

Valerie got her first part.

"You're on contract to Rank," Lewin told her.

70

"Time to get something back for all we've put in. Report to Shepperton Studios tomorrow. Unless you make a complete ass of yourself, they've got something for you."

What they had was a walk-on part with two lines to go with it. A speaking part, just. Valerie was now classified as a starlet; her salary was very nearly doubled.

After the first week's rehearsal, in which she spent a great deal of time in a dressing gown doing nothing, she rented a mansion flat in the fashionable end of Kensington. It had two bedrooms and one for a maid. There was a minute dining room and from the bay window in the drawing room, if she craned her neck, she could see a patch of green, Kensington Gardens. The flat was sparsely furnished, and the carpets were worn. Maples were called in to correct the deficiencies.

A cook-general was next. The domestic employment agency in Beauchamp Place sent a number of girls round for Valerie to interview. It had to be in the evening because, as she explained, she had to be on the set so early. She enjoyed telling them that.

She was in the midst of regaling a stage-struck country girl with the doings of the Rank Films glitterati when her husband telephoned.

"Darling?"

"Who's this?" His voice, so close, seemed to emanate from a great distance in time. Like a long-delayed echo.

"It's Roddy, darling. Look, I'm at my club. I've had the devil's own job tracking you down. Eric said he wasn't sure where you'd moved. Had to get onto Gainsborough Pictures, they sent me onto Rank."

He went on talking as if nothing had happened.

"Look, I know I've been a rotter and all that, but we've got to talk, haven't we? Shall I come around or will you meet me at Quag's in an hour? Remember, there's Robert."

CHAPTER SIX

Quaglino's was crowded. In the available twelve square inches of space nearest the band, Roddy held Valerie to him tightly, his dinner jacket already damp.

"I shan't divorce you, of course."

An ear-splitting explosion of saxophone notes carried the words away. Valerie looked up in time to see the shape of them die on Roddy's lips. Enjoying herself, she blew the wisp of meaning away. Ridiculous, he couldn't have said that.

"I said," Roddy mouthed, pushing his face close to Valerie's ear, "I shan't divorce you."

A climactic drum solo made any reply impossible. Roddy's features wore an expression of beatific self-satisfaction. Emitting a peal of laughter, Valerie dragged him, protesting from the floor. She collapsed breathlessly onto the plush banquette beside their table.

"What were you trying to say to me?"

"I was telling you I don't intend to petition for divorce. We're a team, you and me. A going concern, or we could be." Roddy lifted the bottle from the bucket and turned it upside down, it was empty.

"Oh dear! Order some more, darling, won't you?"

Valerie made sure of her supply before deflating the supplier with bad news. Funny or tragic, life was quite impossible without champagne. Just now, life was hilarious, or ironic, it depended which way you looked at it. Poor Roddy what a dunce he was, there was nothing left between them but debts and failure.

"Darling, I'm going to divorce you. There's nothing for you to worry about." Valerie stretched her upper lip tight against her teeth, retouching her lipstick before snapping the compact shut.

"And as I don't suppose you've got any money, I shan't be coming onto you for any maintenance."

Roddy grasped her hand and held it, feeling the place where his ring should have been, while the waiter placed an ice-frosted pail on the table.

"On the bill, sir?" Roddy nodded.

"No more divorce talk. Let's drink to us, the three of us and the future. We'll have to start making plans, and some little brothers and sisters for Robert. Why don't we start on that tonight, darling? At your flat, I still love you, Val."

Valerie took the frothing champagne saucer from his hand in silence and put it down. It was a pity to ruin the evening, but some things would have to be made terribly plain.

"Roddy, you've got it all wrong. I'm fond of you, of course, but I don't love you. Not after what you did, and I'm going to divorce you. I'm still young and I've got the whole of my life in front of me. My career ..."

The beaming smile on Roddy's face faded abruptly.

"After what I did? Your career? Oh Val, I think you've got things a bit mixed up, haven't you? What on earth do you think you can divorce me for? I'm the one with grounds. You deserted me, but we've got a son, responsibilities and I'm prepared to forgive."

"You're prepared to forgive!" Valerie stormed at him.

"What about me. All that drinking ... the debts ... the rows."

"Average sort of performance for our crowd, I would have thought. You can't divorce a chap for being poor, or for having a few drinks. Those aren't grounds, desertion is."

"Being drunk enough to kill a man is grounds."

"Shut up!"

Nearby, the hum of conversation running a layer beneath the drumbeat stopped. This time, the stares were cold with surprise.

"Come on, let's get out of here, we've got some talking to do." Roddy signalled the waiter and signed the bill. Hustling her from the room, the pressure of his grasp on her elbow left a bruise.

Thrashing it out, at Valerie's flat, took most of the night.

The murder of Lord Erroll still lingered in the gossip of certain circles. Roddy and his wife had more reason than most to remember it but little desire to speak of it. "You stupid, blackmailing bitch!" Roddy flung the words at her. "You can't stick that one on me. Nobody knows who killed Joss, and if it hadn't been for you, I should never have had to wonder."

Valerie froze. What the hell was he talking about? She should never have agreed to see Roddy. It had been a mistake. She could have left him at Quaglino's. What was he doing here, standing in her beautiful new drawing room, spoiling things as usual? None of that awful business in Kenya need ever have been mentioned again.

"You'd better help yourself to whiskey or whatever you want. You can pour me a small one. I'm going to change out of this dress."

As she closed her bedroom door, the past came flooding back to her like a backwash of sewage. It was her fault, Valerie acknowledged to her reflection in the mirror. She should never have brought the matter up. Roddy knew where he stood without that, on shaky ground.

The night Joss died, Roddy had returned rolling drunk to her parents' house in Muthaiga. It was the sound of the Buick's squealing brakes that had woken her. Hours had passed since she'd last seen him. Opening the bedroom window, she had looked down to find him stumbling around in the dark bellowing like an enraged bull elephant. "Shut up, you fool, you'll waken the servants!"

Down the stairs, through the dim spaces she had crept, glancing nervously at the closed door of her parents' room as she passed. Please God don't let them wake up! She had managed to get Roddy inside and upstairs.

He collapsed on the bed like a dead man. Only dead men were silent, and Roddy would not stop talking.

Bit by bit, she had got it out of him, or most of it. Roddy had gone on from the Muthaiga Club to the Claremont nightclub after all. She hadn't wanted to go. First Roddy had taken her home and then driven to the Claremont, so much Valerie already knew.

According to Roddy's halting account, Joss and Diana had arrived there already and were quarrelling. Roddy didn't know what it was about. At the start, he'd tried to make peace between them, but Joss was angry, he had turned on Roddy.

"I wanted to kill the bastard, better he's dead, better for all of us. A bad man, I must have shot him. Where's he gone? I never meant to shoot him." Roddy twisted his head from side to side on the pillow feverishly.

Joss Hay and Diana had left the Claremont together. Roddy had blundered after them and followed them in Valerie's Buick to Diana's house. He'd waited outside the house until Joss started his car again. Roddy had chased him in the Buick, fast. Down the Ngong road, yes, that's where he'd woken up anyway, sober. He'd no idea how long he'd been unconscious. Roddy got out of the car and found Joss sprawled on the floor of the overturned Buick. He looked dead, a head wound. Then Roddy got back into Valerie's Buick and found his own revolver on the passenger seat beside him, there were two bullets missing.

Roddy had sat there in the car for some minutes, sweating. He couldn't remember shooting Joss. He had wanted to fight him, yes. Strangle him with his bare hands, but shoot him?

Valerie had shaken him then as hard as she could. It was no good. Roddy didn't remember where he'd gone next. Somewhere he'd stopped the car again. There was a bottle of brandy in the back. He'd drunk that, yes, all of it.

The facts had penetrated Valerie's brain rapidly. Where was the revolver now?

Leaving Roddy comatose on the bed, Valerie had pulled on some slacks and retraced her steps down the staircase. She would have to hurry. Soon the household would begin to wake. The revolver was there, still on the Buick's passenger seat.

What a fool Roddy was, but not guilty, this proved it. Catching sight of her father's head boy approaching from his quarters, she had done the only thing possible. She decided to trust him; there was no time for anything else.

Valerie beckoned to the elderly Kikuyu. He came and stood beside her, courteous and patient. She was Msabu Ward now. But to him, she would, always be Baba Valerie. His gaze followed the direction of her pointing finger, something in the car.

"You see that?" Puzzled, the Kikuyu nodded. A revolver in a white settler's car was routine.

"I am going to open the door of this car and you are going to lift it out." Valerie spoke to him in Swahili. "And then I want you to make sure it is never seen again … ever. Do you understand, Kinsu?"

Kinsu did. He took the revolver from the car and checking the safety catch, hid it from view amongst the folds of his robe.

By the time of Superintendent Poppy's visit to the house later in the morning, the supposed murder weapon was in the hands of Kinsu's granddaughter's husband. In a matter of days, the gun had travelled miles along the Rift Valley towards the Ugandan border, passing from hand to hand, exchanged many times for cattle. A Colt .32, there was nothing left to connect it to Roddy Ward, Muthaiga or the murder of Joss Hay.

Thanks to Valerie, whatever Roddy had or had not done, he was safe. They had never found Joss's murder weapon and they never would, it was too late, all over.

"You got out of that because of me, I think the least you can do is give me my freedom. It's not much to ask after what I did for you."

The expression in Roddy's eyes dried the words in her mouth. It was almost like pity.

"Val," Roddy slumped on the sofa opposite her. "Do you really believe I killed Joss?"

"Of course I don't, not really. Somebody framed you but …"

"Let's hope so. Here, you'd better have this," he leaned across and handed her a cut-glass tumbler with a finger of whiskey in it.

There was something in Roddy's voice that arrested the shuttle flight of the nail file in Valerie's hands. She refused the drink; her head ached with the champagne.

"Well, get on with it."

"The reason I went after Joss was, he said some terrible things about you, said you were an army mattress."

"That's enough!" Valerie cut him short, her face flaming with anger and mortification. "It's not true!"

"I know that, Joss did too, but he was roaring drunk at the time and so was I. That's not the point. The point is this; it gives me a motive for murder and you a motive for helping me."

"But I didn't know. I didn't know what he said about me until this moment," Valerie got up and walked swiftly, nervously about the room pacing the pale grey carpet, looking at her shadowy reflection in the mirror and polished cabinets. Oh God! How she hated Joss Hay, he had never wanted her.

"Yes, but nobody knows what you did and didn't know. It could look as if you were an accessory, so Val, give me away, and I'll give you away. It's like I said, darling. We stand or fall together, and I don't want a divorce. I love you.

Leaning against the back of the sofa, Roddy shook the empty glass in his hand. "Say, can I have another of these?"

Valerie flew at him then, biting and scratching like a cat. Laughing, Roddy held her from him easily. It was good to hold her again, even like this. Shrill with panic, she showered him with insults, turning spiteful knives of truth in his heart. She didn't want him for a husband. He'd had his chance and failed. She spat the venom, darting it between every gap in his defences.

Valerie screeched and Roddy, with the last surviving shreds of his pride destroyed, boomed out his pain. It went on for hours; neither of them noticed the tenant above banging on the ceiling. When the doorbell rang at six o'clock in the morning, Valerie went to answer the door smoothing the contortions of rage from her features and dabbing away the tears.

"I say, couldn't you two just put a sock in it?"

Stupefied, Valerie stared at the man in the brocade dressing gown. He was so handsome. A blond, pre-Raphaelite angel. His voice, like the quizzical lift of his eyebrow was lightly satirical. Whatever must she look like?

"And by the way, here's my card."

"Dennis Dangan," it read. "Barrister at Law." The answer to a prayer, another of fate's timely interventions. Valerie turned the card over and pouted charmingly, like a child caught out of bed by a strict nanny

Dennis fell in love with her there and then.

Valerie was late at the studio that morning and although immaculate as usual, she looked drawn.

"Like death warmed up," the studio manager snarled at her. "That's not what we pay you for. You'd better go home and get some sleep. We'll rejig the shooting schedule and do your scenes tomorrow. Don't let it happen again, there's plenty of pretty girls about who'd kill to be in your shoes."

Valerie knew it and she bore the rebuke with dignity. Excuses would be a waste of everyone's time. Mollified by her silence and downcast eyes, the studio manager put a car at her disposal.

"The quicker you get some shut-eye the better. Rank want to do some portrait shots of you tomorrow so pull yourself together. Let's see that face of yours dew-drop fresh in the morning … or else."

It occurred to Valerie that what she needed was a lawyer. They were expensive, and the results of their work could be neither worn, nor eaten nor displayed. But Dennis Dangan, so obviously a gentleman, would help.

Life's every need, it seemed to Valerie, was satisfied by resources close to hand. Roddy was the nettle sting and Dennis was the dock leaf. Valerie giggled to herself, pleased with the cleverness of her own comparison.

"Back so soon, Madam?" The hall porter enquired with cheerful inquisitiveness.

"I wonder if you can help me, George."

78

"Anything, Madam, always glad to be of assistance to a lady like yourself." He touched the peak of his cap in salute. She was smashing, was Miss Ward.

"I'm afraid I had …. a little party in my flat last night," Valerie improvised. "And I think we disturbed my neighbour directly above. I should so like to apologise, perhaps a note. Could you just tell me …?"

George Potter told her everything he possibly could. Mr Dangan? He was a lovely gentleman, he was. Of course, he was really Lord Dangan. Viscount, he was. Heir to Lord Cowley. Of course, he was one of those there theatrical agents. Well, he was a lawyer too. His lordship spent most of his time messing around with actors and actresses, saving Madam's presence.

Valerie floated into the lift, out of it on the second floor, along the corridor, and into her flat. Just think, if she had never had that awful row with Roddy, she would have never met him, never have known who he was. Dennis Dangan, Lord Dennis Dangan. As she undressed and slid between the sheets, Valerie tasted his name over and over again. Dennis, she was sure, would soon be everything to her. She felt beautiful again.

When she woke, Valerie examined herself in the looking glass strategically placed opposite her bed. Perfect. Misty, like a Renoir painting, well, one of those painter people, anyway, rosy and golden with eyes like Kashmiri sapphires, gifts from God not to be wasted. Dennis Dangan didn't stand a chance.

Dennis wanted only the chance to know Valerie and it came on the following Saturday morning.

He was standing by the porter's desk when she emerged from the lift glorious in a full, soft blue cashmere coat that matched her eyes.

"'Ere she is now, sir," George Potter removed the momentary awkwardness. "I was just telling Mr Dangan here 'ow you was in the films."

The naked admiration in Dennis's eyes told Valerie all she needed to know.

Valerie flushed entrancingly, sweeping her lashes down over her eyes. She removed one elegantly-gloved hand from the little muff she carried and held it out to him.

"I was going to write to you and say how dreadfully ashamed I was."

Dennis would not let her continue. Where was she going? Might he give her a lift? Might he be so impertinent as to offer her lunch, or dinner, or a drink? Thinking quickly, Valerie agreed to a drink in the basement cocktail bar beneath the flats that evening. For lunch and dinner, regrettably, she was engaged. To have been free for either would have been terribly gauche, but of course, Dennis upbraided his own crassness. How could he have thought otherwise? He would look forward to it so much.

Dennis would feel privileged to look after Valerie's career, he said, and meant it. Valerie confided some of her marital problems, not all. Dennis knew many good men in the profession. If necessary, they would fight for her freedom all the way to the Privy Council, sword in hand.

"Will you dine with me one day next week?" Dennis asked as he parted from her that evening. Nothing could have been more touchingly forlorn than his face when he handed her into the taxi destined to carry her away from him. "You're quite the nicest thing that's happened to me for a long, long time. Where are you going?"

'The Ivy," Valerie told him, startled that he should ask. Dennis paid the fare.

Like any woman in love, Valerie spent a fortune not only on clothes but also on embellishments for her little flat. The thousand pounds she had won from Farouk was gone. There were wages to pay, Valerie could not cook. Shoe leather omelettes, chops with the consistency of coke and glutinous meringues, Dennis had borne it all with the charity of the true worshipper.

The turnover in maids quickened as Valerie and Dennis allowed their relationship to blossom in the open. Friends, both hers and his, they were so often the same anyway, were in and out of the flat day and night, rowdy parties, the noise and the mess.

80

It wasn't as if Valerie was easy going. Oh no, Mrs Ward wanted everything just so. Gleaming surfaces smelling of polish, not so much as a thread on the carpet and woe betide the hapless woman who let a soiled ashtray escape her attention. No, Valerie was not an easy person to work for. If anything, her happiness sharpened her appetite for perfection.

Valerie's contract with Rank was coming to an end. It might well be renewed, she thought. But the studio system was stultifying. It stopped you taking chances and they got you on the cheap.

"Take a chance then, darling," Dennis urged indulgently. "Tell them you won't renew. How I should like to see their faces!"

"Nice knowin' you kid," they said from makeup to scene building. "What you going to do? Settle down with some nice guy and have kids? Best things."

No longer quite as confident, Valerie went to Korda's offices as he had once invited her to do, but the casting director was a woman and she brushed Valerie off like a fly.

"I'm sorry, we've nothing for you. You were with Rank? What happened?" The casting director was too busy to listen to Valerie's reply. "Oh yes, I know. Mr Korda's very good at making idle promises to odd girls but I make the decisions here."

A nasty, jealous woman, Valerie had thought her. She would never go there again. But the problem remained. What should she do next; there was money to think of?

"You need never give the sordid subject a thought while I'm around Val, darling," Dennis told her.

Valerie was mightily relieved to hear it. Dennis already paid the maid's wages and the previous month, he'd paid her rent as well, things were so terribly expensive.

Dennis then had a most exciting suggestion. Trevor Ransome was doing a film and was on the lookout for a likely lass to fill a small role. Valerie should go to the audition.

Trevor Ransome!

The day of the audition, it seemed to Valerie that there must be a hundred girls waiting in the corridors of the administrative block at Ealing studios. What chance did she have? Every chance, she told herself firmly, lifting her chin. She had experience and contacts. Looking into her powder compact mirror, she knew she had never looked lovelier, that was Dennis. The wait was interminable.

It gave Valerie plenty of time to think. The experience of love had changed her. She realised now that she had never really loved Roddy. Or if she had, it had been something quite different.

Three hours later, it was her turn, the seventy-fifth in line. The star glanced at Valerie and decided. Dennis Dangan's girlfriend looked fine. They said she wasn't much of an actress really, but so what? A favour to the future Marquess of Mann might one day bear dividends. Ransome was a Newmarket saddler's son and a snob by nature.

"You've worked before, haven't you?"

"I have, yes, Mr Ransome."

"So, there's a reel of you somewhere." It was a statement, not a question. "If it's all right, the part's yours; you're just what I want,"

Valerie never knew how she got home to Kensington.

"I got it! Oh, darling, I got it!

"Of course, you did, my beloved," Dennis answered her with a sly smile. He had done quite a lot of spadework himself. A word here, a suggestion and a couple of drinks there. Still in the end, it all came down to Val herself, he was proud of her.

"And to celebrate, we shall dine at the Ritz and dance until first light. You can have as much champagne as I think wise for a girl of your age."

It was a surprise party. Dennis had got around twenty people to meet them at the Ritz, with more coming on after dinner. Film people, all of them, though Eric and Laura Dudley were there. Congratulations, hugs, kisses and of course, champagne. And everybody, but everybody, called each other darling.

"Have you seen anything of Roddy lately?" Laura asked Valerie. They sat side by side in the rococo magnificence of the powder room repairing the ravages of joy.

"No," Valerie sighed. "He won't let me divorce him, you know. Or he says he'll cross petition if I do."

"Don't be silly, darling," Laura flourished a swans-down powder puff. "He'll have to, he's got a lady friend ... didn't you know?"

Valerie did not know. She had pushed Roddy to the back of her mind. He was a dark cloud on the far horizon of her happiness, one that would not go away.

"Well, he has," Laura confirmed. "And if you ask me, the lady's expecting a baby. Or that's the rumour. So, I shouldn't worry if I were you darling. Sooner or later, he'll be begging you for a divorce."

No news could have given Valerie greater relief. They walked all the way home through Green Park and deserted streets in the summer's day dawn. Now and again they stopped just for the pleasure of gazing into each other's eyes. London bobbies finishing a weary night's duty on the beat smiled at the flaxen-haired couple in evening dress. Lovers. The river of a clattering milk float started to sing. There were angels dining at the Ritz and a Nightingale sang in Berkeley Square. The song could have been written for them alone. Valerie saw and heard nothing, outside the circle of Dennis's arms, nothing existed.

"Wilt thou, Valerie Maud, take me Dennis David Jonathan," Dennis intoned on the doorstep of Kensington Close, half solemn, half laughing. "To be thy lawful wedded husband?"

Valerie said that she would.

CHAPTER SEVEN

There was no rush either to announce the engagement or name the wedding day. Valerie had her reasons. Some of them, Dennis reluctantly understood, others, he was not told of.

Her delicacy in not wishing to announce her engagement before she was divorced from Roddy Ward was also admirable. The divorce itself, he was convinced, was a formality. Twelve weeks from start to finish, at the very most. A little patience and then she would be his.

Darkly, Dennis had begun to suspect that Valerie would never play a Colonel film role. Although most were careful to drop the subject when he was around, he caught the fag end of industry tittle-tattle. Little Valerie Ward had reached her ceiling, and a low one it was too.

Dennis's heart ached for her. Val had worked so hard to achieve the little she had. Let her live with her illusions as long as she liked, she'd earned them, he would be there to comfort her when they shattered.

Immediately after Dennis's proposal, she had written, unthinkingly, in high excitement to her mother. Mummie, she was quite sure, would simply adore Dennis. He was witty, charming, generous and terribly well connected. They were head over heels in love. Valerie would have married Dennis Dangan if he had been a bus conductor. Except of course, that one just didn't meet the bus conductors, did one? Oh, darling Mummie, I am the luckiest girl alive to have found him. I know I don't deserve him, not really.

It was those last words that impressed themselves most forcibly on Mrs Skelton. She knew her daughter and dearly though she loved her, she would not have put humility top of the list of her virtues.

Only the nearest possible approximation to true love could have produced this effect on Valerie.

"I think it will stick," she remarked to Bobby as they sat in their Muthaiga garden. "Not many men can offer a girl a position like that and put up with her working as well." She handed him the photograph of Dennis, which Valerie had enclosed as she spoke. "A much better type than Ward."

"Looks a proper Nancy to me," Bobby answered her gruffly after a cursory glance at the photograph. He was more interested in Robert and the child's crows of delight as his black nurse sent him sailing higher and higher in the air on his new swing. The pain of losing his grandson to a man he didn't know outweighed any satisfaction in his daughter's success.

"Nonsense, Bobby," Alice almost snatched the picture from him. "We must be practical. Robert belongs with his mother and I think this Mr Dangan might do very well. He looks sensitive and intelligent to me."

"Oh aye," said Bobby pulling on his pipe. "Well, that'll make a nice change. Let's hope he's solvent an'all."

"That's enough now," Alice called to the nurse. "Don't let him get over excited before bed.

Robert, fat-legged and smiling, ran to his grandmother and scrambled onto her lap. He loved the way she smelled, the soft strength of her arms.

His memories of Valerie were dim. She was a Christmas-tree-fairy presence in his life. Glitteringly remote. Conscientiously, Alice kept her memory ever before him. A person called 'Mummie' in England, who loved him so much was working very hard so that he could go to England too. Robert had no great opinion of this place called 'England'. He wanted to stay at home with Granny.

Once, after his prayers, they had said a prayer for Mummie in England. "Do I have to go to England? I want to stay here with you and Grandpa forever."

Alice had regarded him sorrowfully. "And I should like you to, sweetheart. But we mustn't be selfish. Your Mummie will be missing you quite dreadfully and what would she say to me if I'd let you forget her? She'd be very cross and then Granny would cry."

The prospect of the biggest and strongest person in his life crying was too awful to contemplate. Robert, burdened at four years old with responsibility for his elders' emotions, vowed to do whatever was needed to prevent Granny from crying.

"Is that letter from Mummie?" he asked bravely. Each day now he lived in silent dread of being torn from the safety of his grandparent's home. Alice nuzzled his head, sick with fear of the parting that must come soon. "Yes, it is. Mummie's got a lovely new job and has met a nice gentleman who she says she's going to marry. So, you'll have a new Daddy and a beautiful new home, isn't it exciting?"

Robert's heart sank. Inwardly, he steeled his infant courage. Granny must have no reason to cry. They must all smile all the time. Then everything would be all right.

A few days later, Alice wrote to Valerie. She was, she said, overjoyed to hear of her daughter's happiness. It would surely be sensible if she were to book a passage and bring Robert over to meet his new stepfather so that they could all get to know each other before the wedding. Could Valerie please give some idea of the proposed date?

Reading her mother's letter, Valerie found that Robert, a distant reality, had come home to roost. She was too young for motherhood; life was so rich and full. The truth was, that Robert had ceased to play any part in her life. He had no function that Valerie could identify. She had her career now and Dennis, Robert did not fit into either of these galaxies of Valerie's universe. Dennis wanted him, of course, but did she? She loved him, she thought, she must do, he was her son. Somehow, the fact rang hollow in Valerie's head. Meaningless.

A day later, a solution appeared to offer itself. A letter from Roddy's solicitors stated that she could divorce him on grounds of his own adultery. There would be no question of any financial settlement, but Mr Ward intended to apply for custody of the only child of the marriage.

Valerie shook with a combination of guilt and some kind of unmentionable hope. She rang Laura at Dudley Hall. No, Roddy wasn't there but he would be that evening as it happened. Had Laura heard about Roddy's idea of applying for custody?

"Yes, actually, I have. Naturally, I told him he didn't stand a chance, the whole thing's unthinkable. The court always awards custody to the mother unless there's some terribly good reason why it shouldn't."

"Like what?"

"Darling, why don't you ask Dennis these things? He's the one who's qualified to answer them, much the best person. All I know is that Roddy's got a hare-brained scheme to give Robert to some childless Ward cousins to bring up. He'd be fine, but that's not the point, Roddy thinks it is. He says Robert is a Ward and ought to be with his own family, all that kind of thing, you know. Anyway, it won't come to anything; I shouldn't give it another thought if I were you. Dennis will know how to deal with it."

But Valerie did give it some thought. She decided to say nothing to Dennis just yet. A childless couple with the name of Ward? Why not? It might be the best thing after all. In the meantime, there was no hurry for anything; she would see how things developed. Alice Skelton got a letter informing her that Roddy Ward was seeking custody of her grandson. It might, Valerie wrote, be the best thing for Robert himself

Alice had a mild heart attack.

The news disturbed Valerie, of course. She loved her mother, but once reassured that she was out of immediate danger, Valerie was not sorry that Mrs Skelton's energy, was for the time being, a spent force. She had acquired other interests that lay outside either the dilemma over Robert, her work or her engagement - money.

In Valerie's experience, that desirable commodity was inextricably linked with men. Dennis alone, could not or would not supply all her wants. It would be a long time before he inherited the title and his tastes were simple, Valerie's were not.

Secure in Dennis's unswerving devotion and solid financial support, Valerie had begun to chafe at the domestic round. Dennis was beginning to behave like a married man.

"We really had better get our finances in order, Val," he said. "We can't go on at this rate. Look at all the hospitality we hand out to people, we don't get a tenth of it back, and you really don't need a full-time, live-in maid, you never get on with them and they're never very satisfactory. Couldn't you manage with a daily two or three times a week?"

"Of course, I need a maid," Valerie stated firmly, "in my position."

"Oh, come off it, Val," Dennis waved a sheaf of unpaid bills in exasperation. "Let's try and keep our feet on the ground for once. We're not yet married, your choice let me remind you and …"

"That's not fair," Valerie allowed a few tears to shine in her eyes. "You know I'm worried about Mummie."

But for once, Dennis was not to be deflected. He had his say. Accordingly, Valerie made certain radical adjustments to her routine. As Dennis turned the financial tap off, she began to accept invitations from other men.

It all started innocently enough. A dinner now and again, when Dennis was away, a tea dance at the Ritz, perhaps. And little presents, all perfectly respectable, Valerie excused herself. Anyway, Dennis was smothering her. She needed to get out, but one thing led to another, soon, longer interludes were suggested, greater distances and deeper involvement. Oblique hints from this unofficial boyfriend and that, that the presents would get correspondingly larger, ensnared Valerie. It wasn't too difficult to arrange. There was a girlfriend in the country, she told Dennis, who was pining for a visit.

"The poor dear doesn't have much fun and I bring a touch of glamour into her life. You must know I don't really want to leave you this weekend, but I feel a duty to cheer poor Irene up. It's only right when people have been so much less fortunate than one has oneself."

Dennis would kiss her and call her his 'unselfish little saint'. Neither jealousy nor suspicion were in his nature. He sped her errands of mercy with blessings. If a chap engaged himself to a girl like Valerie, he must be prepared to share her sometimes.

The Irenes, Sylvias and Colonelies on whom Valerie so thoughtfully bestowed her brightness were really Toms, Dicks and Harrys. Valerie was an expensive playmate for a man, but then, she was rewarding.

Her caution when fully clothed was juxtaposed with an exciting abandon in bed. Her arousal by Dennis had released a more genuine seam of inventiveness in her than the stage ever would. Once her hyacinth eyes had clouded over and her breath came short and quick, Valerie's sense of fun found its truest expression. She could play rough, too. There was a score of men who, exploring the nail gouges on their backs and buttocks, exulted at the memory.

No man ever dared to entertain Valerie on the cheap. On the contrary, they were grateful for her exclusive all-embracing passion. It might last more than one weekend. Whether it did or not, there was always some little memento of the enchanting conspiracy. A pretty watch, a diamond brooch, a collar of pearls or best of all, a large cheque.

"So sweet of you! You are a naughty man, I really ought not to accept this," she would exclaim girlishly as her surprisingly-capable hands closed over the tributes. Not everything was easy.

Clement Watkyn-Dane, for example, was agony. He sold Rolls Royces on Park Lane. The third son of a coal-owing family, in Wales, he said he was. There was not enough coal to go around five brothers, he said. "Alack and Alas." So charming. His black curls, ever so slightly oily and fascinatingly symmetrical, framed a dark, even-featured face.

He began by taking her to the British Museum, which she found rather odd. The Greek vases, of which there were a lot, were chief interest, and to Valerie's glazing eyes, very dull they were as well. The vases, Clement pointed out, were painted with chaps who looked a lot like him. He had a point, Valerie agreed.

In a place near Oxford on the Banbury road, Valerie suddenly saw the point of the vases and the painted penises turned out to be less than humorous, stark reality, in fact.

Valerie had drunk close to a bottle of champagne, but she sobered fast when Clement's own cock sprang out of his underpants with all the charm of the truncheon in a *Punch and Judy Show*. She braced her back against the buttoned satin of the headboard. A bargain, albeit unspoken, had been struck. She scorned to flinch; one must see things through to the end.

He launched himself upon her with joy. A real woman at last. Valerie spread her legs, knowing that she was as dry as a desert. It was a noble leap into a universe of pain. How she would disguise it, she couldn't imagine, she need not have worried. Clement's member, as he called it, didn't know the difference between a reluctant lover and the Bank of England's strong room. Muscle and tissue were nothing to him. Valerie's shrieks only urged him to deeper, more violent thrusts. It was always the way. Women loved it, plumbed them to their very depths, it did, as the dew of Valerie's tears upon his shoulder told him. Clement climaxed and was still. Valerie could hardly believe she was still alive, suppose he wanted to do it again

"You'll search the world over," Clement grunted, "before you'll feel the measure of a man like me again. Marry me, why don't you?"

Before she could answer, Clement was snoring. Valerie cushioned the soreness between her legs with her hand and slept warily on the edge of the bed.

In the morning, Clement wanted more. His wretched thing was stiff as a broom handle and almost as long.

A compromise was called for; Valerie licked and sucked him into submission. A sticky lake of stinking semen between her breasts was the penalty. Repulsive, but painless.

He gave her a very ordinary string of pearls. They looked like a row of bad teeth, but real enough. Small, uneven and yellow. Valerie gazed disdainfully upon them.

"Clement! What a large gesture."

Unconscious of sarcasm, Clement Watkyn-Dane grinned as Valerie fingered the pearls. Val was good value, and he'd given value in return. A deal was a deal, mutual satisfaction.

The story of Clement and his cock was told repeatedly. It always got a laugh. Something amusing, Valerie always said, that happened to a friend. The coarse story dropped innocently from her lips, leaving them as pure and pretty as before she had spoken. Unsuspicious, Dennis, too was amused by the tale.

Prostitution was not a word in Valerie's vocabulary.

Only love, or fun, nothing else could have justified her accepting so much kindness at the hands of her friends. It was nice to think too, that none of her 'dependents' need be disappointed. Valerie's conscience was clear, and her diary innocent of any entry regarding these adventures.

Dennis found out.

Valerie was betrayed inadvertently by one of the transient bachelors who haunted Kensington Gate Mansions. It had been foolish to play with fire so near to home, but then, she had expenses. The danger had added spice to the overnight sojourn in a flashy chromium-plated hotel just outside Basingstoke.

Dennis confronted her one day as she got home from the studio. A pair of emerald earrings lay in his open palm.

"What did you pay for these, Val?" he asked her quietly as she removed her hat. "I've never seen you wear them. They're new, aren't they?"

Valerie backed away, her face drained of all colour. "How dare you go through my things! What gives you the right?"

"Where did you get them, Val?" Dennis stood his ground.

"My mother," Valerie improvised cleverly but her voice shook. "She gave them to me as a wedding present when I married Roddy."

Dennis placed them slowly on the hall table. "In that case darling, I owe you a most humble apology. I suppose, if I ask your mother what she paid for them, so I can work out whether or not I can afford to give you a matching piece for our wedding, she won't mind, will she?"

Valerie was rooted to the spot. Her tongue worked in her mouth, there was no saliva, Dennis's voice went on, inexorably soft and very, very dangerous.

"You see, I know that's what you like, Val, collecting jewellery. It's a funny thing, but there's a chap downstairs in the bar at the moment talking about the cost of a pair of emerald earrings he bought at Blooms the other week.

A tip for a lady friend, a firecracker in the sack, he said. A starlet, no less, lives here, in this building, he says. Blonde with blue eyes and the neatest little figure you ever saw."

Dennis was silent for a moment, his features working. Valerie stood frozen with horror, there was no escape.

"You must forgive a jealous man, darling, but I couldn't help thinking how like my Val this fellow's lady friend sounded. Of course, I knew it couldn't be. What a fool I felt, coming up here and searching round in your jewel case like a burglar. I had to be quite, quite sure you see. And then I found this box, with Blooms printed on the satin inside the lid. Just a coincidence, I know that now. After all, Blooms will keep records of these sales, and I know the man's name. I can check, so there'll be absolutely no need for me to ever doubt you again, will there, Val?"

Dennis had not trained as a barrister for nothing. Valerie resorted to remorse and crumpled in a sobbing heap. She could not afford to lose Dennis, nor did she wish to. She loved him more than she had loved any other man.

Dennis wept himself. The sight broke Valerie's heart.

They talked all night. Valerie confessed and Dennis, pierced to the very marrow of his bones by her evident sorrow, forgave her. Valerie had never acted any part with more desperate sincerity.

"It's all over now, darling," he said as she lay in his arms towards dawn. For once, her lovely face was ravaged by tears. Dennis kissed it repeatedly, more moved by its devastation than he had ever been by its beauty. "We'll set a date for the wedding, and then we must look for a house. Somewhere with a garden for Robert, he will be our son, I shall adopt him, don't worry anymore."

There was one other thing. Dennis made Valerie promise to return all the gifts she had received from men other than himself. Unutterably grateful that her engagement was safe, Valerie promised before she slept.

The next day, she had recovered complete command of her senses. It was impractical to return the gifts. The money, about which Dennis knew nothing, had been largely spent, and the jewels, well, it would be so embarrassing and hurtful to her friends. Dennis didn't realise. So, Valerie rented a safe deposit box in a branch of the Westminster bank and left the jewels there. She walked away from the bank's premises completely happy. She had fulfilled the spirit of Dennis's law, gone as far as she could, a sensible compromise. There was a spring in her step.

Dennis embarked on a policy of continual, tender surveillance. His beloved, fallible Valerie, should not be exposed to temptation, as far as practicable, they went everywhere together, and when they must be apart, Dennis made sure that he knew where Valerie would be and with whom.

There was one place in which he had absolute confidence, Coneyhurst. The house, which lay conveniently close to Wyton Airfield, belonged to an old RAF friend of Dennis's. He and his open-faced Scottish fiancée were lively, wholesome company. They had a welcome for anyone who loved aircraft and flying. Many a time, Valerie's weekend flying lessons would end in an impromptu supper party around Coneyhurst's generous dining table.

Valerie never got off the ground in the role of temptress here. She was engaged, wasn't she? Off limits. Dennis had every reason to feel secure.

He was unconcerned when the grandson of a famous aircraft manufacturer and his wife were bidden to join the party at Coneyhurst one evening. Nothing could have been more natural. Wherever interest was focussed on aeroplanes, this couple were eagerly sought after. They begged leave to bring a house guest of their own.

"Do anything to come, old boy. Snag is we have an old school chum of mine staying. Dick Barwick can't very well leave him on his own."

Of course, Richard Barwick was invited. The occasion was informal. One more would make no difference.

"Hell's bells!" Coneyhurst's future mistress railed at her fiancé, "Have you ever seen that man eat? I just hope the food stretches, that's all. He drinks enough for three normal men," she added bitterly. Richard Barwick's reputation went before him.

Valerie did not know Richard Barwick, nor did Dennis. His arrival, a noisy, house-filling affair, shook Coneyhurst to the foundations. His huge body blocked the light of the westering sun shafting through the windows. People had a tendency to lean away from Richard Barwick. Like the shadow of his bulk, the bassoon note of his voice was oppressive.

Valerie was seated next to Richard at dinner, the other women had refused. It was hardly surprising.

Many questions were shot from the side of his mouth when he could spare a moment from his plate or from dominating the table talk. Valerie's negative replies were ignored; she might as well have lacked the power of speech entirely. Dennis, seated on Valerie's other side, was distracted by the general conversation.

Throughout the meal, Barwick's left hand wandered over Valerie's thigh. Repeatedly, she threw the hand from her. Unperturbed by the rebuff it came back, over and over again. It seemed less a part of Richard's body than some dreadful mechanical attachment.

94

Squeezing and kneading from knee to hip joint, the hand was never still. Once it insinuated itself beneath the damask napkin that lay on her lap finding the fork in her legs.

A low moan escaped Valerie's parted lips.

"Darling! Are you all right?" Dennis turned to her in alarm. Her eyes looked shocked, sightless.

He had seen that look so often before, when they were alone in her bed, but of course, in these circumstances, he did not make the connection. Valerie did not know how to extricate herself.

"Yes, yes. I'm all right," she muttered the words in a gruff, funny little voice. The faces round the table swam before her eyes. Richard Barwick was speaking. The lady on Dennis's left claimed his attention once more. Valerie was back in her capsule of confusion and appalled fascination.

After the dessert was eaten, the ladies rose. It wasn't the usual practice at Coneyhurst, to leave the men alone with their cigars and decanters, but at a signal from their hostess, all the women guests prepared gratefully to leave the dining room. Anything to get away from that frightful man's voice.

"You boys take as long as you want."

"We have masses to talk about."

Richard Barwick got up from his chair to assist Valerie from hers. There was a moment's check whilst she sought her handbag, lost beneath the table.

Richard dived down to find it for her and in the general confusion of skirts and chair legs, ran his hand up from her ankle to the slack gusset of her cami-knickers. Reeling with a sense of unreality, she took her handbag and left the dining room, Dennis patted her shoulder as she passed

"I should get a breath of fresh air, if I were you, darling. See you later."

Shortly after this, Dennis went to America.

The separation was not to last more than four weeks. Commissioned to deal with some business affairs of his father's in the States, Dennis left Valerie behind deliberately. It wasn't easy.

"I hope you don't mind, Val," he said casually as he unpacked a half-dozen new shirts ordered for his trip. "But I've jacked up a recording test with Parlophone for you. You'll need to pick out a couple of songs … work on them for a bit and then this studio here," he handed her a card, "will help you cut a demonstration disc. Don't neglect your voice, it deserves an audience." Valerie skipped to the piano.

Conveniently, Mrs Skelton wrote. She was quite recovered from her minor heart attack, and proposed embarking for England with her husband and Robert, almost immediately. Her doctors thought a sea voyage the best possible convalescence for her. The business of Robert's future must certainly be sorted out, and besides, she was impatient to meet her new son-in-law. By the time her letter arrived, the Skeltons were already sailing home. Valerie must certainly remain behind to see to the arrangements; there was much to be done.

A temporary nanny must be recruited for Robert, a flat to accommodate the Skeltons for a longish stay, must be rented, and of course, their daughter must be there to greet them when they docked. The wedding plans could then go ahead without further delay. On that point, Dennis displayed some of the firmness he generally held in reserve.

"By the time I'm back, darling," he said. "You'll have set a date unless you've changed your mind, that is and the next time I cross the pond, you'll come with me as Lady Dangan, or not at all."

Valerie drove him down to Southampton herself. Dennis had a first-class stateroom on the Queen Mary. For once, he was travelling under his true identity, all part of the campaign. Lord Dangan. A certain amount of flattering fuss was made of the young nobleman and his pretty fiancée.

It would probably have happened anyway, but Dennis left nothing to chance. He knew Valerie's strengths and weaknesses in equal measure. The deferential smiles of stewards and purser's assistants were well lubricated with cash. Dennis was not ashamed to fight for Valerie with any weapons that came to hand. For better or worse, he loved her.

Valerie with her parents – Bobby and Alice Skelton

Family home in Nyali, Mombasa

Valerie with her parents – Bobby and Alice Skelton

Alice and Bobby with 'Pekin'

Robert with Grandma (Alice)

Macheria and Kinsu (servant boys)

Roddy and Valerie with their best man, Lizzie Lezard on
their wedding day at the District Commissioner's
Office in Nairobi

Robert and Valerie

Robert and Valerie on his first birthday –
25th August 1943

Richard and Valerie Barwick

Richard and Valerie Barwick with Robert – Port Said 1949

As the tugs pulled the great liner away from the quayside, Valerie knew that she wanted to be Lady Dangan, nobody else. What a fool she had been to make Dennis wait.

Much of the time, she was occupied with estate agents' particulars. Finding a flat for her parents was the first priority. What would they expect? There were so many it was hard to decide which to inspect and which to ignore.

She supposed that Dennis must be banished from her own flat until the wedding now. And Robert? Where was he to go? Would he suddenly be her responsibility ... or what? Perhaps he could continue to live with her mother and father until this awful legal business was sorted out.

Only two days after Dennis's departure, Valerie opened an incomprehensible letter from her solicitors.

Unless awarded custody of the child of the marriage, Mr Ward would repudiate the child. 'Perhaps you would consider your further instructions in the light of this development and communicate them to us in due course ...' What on earth were they talking about? If only Dennis were here. He always dealt with the solicitors

The rest of the mail was as bad. Dennis had paid the rent on the flat up until the end of the quarter, but electricity, gas and telephone bills flooded in. The restaurant bills she had signed in the basement of Kensington Gate Mansions and elsewhere were brought politely to her attention. Surely these people realised it was Dennis who paid for things like that. What was the point of harassing her about it all?

Not unaware of these accounts, Dennis knew exactly how long they could be staved off. Long enough to give Valerie a fright without actually exposing her to embarrassment. It would, he had calculated, do her no harm to realise his value as a provider. She would be very glad to see him on his return. There were other things of which he was not aware.

A furrier had remodelled a phantom beaver stole. He was suing for payment. So was a jeweller who had copied in paste a pair of diamond dress clips Dennis had given her. Valerie had sold them to pay the lingerie shop in Beauchamp Place, she couldn't help it. They had been threatening to take her to court. And now this!

Valerie hated being alone; she lay low and did nothing. The problems might dissolve of their own accord. Of course, they didn't.

It was Richard Barwick who offered an escape from her own company. Horrified at first, to hear his harsh, barking tones on the telephone, she snapped at him.

"How the hell did you get my number?"

"The easy way, you're in the telephone book. Or didn't you know?"

Of course.

"Don't suppose a popular girl like you has an evening free to comfort a lonely fellow like me," he wheedled.

Valerie was lonely herself. Bored and hungry, too. Dennis should never have left her.

"I might have. If you promise to keep your hands to yourself."

"Where do you want to go? The Caprice? Les Ambassadeurs? Make your mind up in the bath. I'll pick you up in half an hour." The telephone went dead in Valerie's hand.

She was furious. How dare he? She started to ring him back. But of course, she did not know his number. There was nothing for it, she would have to dress. Well, it was nice to be going out, even with that gorilla. He rang the bell just as she was blotting her lipstick for the third time, a new technique.

Cocking her head on one side, Valerie examined herself critically in the looking glass. Richard Barwick could wait a little longer on the doorstep, do him good. Yes, she looked wonderful. The new look, wide, sweeping skirts of ivory grosgrain over layers of white tulle.

98

They had a surprisingly agreeable evening. Richard stuck to his side of the bargain and indeed, kept his hands to himself. It began to seem to Valerie that she must have been mistaken about their last encounter; he was a good listener too. Valerie poured out her troubles. All about Robert, about finding a flat for her parents and of course, about her little financial difficulties.

"How much do you want?" Richard asked bluntly. "Come on, how much?" He insisted as he saw Valerie hesitate.

"Oh, I couldn't. Not possibly … If my fiancé found out."

"Not going to find out, is he? More fool him for leaving you stuck." Valerie's hesitation was short lived. The temptation to be free of worry was too great.

"Look, this is very kind of you," she said. "But you must understand, I mean …"

"I don't buy my women, if that's what you're trying to say," Richard withdrew a chequebook from the inside pocket of his dinner jacket. "Now, say, a thousand? Two … three … five thousand. Come on."

Valerie looked down. She must not be foolish. If she borrowed just a little it would not be so bad.

"Please, Richard, five hundred, as a loan. I'm terribly grateful."

Richard pursed his lips and wrote the cheque for one thousand pounds. He did not expect to see it back. When a woman talked about a loan, she meant she didn't like taking the money. Still, he smiled drily to himself as he completed his signature with a flourish, money was habit-forming stuff, and Valerie he guessed, was an addict.

"There, stuff that down your front. Feel up to dancing?"

Valerie was in no position to refuse.

They went out several times after that. Richard was a generous host and when he cared to, he knew how to please, he could be amusing.

One evening, about a week before her parents were due, Richard's spirits seemed les ebullient. Valerie had been chattering about all sorts of ideas for her wedding.

Dennis would like to get married in church, poor boy, it wasn't possible, Valerie said, because she'd been married before.

"Don't you like that?" Richard interrupted her prattle testily. "Shall I send it back?" he gestured towards the Lobster Thermidor Valerie was consuming rather slowly. Richard's purchasing power had left her with little appetite lately. She had never been so well fed. They'd been to Prunier's two nights in a row. A lot of things were off the ration there.

"No, it's delicious," Valerie looked at him in surprise. "I'm just not very hungry, that's all."

"Look, Val, there's something I've got to tell you. It's damn difficult and I don't know where to begin."

"At the beginning," Valerie replied casually. "Whatever it is, you'd better get it off your chest. You're being a bit of a bore."

Richard sighed heavily.

"It's Dangan."

Valerie put the lobster pick down and looked up in surprise.

"Dennis? You don't know him, well, hardly. What about him, anyway?"

Valerie felt goose pimples of apprehension begin to spring up along her forearms. Something was wrong. Richard's voice had become so gentle ... And his face wore an expression of peculiar serenity.

"Val, somebody has to tell you this, and your friends thought it had better be me." Richard started to make absent-minded patterns on the damask cloth with the tines of a fork. "We've been getting on pretty well but, let's face it. I'm very nearly a stranger to you. So, it won't matter if you never want to see me again ... or throw something. No harm done."

"Dennis. What about Dennis?"

"I'm afraid he's backed out. The wedding's off. If I could get my hands on the fellow, I'd kick him into the middle of next year."

"I don't know what you're talking about," Valerie began to gather her evening bag and gloves together, shaking with indignation. "I think you must be quite, quite mad."

Richard regarded her covertly. She was shivering, half risen in her chair. He stood himself and leaning across the table, placed his hands on her shoulders and forced her to resume her seat.

"Val, I know this is hard to bear, but there's no point in running away. You've got to face facts. Dangan's a swine."

Richard signalled urbanely to a passing waiter.

"Bring Madam a glass of cognac, please. At once."

Valerie needed it. Her world was disintegrating. It was as if her own body were crumbling to dust. In a minute, she would simply cease to exist.

"Here, take a swig of this. No, not lady like little sips, knock it back, do you good." Richard thrust the brandy at her. A faint wash of colour returned to her face.

"But..." Valerie spluttered, not knowing where to begin exploring the terrifying new landscape within. "Even if I believe what you say ... Why? Why? For God's sake ... why?"

Richard seemed reluctant to answer. He glanced down and placed his fingertips together. After a pause, he took a deep breath and looked up into her face. The pupils of his brown eyes were hugely dilated.

"Some trouble with his people, I think. Apparently, you're not quite what they had in mind for Dennis ... a touch too ..." Richard sought inspiration among the ceiling fans, "Sophisticated for them ... er, experienced ... if you want to put it another way."

Valerie felt a slow flush spreading hotly from her waist. "You mean because I've been married before ... because I'm in films ..."

Richard snatched another glance at her, his mouth compressed. Great care was needed here.

"Something like that, yes."

Valerie knew it was hopeless. Who had been talking? Not Dennis ... Oh, not Dennis. He was deserting her. He loved her.

"Come on now," Richard was suddenly brisk. "Let's be practical. He's run out on you. Left you in the mire. We've got to find a way out of it. Square up to the situation. Let's start with another cognac."

It was so easy to lean on Richard. He seemed to know just what to do about everything. Valerie hadn't realised quite how much she had told him about herself and her affairs. Thank heavens she didn't have to explain anything to him now.

"Dangan will write to you from New York. The letter's probably on the high seas at this moment. Where's he staying?"

"The Waldorf Astoria," Valerie replied dully.

"Right, first thing tomorrow morning, you send him a wire saying the engagement's off. Give him a reason. Preferably one that hurts. That way you come off with your dignity intact at least. Chuck him before he chucks you. OK?"

Valerie nodded. Dignity. That was important.

"Next, you've got your parents arriving in seven days' time. You still haven't got a flat for them ... and so, far as I know, no means of paying for it when you do. Correct?"

Again, Valerie nodded.

"What's more, Mamma and Papa are expecting to meet a bridegroom for you and a stepfather for their grandson. That's right, isn't it?"

Richard ticked off the horrendous features of her situation one by one with devastating accuracy. She had debts ... but no job and no income and Robert. Would her parents take him back to Kenya with them? Would the court allow them to? The legal business, who would deal with that now?

Caught in the jaws of a trap, it never occurred to Valerie that it was of Richard Barwick's own devising.

The whole thing was so logical. Dennis had never introduced her to his family. She had never previously wondered about that. They hadn't bothered with family things. Old people, the dim and the distant future, now she saw why.

"As I see it, you can solve the whole mess at a single stroke."

"Can I?" Valerie reached apathetically for the reed floating on the wreckage of her expectations.

"Yes," Richard shot the bolt home, "You can marry me."

There was no choice.

Richard lit a fresh cigar and blew three smoke rings. Ascending garlands of triumph.

Forty-eight hours later, Dennis had just begun what was to be a long and loving letter to Valerie when the bellboy brought him her wire.

"Gee, sir! Thanks!" The lad flourished the dollar bill Dennis gave him. It wasn't so much the generosity of the tip as the Englishman's grace in giving it. Lord Dangan was a swell.

Smoothing the folds from the telegraph form, Dennis had no sense of what was in store. He read the clumsy typescript and misspelt phrases without absorbing the messages fed to his brain. He read it three more times before the meaning soaked in, like an indelible stain, into his mind.

WHIRLWIND ROMANCE WITH RICHARD BARWICK MEANS OUR ENGAGEMENT OFF; GETTING MARRIED; KNOW YOU'LL UNDERSTAND; VAL.

Dennis walked down to the lobby and bought a copy of the *London Times* from the hall porter. Yesterdays. The marriage had already been announced.

PART TWO
Lady Barwick

CHAPTER EIGHT

For a woman, there is no choice, ever.

Surrounded by the opulence of one of the Dorchester's best suites and on the brink of marriage with a man of seemingly limitless wealth, Valerie told herself she was in love and was loved in return. The three large, blindingly white diamonds on her finger proved it, so did the brand-new Bentley already waiting in Paris with a chauffeur to drive them down to Cannes for their honeymoon. Luxury and love. In Valerie's mind, they were inextricably linked.

She would have everything. A stately home in North Yorkshire, a title when Richard's seventy-five-year-old father and his poor, drink-sodden brother died, as they would, quite soon. Tragic, of course. She would have servants and a fabulous dress allowance. Richard hadn't yet said how much that would be, but as long as she lived, she would never have to worry about money again.

Lucky? Some of her friends had dared to say it. But they knew nothing. Great wealth and privilege were always balanced by sacrifice and responsibility. Richard said so. Valerie relished the path of duty that lay before her. She had always expected it. She had been born to this.

There was something very satisfying in the long talks she had had with Richard. His vast-looking physique and seniority in years, (he was nearly twice Valerie's age), gave him a kind of priestly gravity when he came to speak of their future together. It would be rich in activity, in achievement. Of what sort precisely, he did not say. 'Rich' was the word that curled around her heartstrings.

Every seductive syllable thrilled along Valerie's nerves bringing her to a point of rapturous sexual excitement. Not that she would have recognised it for what it was. The radiance she saw in her looking glass, she was sure, had nothing to do with Richard's four thousand acres or the list of Company directorships he held.

Romance was uncalculating. Cupid's arrow had struck randomly in a place where thousands were the smallest unit of exchange ever mentioned. Richard could have anything he wanted … gratify the most extravagant whim. Valerie was to have a diamond tiara and a Rolls Royce of her own, they went with the position.

Titillating Valerie in this way, Richard gloated inwardly over her mounting desire. Neither handsome nor particularly intelligent, he possessed that most potent of all attractions, money. From adolescence, Richard had known how to use it without in any way dissipating it. He flirted and flaunted it like a matador with a cape. It rarely fell from his grasp. The promise of presents worked better, he had noticed, than the reality. Too many titbits and girls, like dogs, became snappish and spoiled. He put Valerie through the most exquisite torments with a word and a look. She was enslaved. Richard drew back, restraining her embraces.

Exalted position, he warned, entailed a degree of self-denial. Their marriage was a serious affair, not to be anticipated for selfish pleasure. Every child born of their union must be of undisputed legitimacy. They could not afford to risk sniggering comparisons of dates …

"You of all people, Val, know how envious little people like to drag people like us down to their level if they can. When you present me with an heir, darling, I want to hear nothing but the silence of respect."

Purity, dignity … respect. Valerie shuddered in ecstasy. Already she felt like a queen. In Richard Barwick, she had found the twin half of her soul.

"And a male heir there must be, Val. I hope you understand that."

Here again, Richard struck precisely the right note with Valerie. She felt a little like Anne Boleyn or an oriental potentate's wife. Beloved but threatened by the very power of the man who adored her. She shivered with the delicious hint of fear that Richard's words induced.

He watched her intently, suppressing a grunt of satisfaction. He was an experienced man. By the time he bedded this bride of his, she would barely need to be touched. One glance and she would flow with juice for him. Beneath that enamelled surface sophistication, she was greedy for him now.

"I must, I'm afraid, ask another sacrifice of you," Richard had continued. "In fact, darling, I must insist. There are to be no more professional stage or film appearances. My wife cannot do any paid work or be exposed to publicity which is not consistent with her dignity as my wife. I suppose it boils down to whether you're willing to play second fiddle to me," Richard smiled disarmingly. "Rather old fashioned, but necessary. Hope it isn't too much of a wrench, darling."

Valerie's eyelids drooped in submission. The opportunity to dedicate herself voluntarily to the role of chatelaine of a great house and upholder of traditional values was heaven sent. After all, there was no film work available to her. Suddenly, she was no longer 'resting' but retiring gracefully ... with only a few, trifling regrets. An announcement along those lines would look good in the industry press.

"I want nothing," Valerie said fervently, "but to devote myself to you, our children, our home and," she added with a becoming sigh of resignation, "your tenants and employees."

"Splendid," Richard ejaculated a little too heartily. Val wasn't an actress for nothing. She really knew how to play these games. By the time their wedding night came, they'd both be at screaming pitch. Richard was undergoing a period of unusual continence himself. Val's surrender was a treat worth waiting for. How she could ever have tolerated the vapid caresses of Dennis Dangan, let alone Ward's lumbering efforts was a mystery. She had appetite ... as few women did. Finesse? Richard had no use for it.

106

Indeed, Dennis had faded swiftly from Valerie's memory. She received none of the many anguished cables and letters he sent. These were intercepted by Richard. The desk porter at Kensington Gate Mansions had changed ... the new one was easily bribed.

The flat there was soon given up; Valerie had said she'd grown out of it. A small house in Montpellier Place was taken for Valerie's parents, Robert and his nanny. Richard attended to everything.

And if he was not the bridegroom that the Skeltons had expected to meet, their bewildered enquiries were smothered by the crushing impact of Richard's personality. The size of his fortune and handsome undertakings regarding little Robert's future went a long way towards silencing any protests about this extraordinary change of plan. It was Robert, after all, that mattered most to his grandparents. One way and another, Val could look after herself as her ravishing appearance and costly possessions showed. Alice chose not to probe too deeply into the manner in which her daughter had acquired such a collection of furs and jewels.

"You'll miss it, you know, Val. The stage and all that. I'm surprised you gave in to Barwick over that."

Valerie dimpled prettily and muttered something about Richard being masterful before dropping a perfunctory kiss on Robert's head. She must go.

She had a fitting for her wedding gown. Everything was such a rush. Bobby chuckled as the front door slammed behind her. She might fool most people, but not him. She was his little girl, God knew what she'd been up to during the past four years, he was too tired to find out. Better now to let things ride. Val was astonishing ... and exhausting.

"I don't know how she does it," he remarked to his grandson. "But one thing's for certain, your mother has worked damned hard to find a silver spoon to put in your mouth. Go to Nanny, now."

Robert toddled off obediently. He missed the big, green garden in Muthaiga and his comfortable black nurse. Nanny's lap, like her rules, crackled with starch.

Mummie was hardly a disappointment. She was much as he had imagined her.

Somebody who came and went on a cloud of perfume, tinkling with laughter … always in a hurry to be somewhere else.

She was getting married Granny said. Brides were always like that. Someday soon, it would be over and then she would be able to settle down and cuddle him. Robert knew better. Brightly coloured butterflies, he had observed, never settled down. They alighted for a moment, long enough to be admired before they flew away again on restless, delicate wings.

Still, he ought to be proud of Mummie. Grown-ups were never tired of telling him that. Particularly the huge, dark man she was going to marry. He was always picking Robert up and putting him on his knee, like a doll. Then he tickled him with his moustache and whispered incomprehensible things. Robert felt uneasy with Richard Barwick. He was supposed to love him. Richard was going to be his new Daddy. He was so ugly with his vague, fleshy face and little black eyes. Robert didn't see how Mummie could possibly like him when she was so pretty herself.

Sitting in his pyjamas one night, with his legs slotted through the third-floor landing balusters. Robert had overheard something that might explain it all. It was Nanny's night off, so he had ample leisure time to stare down the staircase well into the tiled hall far below. Mummie and Richard Barwick were all dressed up. They were going to a party. Granny and Grandpa were seeing them off. The grown-ups' voices floated up quite clearly.

"I shall always do right by Robert, you know. He shall be educated as befits my son and in time …" Richard Barwick's voice was interrupted by his grandmother's.

"He is down for Eton already."

"Quite. After that, he shall go to Oxford or Cambridge, then he will need an adequate allowance while he does a couple of years in the Brigade of Guards, and then we'll see. Agricultural College, perhaps; or the City ... anything at all. Robert shall lack for nothing."

"The boy's own father is trying to wriggle out." That was Grandpa speaking.

"Bugger the Wards," Barwick boomed. "We don't need any tuppeny halfpenny maintenance payments from them. Everything the boy wants, he'll get from me."

Then Robert could see a lot of hand shaking and kissing going on. His mother was hanging on Richard Barwick's arm and gazing up at him.

There were murmurs of half-audible gratitude and Robert heard his name again amongst snatches of conversation. This whole thing seemed to be about him. Mummie had been working on getting married all this time just for him. Robert tried to feel appropriately thankful and couldn't. Just at that moment, Richard Barwick looked upward and caught sight of the small boy.

"What the devil are you doing up there? Get back into bed or I'll come and put you there."

Robert ran away terrified. He hated Richard Barwick. It was all his fault Mummie was marrying him. And he couldn't do anything to stop it. Granny and Grandpa would go, and he'd be left alone.

"He needs a man's hand," Richard assured the Skeltons as he shepherded Valerie across the threshold.

"I'll give him a man's bloody hand," Bobby gave vent to his affront as the door closed behind the departing couple. "Or I would if I were five years' younger. One thing's certain. You needn't think I'm going through any bloody pantomime of giving that swine Val's hand.

I shan't be here."

Valerie was not unduly distressed when her father went back to Kenya before the wedding. He had been difficult to account for.

"My darling father," she told a few people at a pre-wedding reception given for her and Richard "was most terribly injured in the first war. Shell shock was the worst thing, he couldn't speak for months. When he did begin to speak again it was with a Yorkshire accent!"

"Too, too inventive," murmured one woman. Valerie flushed angrily and blotted the woman from her consciousness. She was of no importance.

Valerie was too beautiful to be scorned, too vulnerable in her ignorance to be challenged. The more outrageous the lie on her lips, the more reverently her admirers received it. So, she got away with the 'Yorkshire accent' story as she got away with everything else.

Even her father, to whom the tale was chaffingly relayed, grinned with affectionate pride. She was a cheeky young monkey, was his Val, a comic turn. She'd have done better to carry on with her career than to be marrying this Barwick fellow. But apart from his single outburst to Alice and premature return to his duties in Kenya, Bobby kept his feelings to himself. Valerie, he was well aware, was impossible to advise. She always knew best.

God alone knew what kind of bed she was preparing for herself to lie upon.

Valerie had no reason to believe that it would be anything but soft. The loosely constructed gown of satin jersey in which she chose to be married certainly suggested an eagerness of consummation. Enfolding Valerie's figure in the defenceless drapery of a sacrificial victim, the gown pleased Richard ... as it had been designed to do. The bride and groom mingled among the wedding guests at Kensington Register office and later at Holy Trinity, Brompton. Then on to the reception at the Dorchester, where three hundred guests were entertained to champagne, smoked salmon, caviar and any other ostentatious delicacy, which was off the ration and in conspicuously short supply. The atmosphere was musky with the smell of perspiration mingled with perfume and money.

Robert, temporarily evading the supervision of Nanny, tasted the dregs from the bottom of a number of cocktail glasses left on a tray making him feel very peculiar. People with large, red faces kept bending down to talk to him. They wanted to know who he was, he smiled tolerantly. Eventually he was sick over somebody's striped trousers and was taken away.

Later, Valerie would say the speeches were outstandingly witty. They were certainly long. All made oblique reference to Richard's financial resources and extolled Valerie's beauty in the most fulsome terms. Even fame was mentioned. She was offering up her career on the altar of Richard's dynasty. No flattery is too gross for a wealthy man's bride on her wedding day.

Valerie accepted the tributes in a daze of happiness, her skin exuding a faint dew under the powder. When she rose to go and change, everybody clapped and cheered. Valerie kissed the tips of her fingers to them all. When she reappeared, in her going away outfit, she swept down the staircases and across the foyer with her arm extended.

Richard and Valerie flew off to Paris from Gatwick in the late afternoon. A privately-chartered aircraft. A knot of top-hatted men waved from the tarmac as the plane taxied down the runway.

"Oh darling, we're going to have such a wonderful life," Valerie snuggled into Richard's shoulder.

He stroked her cheek and smiled. How utterly typical. It was one of the things he loved about Val, her banal romanticism. These Skeltons were a push over. They hadn't asked him, any of them, to make a marriage settlement on Valerie. Not a penny piece. She was utterly helpless, as a good wife ought to be. Independent women were an expensive nuisance.

For the first two days of her honeymoon, Valerie's principal impression was one of hot, wet blackness. Richard had stored a reservoir of lust until his body was as full and heavy with it as a tropical rain cloud tantalising the parched earth beneath.

In a hotel, somewhere near Place Vendôme, Richard released the torrent of his loins on Valerie. It came on her like waves of wind-driven rain, pumped by his relentless energy.

111

All thought of past and future was squeezed to the margins of Valerie's imagination as she absorbed the battering force of her husband's desire. She was powerless to control or direct the onslaught.

Richard turned and manipulated her effortlessly. He probed every orifice, sucked buttock, nipple and breast without mercy. She was covered in dark bruises.

No impulse of her own was noticed. No skill she possessed could arrest the pace of his invasion.

In brief intervals of calm, she arched her aching body and sought to slide from underneath him. Sweat caked her hair, her skin tasted of salt. Once he slept Valerie managed to take a bath. When she came back, he was awake, angry that she had not been there beside him. Food came brought on a trolley by a waiter with an apron down to his feet. Valerie scarcely remembered what she ate. There was champagne which Richard drank most of, in large impatient gulps.

If fatigue is a measure of sexual satisfaction, then Valerie was satisfied. She slept every mile of the way south. Only the chauffeur's necessary presence prevented Richard from waking her. She might be sated, but he was not.

"Madam is tired," the chauffeur remarked with matter-of-fact innocence, cruising the Bentley through the Porte de Gentilly traffic.

Richard glanced at Valerie; her head was thrown back, her lips slightly parted. She looked like a bruised rose. There had been no time, he had insisted, for her to go to the hairdressers and her manicure was two days old. It pleased him to see his immaculate fiancée transformed thus. Now she was his wife in every corner of her conquered being.

"Yes," he agreed with the chauffeur pleasantly, "Madam is tired." The man should be paid off on their return to England for his impudence. Madam would be a lot more tired yet, but she was his wife. The future Lady entitled respect.

112

The Côte d'Azur was beautiful, of course. White, wedding cake villas, set between well-watered lawns and the hard-baked brilliance of cerulean skies smiling down on a smooth aquamarine sea.

There were palm trees marching along the promenades, bougainvillea tumbling like purple gushing wounds over garden walls where orange, lemon and peach trees spread umbrellas of shade and dangled bright globes within reach of languidly-reaching hands.

Even the policeman seemed made for pleasure with their handsome, tanned faced and white truncheons symbolising a potency held in reserve.

The Carlton Hotel at Cannes was a voluptuous inner citadel. The cool lobbies, banked with flowers, provided a haven from the ferocious heat and glare of the midsummer sun.

"Premier etage, Madame," the top-hatted, cockaded lift attendant would announce with superb indifference to decayed royalty and American dog-biscuit-manufacturer's wife alike. It was the business of his life to notice no gradation of rank until persuaded to do so by a large tip. He kept an especially warm, conspiratorial smile for Valerie, however. There was something so charming about her breathless smiles and ribbon-tied parcels on her ascending trips to the honeymoon suite … so ingenuous when she descended en-grande toilette all primly dignified and with the ineradicable flush of recent copulation warming her delectable flesh.

She liked to speak French, Georges had noted. Her French was of the execrable schoolgirl variety. It did no harm to call her 'Milady' either … although she was only Mrs Richard Barwick. The error was good for a few more francs every time. Georges knew the English Peerage and Baronetage pretty thoroughly. He intended to have his own hotel one day.

113

Valerie was happy. Richard's urgency had slackened. He wanted her in the mornings when they awoke and perhaps once again at night. It gave her an opportunity to display her own enthusiasm for married coupling. Scope for tenderness and technique. Now there was time for conversation. Valerie's chosen topics were inharmonious in Richard's ear. Nagging.

"I don't see," she told him whilst scanning the Carlton's epic menu, "why we shouldn't keep the town house on as well. Property in London is bound to soar in value in the next ten years."

Richard sighed impatiently. This was already a bone of contention. The Brook Street house had seventeen rooms and a staff cottage. During the war, it had been requisitioned by the Ministry of Fuel and Power.

"I told you before. You had the choice. Thimbleby Hall … The Morgue, my father calls it or the Brook Street dump. I can't afford to redecorate and staff both." Richard summoned the head waiter with a jerk of his head. "Try to remember, having money isn't an excuse for throwing it around."

"But we'll need a place in London too …"

Valerie bit off the rest of her sentence at the approach of the head waiter. Nothing must disturb the picture of them as the perfect couple. Arguments about money were unseemly. Tears formed in the corners of Valerie's eyes.

"Here," Richard shoved the wine list into the waiter's hands, who inclined his head at an angle that combined withering reproof with deference. "Tell the sommelier I don't need to see him. Bring me a whiskey and soda. My wife will have some mineral water."

"Monsieur," the waiter assented disapprovingly. The new little Mrs Barwick was bewitching. It was a shame that she shouldn't have her wine.

"Richard!" Valerie hissed across the table. "How could you be so mean? You've humiliated me!"

Valerie looked out of the tall windows onto the broad terrace fronting the sea. How was it possible to be unhappy amid all of this? They were fortunate, heaven-blessed couple and now Richard was hurling insults at her in public.

"Why are you so unreasonable?" she said after a moment. "I only want to help. If you let me convert the Brook Street house into flats, we'll have the letting income and the staff cottage as a nice little pied-à-terre for ourselves."

"Since when do you know the first thing about property, Val? When I met you, let me remind you, you couldn't even pay your own rent."

Valerie left the table fighting back tears of anger. She was puzzled when Richard did not follow her at once, puzzlement turned to gnawing anxiety when after an hour in their suite, he did not come.

Richard did not return before dinner time or at any time during the night. Valerie took off the new, halter-necked evening gown at a quarter past one in the morning. She had not eaten since breakfast. She could order some food now. At the Carlton, service was uninterrupted around the clock, but what would the waiter think when he found her alone? No, it was impossible. Valerie disrobed and removed her make- up, leaving some artistic mascara smudges around her eyes. Tragedy or no tragedy, pink lids were horrid. How awful to think she might, even now, be a widow.

Valerie tossed and turned on the fantastically-canopied bed, rising once to throw off her nightgown and shower, and then again to change into her grandest crêpe de Chine because it would look more dignified when they brought the news ... Richard was energetically employed.

The casino would not let him in without a dinner jacket, which made no matter. Hidden behind the glittering boulevards there were narrow streets with unsavoury cafes, rat holes. They catered for off-duty hotel staff, a shifting, poverty-stricken population. Richard liked these places.

The way small change was banged noisily on zinc-topped bars and the steamy atmosphere misted the exhausted features of the patrons. A view through the narrow keyhole of underprivilege. It was arousing

There was a sharp-faced girl with dark hair down to her shoulders. She was sitting on a bar stool chain smoking and exchanging laconic remarks with the bartender. She was smart, in the brave, cheap and clever way that Frenchwomen of the people often have. A ridiculous black satin bow perched on the crown of her head. A defiant gesture of femininity.

Richard bought her drinks and won her confidence. She was a chambermaid in a modest hotel.

The proprietor was a keen manager … the girl rubbed her fingertips with the thumb of the same hand expressively. After the guests had eaten, there was little left over for the nourishment of the staff. She shrugged philosophically. *Quoi a faire?*

Richard, on the other hand, knew just what to do. He bought her dinner in a discreet restaurant and then took her up against the wall of a shuttered bakery, his trousers crumpled around his knees. It was too hard and too long. He paid the girl a few francs. She shouted after him.

"*Salaud!*"

Retreating down the darkened alley, Richard grinned. Evenings like this were supposed to end that way. A slimy nest of glorious squalor. It made a nice change. An inexpensive treat.

Wandering from bar to bar, he drank some more, carousing with unnoticeable, forgettable people. He had a whore, a professional this time. She sucked him off, she cost too much. Eventually, Richard fell asleep on the grass in a public park. He was robbed, of course. Waking only when drops from a sprinkler mechanism splashed him in the face, Richard went back to the Carlton Hotel and his bride.

Valerie awaited him in a crisply-pressed linen walking dress. She ran to him, her arms wide.

"Oh, my poor darling. I was so frightened. Whatever happened to you?"

116

The smell of spirits, cheap perfume and cheaper sex was strong upon him. Valerie's nostrils dilated with anger. Her eyes blazed.

"You bastard! How could you? Oh, you bastard!"

The Barwicks packed and began the journey home that day. Valerie sat stiffly in the back seat of the Bentley, checking her make up in her powder compact at intervals. Apart from the snap of the compact, there was silence.

Valerie exacted a high price for her forgiveness, a second honeymoon. There would be no time to go up to North Yorkshire before embarkation. Thimbleby Hall could await its new mistress a little longer.

"Are you going away again, Mummie?" Robert asked wide eyed as Valerie packed a steamer trunk.

The small master bedroom in Montpellier Place was littered with boxes and tissue paper. A camera safari through Kenya, Uganda and The Congo called for a very specialised wardrobe.

"Yes, darling," Valerie answered her small son's question absently. "With Daddy, just for a while, we'll be back again before you know it. Then we must begin to think about school for you, mustn't we, won't that be fun?"

"Where are you going?" Robert persisted, unwilling to be distracted.

"To see Granny and Grandpa."

"Can't I come?"

"Not this time, darling. Good heavens, what a restless little boy you are! You've only just got here. Don't you like it here, at home with Nanny?"

Robert did not trouble himself to answer. His mother wouldn't be listening anyway; she was busy with her clothes. He trailed his truck full of wooden bricks out of the bedroom onto the landing where Richard, emerging from his dressing room, tripped over the toy. He turned on the child.

"Can't you keep your things out of the bloody way? What are you doing down here? Where's Nanny? Bloody woman."

Shocked and frightened. Robert began to cry. Richard bellowed up the staircase for the nanny.

"Can't you control this child? I don't pay you to sit on your fat backside all day!"

Nanny's indignant face peered over the bannisters. She wasn't taking any more of this. She'd have a word with Mrs Barwick and give her notice. She didn't want to leave Robert in the lurch ... poor little mite ... but there were limits.

Nanny's interview with Valerie involved some plain speaking.

No, she was not particularly sorry her employers would have to cancel their trip.

They'd had one honeymoon. Didn't Mrs Barwick realise that her son needed her? And as for Mr Barwick ... well, Nanny had never been treated like that in her whole life before. She had to think of herself sometimes. It was impossible to create a happy, secure environment for a child in conditions like this. The poor little chap didn't know whether he was coming or going, it was no kind of life for him. Nanny handed over an envelope containing her written resignation. She was entitled to leave after seven days. However, she realised that would be very difficult and for Robert's sake, she would stretch a point. A fortnight's notice. But that was the limit. And now she would take Robert for his walk in the park if Madam would excuse her.

"Now look what you've done!" Valerie confronted Richard crossly. "Before you interfere with my servants again, just think."

Richard said something predictable about being the one who paid the wages and went out to his club. There might be some mail waiting for him there.

Resuming work on her wardrobe, Valerie considered that a lot could be done in a fortnight. She could get somebody else in time for her and Richard to leave as planned. How could he have behaved so badly? Didn't he realise you couldn't keep children permanently hidden? She wondered if it would be any different when his own children arrived.

By the end of the afternoon, there was a further change of plan.

Nanny returned within half an hour of leaving the house with Robert. She was screaming when Valerie ran down the stairs with her heart beating. Robert, she was sure had been run over and killed. In the endless moments before she actually saw him, the whole history of relationship with her son passed through her shrinking memory. Her callousness and neglect were punished. How could she face her mother? But Robert was there, in the hall. He was standing quite calmly while blood spurted from his eye.

Somehow or other, Valerie extracted the story from the hysterical nanny. Robert had rushed off into a shrubbery. She had seen the whole thing.

A protruding twig with a thorn, Robert hadn't seen it, as it pierced the corner of his eyeball. His screams had attracted a gentleman. The gentleman got them a taxi. Why, Valerie demanded, had they not gone first to a hospital? She was already dialling the number of her own doctor.

"I don't know, Madam. I couldn't think what to do … and after everything I said," the woman was quite incoherent. The tortoiseshell pins were coming out of her hair. Where was her hat?

Robert sat on his mother's lap on a hall chair. He was quiet and pale. His skin felt cold. Shock. There was blood all over Valerie's dress when the doctor arrived, she didn't notice. The nanny was sobbing, clasping and unclasping her work-roughened hands.

"Do be quiet, Nanny," Valerie ordered her. "Go and make a cup of tea or something. There's the doctor. Let him in for God's sake."

Robert began to whimper.

"Hmm," the doctor squatted down before Valerie's chair and examined Robert's eye with an ophthalmoscope. "I'm afraid there's a splinter stuck behind the eyeball. I'll have to remove it."

'Yes, yes, of course."

"I don't think you quite understand what I mean," the doctor said gently. "It is the eyeball itself which will have to come out. I'll need your help."

There was a muffled thud as the nanny slid to the ground. "Fainted," Valerie commented unnecessarily. "She'll be all right there. Quiet, at least."

The doctor glanced at Valerie in admiration. She was a trooper, not many mothers would have this amount of fortitude. It was an appalling injury. Enough to make anyone faint or throw up. He felt a bit queasy himself. Valerie remained immobile, her arms firmly around Robert's little body while his eyeball was anaesthetised. She was unflinching when the doctor extracted it from its socket. The rest of the operation although gruesome was over in a few moments. Richard entered by the front door just as the eye was about to be reinserted into his stepson's skull.

He stood for a moment, weaving from side to side. Then without a word he bolted up the stairs, the sound of his retching was plainly audible in the hall. The doctor and Valerie smiled at each other.

"He'll do now, Mrs Barwick, brave little fellow, I must say, like his mother. I'll come and see him tomorrow. Might I suggest a cup of strong, sweet tea for Nanny?" Nanny was full of the most abject apologies.

"But it wasn't your fault, Nanny," Valerie reassured her. "One of those things."

Richard came downstairs in his shirt sleeves mopping his brow with an enormous white linen handkerchief. He shared the pot of metal-corroding tea that was brought from the kitchen and served in the drawing room after helping Nanny put Robert to bed. It was the least he could do, he said. A narrow escape does tend to put things in perspective. Richard apologised to Nanny who said she could not possibly think of leaving now.

"Oh Val," Richard turned to Valerie once they were alone. "I could never have done what you did, you're the bravest woman I know."

In Richard, as in many people, the aftermath of shock induced a profligate, babbling generosity. Soon he was apologising all over again for everything he had done and said in Cannes.

In future, he would listen to her counsel even if he could not act as she wished. No, he would never leave her like that again. Yes, it was he who drank too much, not his beautiful, courageous wife. He was the luckiest man on earth.

Valerie was well satisfied. Robert, thank God was sleeping soundly in the nursery. Nanny would stay. The holiday in East Africa was no longer threatened, and more important than any of this, she had mastered Richard Barwick. He would never underestimate her again.

Putting it to the test, Valerie had a pair of diamond ear clips she coveted in Garrard's window delivered to the house the next day. Richard paid for them peaceably, despising his own weakness in silence.

He had been generous enough, he thought sourly, forgetting entirely that most of his munificence had been verbal.

During his mother's absence in Africa, Robert went every week to the doctor's surgery to have his eye checked. The doctor was surprised that Valerie had left him. Nanny, who accompanied her charge, was equally dumbfounded, but Mrs Barwick was a remarkable woman they both agreed.

In East Africa, there was the colony gossip to enjoy. The Barwicks saw a herd of elephant and lodged for a while at the Mountains of the Moon Hotel in Uganda. They saw Idi Amin, a jovial sergeant in the King's African Rifles, squatting on the stoop of a native hut. He obligingly took a photograph of Valerie and Richard, arm in arm. When he had finished, he handed the camera back with a smart salute. Valerie suspected no mockery, still less when Valerie's acquaintance in Muthaiga commented blandly that she and Richard deserved each other. Of course, they did, a perfect match, they hadn't quarrelled for weeks.

When she returned home, Valerie assured herself, she would enter Thimbleby Hall as one who carried the heir. The future fourth baronet would be born in the house of his forbears within a year of his mother's marriage. Her position then would be unassailable, and she would still be only twenty-five.

121

CHAPTER NINE

"The meals I eat in the dining room suit me," Richard snapped. "That's all that matters."

He stood with his back to the fireplace in the West drawing room, hands thrust deep in his pockets. Five hundred brace was all the November day's shooting had produced and Richard was not pleased. Disease in the heather, the gamekeeper claimed, Richard had another word for it, incompetence.

The luncheon for the guns had been passable, thanks to Valerie's intervention but Richard would not admit that, even to himself.

Scowling, he regarded the pastel-painted walls with their frosting of white plaster work. The paintings, blackened rectangles in gilt frames when he was a boy, now revealed their subjects and glowed with colour. Restorers' work. A preposterous expense. Tarting up what she called the art collection was Valerie's latest extravagance. Now it was the food again.

The brocade upholstery in this room alone had cost enough to pay the exorbitant annual wages of the sort of cook Valerie constantly harped about. The trouble with Valerie was that she wanted it all. Not that money was the point at issue, anyway. Mrs Clarke was an old servant, faithful. She'd been good enough for his father and she was good enough for him.

Valerie rose and threw a log on the fire herself, no use ringing the bell; everyone had their hands full as it was. The footman had left a week ago and it was Ernest's weekend off. It was the same old complaint. The food served in the servants' hall was inedible, an undeniable fact. Too often, Valerie had cooked the staff supper herself. Anything to prevent a mass walk out.

122

Now there'd be a new footman's uniform to pay for, when they found a replacement. At least the buttons with the Barwick crest were reusable. Running a great house on a shoestring was no picnic. Not with Richard fighting her every inch of the way.

Valerie's thoughts ran along their familiar track.

"What does Ernest say, anyway?" Richard's tone was truculent. He already knew the answer.

He shifted his bulk while Valerie struggled with the fire irons. He leaned his elbow on the marble chimney piece and took it off again impatiently. Even that was a reminder of Valerie's spendthrift ways; she'd had the thing pulled out of the Brook Street house and lugged all the way up to North Yorkshire to be installed in place of the perfectly decent Victorian job that had been there before. She was never satisfied

"Ernest is discreet," Valerie responded wearily to her husband's question. They'd had this argument so many times before. "He is a professional servant. He's loyal to us and the staff. That's his job. He's the butler."

"Exactly," Richard pounced. "He's the butler. It's his place to report to me, not you. If there were anything seriously amiss, he would tell me. Obviously, he has no complaints. You know your trouble, Val, you're weak. You'll listen to any whining housemaid before you'll listen to me."

"How dare you call me weak?" Valerie sprang from the sofa enraged. The Great Dane at her feet emitting a low, warning growl, black lips curling away from its teeth, sensed the atmosphere. Its mistress was putting herself in danger again.

"Get that bloody dog out of here!"

"No, I won't. Don't you realise that your children are sick because of your precious Mrs Clarke? She hasn't changed her clothes for a year. A year! She stinks. The children have got food poisoning, you stupid man."

Richard raised his hand as if to strike Valerie, but he thought better of it. She had two black eyes as it was. He was sorry about that, but six years and nothing to show for it but two daughters and a pile of bills.

123

That damned dog of hers, the house was lousy with animals.

"Don't you also realise that if you paid a cook four pounds a week instead of forty-five shillings it would actually cost you less?" Valerie would not let the matter drop. If the children's health meant nothing to him, perhaps hard cash would.

"Mrs Clarke can't make cakes, biscuits or puddings. Or she won't. Every sweet thing we eat in this house comes from Lewis and Cooper's of Northallerton. She orders everything in two dozen from them and then most of it is thrown away. She doesn't make soup. It all comes out of cans. In a house like this, that's criminal waste."

Richard refused to discuss it further. Mrs Clarke had become a testing ground between himself and Valerie. A trial of strength. It was not one he felt he could afford to lose. So, the old woman smelled, too bad. Richard stormed out of the room and crossed the hall to his study. Val would come around, she always did. It was just a question of being firm with her. She sank back onto the sofa, exhausted.

When Valerie had first set eyes on Thimbleby Hall, it had been a dilapidated, cockroach-infested barn. A terrible disappointment, and filthy. Apart from foul, old, Mrs Clarke there had been no servants. Any cleaning was done on a part-time basis by the estate workers' wives. Nobody could be persuaded to live in the house. It was too damp and dirty. Since the top, third story had been dismantled before the war, the flat roof, which had replaced its original, pitched predecessor, had been letting in water. Pails and old hip baths stood around the upper rooms and corridors to catch the leaks. Here and there, carpets had rotted away to the floorboards. Valerie's heart had sunk to her shoes. But not for long. She had rolled up her sleeves, scrubbed out the kitchens, and painted the nursery wing herself. Richard wouldn't pay anyone else to do it. In the end, after incessant, appalling rows, he'd let her have some money to make the roof weatherproof. Everything else had been a running battle. A war of attrition fought room by room, a round seventy-five of them.

There had been so much of interest and value here. Furniture, silver, porcelain, rugs and paintings. Nothing had been cared for as it should be. Decades of indifference and neglect had taken their toll. Damp had warped the furniture, springing the veneers and marquetry.

The silver was tarnished to the colour of copper and more than half of it was black, pitted with damp, irretrievable damage. The porcelain had survived best, cupboards and dressers full of it, thick with dust. Meissen, Derby, Sevres and Coalport, all piled up as if nobody either knew or cared what the pieces were.

On the night of Valerie's arrival at Thimbleby Hall, all those years ago, there had been a Flora Danica plate left on the kitchen table with an evil smelling, congealing mess on it, a kipper. The remains of Mrs Clarke's supper. Valerie hadn't known the plate's value then. Nor had she realised that the battered old metal teapot left on the draining board with a sludge of cold tea leaves at the bottom was part of a rare Hester Bateman silver tea service. She knew better now.

Upstairs, some magnificent old linen sheets with drawn thread work cuffs had been placed on her bed. They were wringing with damp. Valerie had slept in her dressing gown and had a chill for weeks afterwards. Even so, those were the best sheets in the house. All the rest were speckled with mildew.

The following day she had emptied the linen room cupboards and consigned the contents to the big old copper in the laundry. Boiling the towels, the table and bed linen which occupied the better part of a month, because there was no modern equipment. The linen had then been spread out to dry in the frosty autumnal sunlight in the central quadrangle. Thank God she hadn't been pregnant. Two years had passed before Sandra had been born.

Little by little, Valerie had converted the neglected palladium mansion into a home for herself, her husband and their two little girls. Wherever feasible, its treasures had been repaired and restored. Experts could only do so much. Richard was forever beefing at their charges. When would he realise that they had saved his heritage from annihilation?

125

For herself, she had long ceased hoping for any thanks. The results were their own reward.

There was light and warmth in the house now, flowers and animals, the cheerful tattoo of children's running feet along the corridors.

Everywhere, beauty and cleanliness, except in the kitchens and staff quarters. Valerie reflected bitterly. That was the sole remaining nest of squalor. Never mind, one day, she would prevail there too.

Robert came home from prep school in the holidays. Seeing his pleasure in the place and Richard's growing pride in the boy's promise with a shotgun made it all worthwhile. Perhaps Robert would inherit the estate one day, after all. She was too worn out to have any more children. The doctor said she mustn't. The title would die with Richard, but Valerie was an optimist. She was Lady Barwick now and there had been some good times.

She had been presented at court. The memory of herself crowned with three white ostrich feathers mounted on the Barwick tiara and a long, sweeping train came back to her now. Her curtsey had been quite perfect, low and straight backed, not a single wobble. The king had looked deeply into her eyes and squeezed her gloved hand, intimate and natural. There had been no photograph, of course, Richard hadn't wanted to spend the money. Such a pity, her daughters would never know how their mother had looked on that day.

If you wanted tradition these days, you had to make it yourself, Valerie said. She had created quite a few. The party for the tenants' children every Christmas and the annual village pantomime. She always produced those herself. Of course, she was a professional and it showed. Nothing in life was ever entirely wasted. The notices in the *Darlington & Stockton Times* were generous. It was good to be appreciated. Richard said she should keep out of the limelight. It was vulgar publicity, but he was just jealous, of course. It was her duty, she pointed out to him, as his wife, to do some public work. It would be selfish not to, and it cost him nothing.

There were the yearly visits to Cannes and to Kenya. She lived for those times. They made so many friends. Important, rich people, like themselves. Richard seemed better tempered in the sun, breezy and expansive. The money he spent then was in a different category, his pleasure was paramount.

Then they were back again at Thimbleby for the shooting. That's all Richard really cared about. The rest of the estate could go to rack and ruin as long as there were enough duck, pheasant and grouse to slaughter. Valerie hated it, all those poor little feathered corpses. It was no good talking to Richard about the rights of animals. Just like Roddy, he lived to kill and to drink. Why did she marry these men?

Introspection didn't help. Reflecting on how she had been wronged, however, did. It gave her the energy of rage. The courage to keep fighting for her rights and those of her children and the estate people, she'd managed to do something there. At least most of the cottage roofs had been repaired now, some would even be getting indoor lavatories soon, but their wages were still pathetic. Once, she'd leaked the figures to a national newspaper and told them what Richard's income was, the story was printed. It made no difference, Richard wasn't even embarrassed.

"I pay my people as little as I can get away with paying them, Val, like every other businessman. You can forget all this Merry England, benevolent country squire stuff."

"But what will people think? Our friends ..."

"Who cares what they think?" Richard tapped the newspaper article contemptuously. "I don't suppose I'll ever find out who squealed these figures to a reporter, but I assure you, an example will be made. I'll turn somebody out in the morning. Pollit, maybe."

Richard had enjoyed watching the colour drain from Valerie's face. That would teach her to meddle in his affairs.

"It wasn't Pollit," Valerie said calmly. "It was me."

She took a severe beating for that but didn't regret it. Richard Barwick brought the best out in Valerie. When it wasn't so depressing, it was quite exciting really, scheming and skirmishing for the people you loved and who loved you … with good reason. They were all in it together.

That's what Valerie thought at times, at others, she just wanted to get away, but it was too late, she was over thirty with three children. The narrow, cramped life of a divorcee held little appeal. She had her title and her beautiful vast home, Thimbleby, standing in its hollow, surrounded by moor and fell, had captured her. It was a little world of which she was queen. She must, she absolutely must make it work.

Three days after the argument about Mrs Clarke, Richard went to London, a board meeting. That was the excuse, Valerie wondered why he bothered. Richard never went to board meetings since his father's death. Business attracted him no more than estate management. It was some woman or other, she was certain, Richard had never been faithful.

For appearance's sake, Valerie kissed him goodbye under the front door portico. Dick stood respectfully at attention, holding the car door open for his employer. There seemed to be a flicker of sympathy in his eyes as he walked round to the driver's seat, saluting her with a nod and two fingers to the peak of his cap.

"Cold morning, my Lady. Do you think we shall have snow?"

"Oh, I do hope so, Dick, in time for Christmas. Then we shall have some tobogganing, won't we? And Santa Claus can bring the presents for the children's party on his sledge again, can't he? Like he did last year."

Dick laughed and agreed, Thimbleby looked its best in the snow. It always lay thickest in the hollow around the house, smothering the trees in billows of fondant icing and drifting up to the drawing room windows. Valerie would never let them sweep it away. And snow curtailed Richard's shooting activities, another advantage.

The chauffeur smiled to himself. It was Lady Barwick who enjoyed the tobogganing most. Excited as a child and as pretty as a picture in her red bobble hat and mittens, careering down the sloped lawns around the house, all bundled up in a fur coat with one of the kids, shrieking with joy, tucked between her legs. When it came to dragging the sledges back up to the top again, she was tireless. Hour after hour she'd go on.

It was shameful the way Sir Richard treated her, shameful. There she was with a couple of shiners again which even thick make-up couldn't hide from those who knew her. No one had done more for Thimbleby than her Ladyship had, no one.

Took an interest in everything, she did. Even helping the Home Farm manager with the calving last year. She was there in the cow barns all through the night for the best part of a week. Not that she knew much about it, like, but she was company for the man and kept the hot coffee coming. Right good with a nervous beast an'all, they said.

It would be a sad day for all of them if Lady Barwick ever took it into her head to up and leave. There wasn't many who'd put up with the treatment she'd had. Not with all the money she must have.

It was there of course, that Dick made his mistake.

Valerie waved until the Bentley had climbed the steep part of the drive up to the garages and was out of sight. Richard did not look back. Sadly, she went back into the house and walked upstairs to her sitting room, her boudoir, she called it, and her desk. She must try to put Richard out of her mind and attend to the accounts, always accounts.

Since the days of being Roddy Ward's wife, Valerie had become an expert on single entry bookkeeping. Her books were immaculate. Every purchase faithfully recorded, from a dog collar to a new bathroom suite. Mrs Clarke was supposed to do the tradesmen's books. She sent them up once a month.

Ernest brought them on a large silver salver. Mrs Clarke didn't like that. She said it was her place to render accounts to her Ladyship. But the one-time Clarke had come up to the boudoir, it had taken a week of open windows and disinfectant to get rid of the stench. Too dreadful to think the woman coughed and sneezed all over their food. The books themselves were bad enough. Valerie did not like handling the things, nor could she make much sense of the entries. She didn't think Clarke was dishonest though, just old and uncaring.

Today it was the wages book that interested Valerie, the head parlour maid had asked for a rise in her remuneration. Nothing much, just five shillings a week but it was going to be hard to find. The budget was stretched to the limit. Where she was going to scrape up enough halfpence to give her rise, Valerie did not know. The girl deserved the extra money. She was efficient and hard-working, like so many of the female staff, now, she was a displaced person. An orphan of the war.

That had been Valerie's idea too. These Polish and German girls were often from quite good families. They were clean and needed little training. On top of that, they were grateful for a roof over their heads and would think twice before giving notice. The English girls the Barwicks had employed had been known simply never to return after a day off. They would send for their things imperiously and post insolent, misspelled letters explaining at length, their reasons for going. Richard's name often figured in these.

Even now, it hurt her that Richard had a new woman, she never got used to it. Valerie's own adventures had receded so far in memory now, buried under the weight of childbearing and responsibility that Richard's philandering seemed quite unforgivable. She had kept her side of the bargain, why shouldn't he keep his?

Although she hid from it, Valerie knew the answer to this conundrum quite well. Every mouthful she ate, every stitch of clothing she wore, she owed to Richard Barwick.

He could do as he liked but she must be above suspicion. Her right to live in the palace of her own creation depended on it. She would never abandon her right, never. Her children belonged here and so did she.

Richard was not thinking of Valerie. As the North Yorkshire countryside slipped by, he drank the contents of his spirit flask and anticipated the diversions that awaited him in London. Thimbleby once out of sight, was out of mind. He spent as little time there as possible.

God knew it was a dead and alive hole except on shooting days. They had a house party once in a while. Val was good at that. He didn't begrudge the money for entertaining. There were some tasty women among the local gentry. Some of them were glad of a little extra-curricular activity. Good sports.

Richard traded on his wife's tenacity. She would never leave. Nor did he wish her to. Valerie was his security, the hard centre of a soft, self-indulgent existence. If she'd had a settlement, it might have been different, but she had none. No means of escape, no means of protest, none that she would use. She was too greedy and snobbish, he calculated, to divorce him. He could do what he liked secure in the knowledge that she would forgive every excess. Dependability, that's what counted in a wife.

If he was drunk, he need only sober up and vow never to be drunk again. If he beat her, he need only fall on her neck and express horror at what he had done. It was generally on those occasions that she managed to squeeze a jewel out of him. As for his women ... well, Val might let on she was a wounded innocent but that was all baloney. She was a woman of the world. Roddy Ward had had something to say about that. And what about Dangan? There were rumours she'd had others. She was a pretty good lay anyway, when nothing else offered.

On balance, Richard loved Valerie, as much as he could. Pretty little thing hadn't worn at all badly, everyone said so. Bert Marlborough liked the look of her. Val was so proud of knowing a Duke. It would be touching if it weren't so bloody funny.

131

Flirted with the old buffer like some frantic spinster in a silent movie. She'd no chance there, whatever she put in that damned diary of hers. He read it quite often. She thought she kept it locked up in the drawer of her desk. It had been worth the small trouble of having a duplicate key made. She really had talent, did Val. She should write for *Peg's Paper*. They'd love it in the servant's hall.

Valerie, whose imagination about herself was infinite, never guessed at her husband's thoughts; she went on loving and forgiving him.

An act of pure will with no feeling in it. Richard was her duty and her livelihood. Juggling the figures in the wages book, she focussed on the bright side of her life's coin. She had most of what she wanted. Only generosity and fidelity were missing. Some day she would have those too, it was just a matter of working at it.

It was less than a year ago that she had caught Richard in a shrubbery with a housemaid. He had looked so perfectly ludicrous with his huge, slug-pale buttocks sticking out of the laurel leaves and his tweed breeches at half-mast. It was the dogs who had found them, grinding and grunting. In retrospect, Valerie could laugh – almost, but at the time, her eyes had stung with tears of humiliation. It was all so sordid.

Mingwong, the peke, had rushed into the bushes and snuffled at the maid's red, scared face affectionately. Even that had seemed like a betrayal. The girl had her uniform frock and starched apron rumpled up round her waist and her legs in the air

"Damn and blast it, Val! What the hell are you doing here?"

"Taking my dogs for a walk in my own grounds. Get up."

The country girl struggled to extricate herself

"He said I'd be turned out without a reference if I didn't."

The girl was dismissed but Valerie found her a new position and gave her a good reference together with a month's wages.

This maid was the last of the local girls. All the rest had gone either because of Richard or on account of Mrs Clarke; it was always one or the other.

That was why Valerie was grateful to the Eastern European girls. Their terrible misfortune was her good luck; she did what she could for them.

Elisabeth was the best. She was a handsome, intelligent woman, tall with dark hair, not Richard's type, thank heaven. Valerie had made her head parlour maid and she doubled as a personal maid. Richard wouldn't let her have a real lady's maid, but she was good with her needle. She could smarten up an old dress and remove stains that had defied the dry cleaners in Northallerton. Valerie liked her, and as much as she confided in anyone these days, she confided in her.

It was nearly lunchtime when Valerie decided that she would have to subsidise her maid's wages from her own dress allowance. It would mean sacrificing the odd hairdo or a cashmere sweater or two. Yes, it didn't seem so bad if you looked at it like that and she was quite good at setting hair. If she did Valerie's more often, that would be a saving. She daren't ask Richard again, not for a while. There must be peace in the house sometimes.

"My Lady ..."

It was Ernest. Elisabeth normally brought her luncheon on a tray when Richard was away, Valerie was surprised to see the butler instead, empty handed.

"I think you'd better come, my Lady, if you will. It's Mrs Clarke ..."

Valerie's stomach fluttered unpleasantly. There was tacit agreement in the house that Ernest dealt with Clarke. Not the usual chain of command but Valerie had long ceased trying to overcome her revulsion and the woman was so hostile ...

"She didn't want me to tell you, but I thought it was my place to inform your Ladyship."

"Yes? What, Ernest. Tell me what?" The butler could be slow in getting to the point when he was nervous.

"She's finds herself indisposed, your Ladyship. Come over all queer, as she expresses it. Quite faint and dizzy ... and Doctor Milne's come to see Miss Rozanne and Miss Sandra ... so with your Ladyship's permission ..."

"Yes, yes. Ernest take Doctor Milne down to the kitchen. I'll come if he needs me, if not, tell him to come up and see me here when he's finished."

She couldn't face the sight of Clarke. Not in front of the dapper Sandy Milne. She would feel responsible for the old woman's bedraggled, dirty grey hair, her clothes and her smell but there was nothing she could do. The very thought of her killed Valerie's appetite.

There was no escape, Ernest returned with a message from the doctor. He required her presence in the kitchen.

Mrs Clarke was slumped there, white faced and shapeless in a chair by the Aga. Sandy Milne leaned on the stove's steel rail, his stethoscope around his neck. He looked at Valerie and shrugged slightly.

"I didn't want to see no doctor, my Lady," the old woman croaked. "I'm just tired. That's all it is tired, I'll be right after a little rest."

There was pleading in her eyes. Valerie turned away unable to look at her.

"Now Mrs Clarke, you don't eat enough, that's your trouble," the doctor addressed the cook robustly. "You're anaemic by the look of you and you need more than a little rest. You need a long rest, in bed, but I'd like to listen to that heart of yours first."

The old woman crossed her hands across her breast in a desperate clutching movement and shrank back in the chair

"She won't let me examine her," Sandy turned to Valerie. "Can you persuade her?"

"I'm not taking my clothes off, catch me death, not in this weather and not with all these people."

With Ernest's help, they got the protesting old woman to a bedroom on the servants' corridor. She was incapable of walking upstairs. Clean sheets were brought and a nightgown from Mrs Clarke's own chest of drawers.

Valerie made the bed up herself. When she had finished, the cook collapsed on it fully clothed. Still she refused to undress. Doctor Milne listened to her heart through her thick knitted cardigan, his eye on Valerie. He seemed unaware of any odour. Valerie admired his professional good manners but could not emulate them.

"She'll have to go to hospital or to relations if she has any. She needs complete bed rest, two months at least."

'I'm not going to no hospital." Tears began to leak from Clarke's eyes, cutting pale channels through the grime on her face. She could not have washed for months. "I shan't go."

A swift private conference took place between Sandy Milne and Valerie.

"I won't have her in the house ill. She must be made to go to hospital, Sandy. I've no staff or facilities to nurse her here."

It was beyond his power, the doctor explained, to forcibly place anyone in a hospital who did not wish to go, Valerie's face fell. What if the old woman died?

"Where's Richard, by the way?" the doctor asked.

"In London," Valerie replied dully. "Dick took him to York to catch the Pullman this morning. He should be back soon."

"Hmm." Sandy Milne shot a quick covert glance at Valerie; she really shouldn't have been left alone with all this mess. Doctor Milne repressed an urge to speak his mind. Lady Barwick was defensive about her husband, still pretending it was a perfect marriage and he preferred not to lose the Barwicks as patients. Private patients weren't thick on the ground in his practice, and Val was a good sort, no side, not with him anyway.

"Anyway, I'm afraid I'm going to have to leave you to it. I have other patients waiting. Call me after six if you need me."

Valerie summoned Dick from the stables on the house telephone in her boudoir. She watched Sandy Milne depart, he turned and waved up at her window as he got into his car.

135

She was in the nursery when Dick sought her out. Nanny was on the rampage; no nursery luncheon had been produced. The children were famished. How did Lady Barwick expect her to carry on in these conditions? The food was always quite unpalatable anyway.

"For God's sake, Nanny! Use your imagination for once and pull yourself together. I've got a crisis on my hands." Valerie pulled herself up short. It would be the last straw if Nanny left. "I'm sorry. It's not your fault."

"You'd better come and see for yourself, my Lady."

The sight that confronted Valerie's eyes when she returned to the kitchen quarters would haunt her all her life. Clarke had left the bedroom and was back in the chair at the side of the Aga. There was sweat on her face and she was heaving and groaning, trying to vomit.

Suddenly, dark viscous blood was pouring from her mouth, and her nose, her eyes were sightless, she knew no one.

Clarke moaned feebly and threw up more blood. Ernest supported her, his trousers were splashed with fluid and clots. The stuff was nearer black than red. Then there was a squelching sound followed by an intense, overwhelming reek of faeces. Ernest stepped back; the old woman had let her bowels go.

"That's it. She goes to hospital. I've had all I can take. Call an ambulance."

Mrs Clarke died there in the kitchen twenty minutes later. The ambulance arrived but went away empty, Lady Barwick's cook was no longer their problem the driver said, ambulances were for the living.

Valerie rang Sandy Milne's surgery. He wasn't there.

"You'll have to get someone to lay her out," the receptionist said.

Of course, that was normal practice in the country. Ernest arranged it, he wouldn't let the younger servants near but with the help of two of the farm men, he got the body back to the bedroom near his own and onto the bed. The gardener's wife, Mrs John Pollit would come and her neighbour Mrs Chapman.

Valerie did as much as she was allowed. She got another clean nightgown from Mrs Clarke's room, stockings too. There were drawers full of fresh underwear in there, new, most of it, untouched. She assembled buckets of hot water, lint, cotton wool, scissors, and Dettol. Everything she had been told the women would need. Cigarettes, Ernest suggested, for the smell. Valerie emptied the big silver box in the West drawing room. Then she retreated upstairs to the nursery again.

"What's happening downstairs, Mummie?" Rozanne's little face was alit with enquiry. A knowing child.

"Somebody's poorly, sweetheart. It's all right. The doctor's coming soon."

Nanny prepared a makeshift tea for them all, buttery toast with sardines. Valerie wolfed her share of the food; she was surprisingly hungry.

"I expect poor Mummie missed her lunch," Nanny said. "Would you like to bath the children tonight, my lady?"·

Valerie was unable to do so. A house maid brought a note to the nursery, Valerie was needed downstairs again. In Ernest's pantry, Mrs Pollit and Mrs Chapman were waiting, vibrating with indignation. Each had a cigarette firmly clamped in the corner of their mouths. Their flowered overalls were horribly soiled.

"I can't do no more, my lady," Mrs Pollit began. "You should have seen the state of her feet when we got her stockings off ... coal black."

"I thought I'd seen it all, my Lady," Mrs Chapman cut across her friend. "But whatever's under them rags on her chest. I don't like to think, it's not right to ask us."

No, of course it was not. It was Valerie who lifted the matted stiffened rags. The right breast was eaten away; a hole the size of a grapefruit oozed and crawled. Alive. Valerie fought for command of herself. She must not be sick, she must hold her dignity.

"Thank you for what you have done. Wash your hands now very thoroughly in Dettol solution. Go home, the body isn't safe to handle. I'm sorry you were asked, I should have known."

Valerie summoned a firm of undertakers. The body was removed to the stables where they built a coffin immediately. Six rolls of cotton wool failed to prevent the putrid contents seeping through at the joints. Hours later, the coffin was screwed down. Ernest served brandy to the shuddering undertakers' men in his pantry. Mr Daniels himself drank a large measure with Valerie in the study.

"The worst corpse I've attended in a lifetime in the business," the undertaker said, taking his leave shortly before midnight. "Who was she then?"

"Our cook," Valerie replied stonily. "An old and faithful servant."

"Bloody poison, more like," the man said in an unprecedented departure from professional etiquette.

He shivered. "You'll have to burn everything she's used. Linen and the like. Blankets, carpets, curtains, food an'all. And get t'rooms fumigated. Think on, or you'll have health inspector down on you like a ton of bricks."

They burnt everything that night including a loathsome cache of soiled rags found in Clarke's room. The kitchen cupboards and the larder were swept bare. There was nothing left to eat in the house. Valerie filled her bath up to the brim and poured the best part of a bottle of Dettol into it!

The fumigators came in the morning. Valerie rang Richard's club as soon as they had finished. He was not there, she hadn't really expected him to be.

Richard returned a week later. Valerie poured out the story of Clarke's death into his unwilling ear.

"This isn't what my parents brought me up for," she stormed. "My life was never supposed to be like this. You always leave me with all the filth."

Richard was unmoved. The repellent details he had heard only hardened his heart against his wife. Why did she bother him with all this unpleasantness? She liked to dwell on things. If she wanted to roll in muck, that was her affair. It was all over and done with anyway. Val exaggerated. She was famous for it. Poor old Clarke.

138

Exasperated Valerie had to pack for a visit to friends in London. Enough was enough.

"Unlike you," she told Richard. "I'm leaving you my address and telephone number. I shall call to speak to you every evening to find out how the children are. I expect to be gone four to five days, it depends how I feel. That's not much to ask is it? I need to go anyway. To see employment agencies about a new cook. Meanwhile you'll just have to manage between Nanny and Mrs Pollit."

Richard demurred. Valerie ran his home smoothly. Her absence would be an inconvenience. There was the fear too, that in London she would spend money. Sensing his wife's brittle temper, he used emollient phrases to dissuade her.

He didn't want her to go. He would miss her. The house was never the same without her. He understood her desire to get away. But just now, Thimbleby needed her stabilising influence. And in truth, Valerie felt a little guilty about leaving them all to fend for themselves but rekindled her anger and stiffened her resolve. The Austrian's clipped, formal speech crystallised Valerie's sense of grievance.

"We will manage, my Lady. You have borne so much, so bravely. It is hard that you had not the support of your husband. A small vacation will be beneficial to your health," she glanced at Valerie's reflection in the dressing table mirror, patting her mistress's blonde curls deftly into place "Shall I accompany you, my Lady?"

Valerie turned on the stool and clasped the young woman's hand warmly.

"No, dear, you deserve a rest too, and without me around, you'll have less to do. There's no room at the Walkers' flat anyway. Oh, and send my heather tweed suit to the cleaners, will you?"

"Very good, my Lady and I shall make Wiener Schnitzel for Sir Richard, that will be my contribution."

"I shall be sorry to miss that," Valerie replied absently. "By the way, I've given you your rise. I only wish it could be more."

Thinking nothing further about her conversation with Elisabeth, Valerie enjoyed her visit to London. Resilient as ever, shopping, lunching and going to the theatre restored her quickly. She saw a John Osborne play and didn't understand a word of it, a kitchen-sink drama. At the Ivy restaurant, afterwards, she made her views known.

In Hamley's next morning, she spent rather more than she ought on presents for the children's Christmas party. Something pretty and original for the girls, something clever and exciting for the boys.

Valerie chose them all individually. Shopping was a never-failing palliative. It blunted the edge of misery. For herself she bought a really rather naughty nightgown. Cyclamen pink to suit her dark colouring. The garment was in good taste, but only just. It would be a private joke between the two of them.

Valerie overspent the remainder of her dress allowance for the rest of the year by a considerable margin, but the dunning letters would be polite for at least four months. By then the accounts would be paid. Richard need know nothing.

There were other, more vexatious interludes. She was forced to raise the matter with Richard during one of their telephone conversations.

"This is where your meanness has got me … again. It will have to be at least another ten shillings unless you want me tied to the Aga for the rest of my life."

"Why can't Elisabeth do the cooking?" he queried mildly.

"Elisabeth?"

"Yes, Elisabeth surely you know your own maid's name. She's put on some smashing grub while you've been away."

Valerie vetoed that as another of Richard's cheese-paring ideas. Elisabeth was an expert in other departments. She understood the management of china, linen and silverware. Well-groomed and industrious, she was an indispensable lieutenant to Ernest, a good example to the younger staff.

140

In her current role, she couldn't be replaced, and she was valuable to Valerie personally. Richard grumbled but to his wife's surprise, he allowed her to offer another ten shillings a week to any potential cook.

"I shall expect Cordon Bleu for that." There was no real menace in Richard's voice, he sounded more sheepish than anything else. It was plain to Valerie that he had seen reason at last. "When are you coming home, darling?"

Valerie thawed.

"Friday evening, late, but I think I'll get off the train at Preston. Could you send Dick for me? The train coming down was freezing. I don't want to go any further on it than I have to."

Richard made no objection; they were all looking forward to having her home again. No hurry, though. Why didn't she stay on a little longer and enjoy herself?

"Or go down to Blenheim for a few days," Richard suggested. "Old Bert would be tickled pink to see you."

Astonished and touched by his sudden consideration for her comfort, Valerie was hardly tempted. The great thing was to get a new cook installed at Thimbleby in time for Christmas.

Valerie put the telephone down, pleased with her easy victory. She accepted Richard's change of heart at face value. No doubt he'd had her story about Clarke confirmed by Ernest. Serve him right, but he did love her, really.

It was not long before Valerie told herself that she had completely forgiven Richard his crassness over Clarke. She attempted no excuses, no rationalisations of his attitudes or behaviour. Richard held the key to Valerie's whole existence, Thimbleby.

Succumbing to a girlish impulse to do the unexpected, Valerie changed her mind and came home on the Thursday. She didn't warn them at Thimbleby. Making an entrance was always pleasant. It would be exciting to arrive by taxi in the night. The dogs would bark, and all the lights of the great house would go on at once, like an enormous smile lighting the darkness just for her, a wonderfully-dramatic scene.

141

Valerie pictured herself under the portico in her fur coat laden with parcels. It would all be like a traditional Christmas card, sprinkled with glitter.

Valerie's reception fell short of expectation.

It was half past three in the morning. The house did not flood with light at her first touch on the bell pull, nor at her second. The dogs barked eerily in the dark. Otherwise, the house seemed deserted. It was raining. Nervously, Valerie dismissed the taxi. There could be nothing seriously wrong, the dogs would waken them all in a moment.

Puzzled, Valerie walked around the house. Ernest's ground floor bedroom was there. To her relief she saw a light. There were moving figures showing behind the drawn blind, waving arms like a shadow puppet show. She tapped on the window. Who did Ernest have in there? Not a maid, surely. Ming her Pekingese was yapping.

"Ernest!"

Throwing up the blind, the butler signified his intention of going to the front door. He was wearing a plaid dressing gown and striped flannelly pyjamas. There was nobody in the room with him.

The door was opened not by Ernest himself but the second housemaid. She was holding the dog in her arms.

"Oh, my Lady, we didn't know how to tell you ... Ernest said we should mind our own business, but I couldn't go on, not with you with your eye blacked."

"Where's Sir Richard?" bewildered, Valerie took Ming from the maid's arms. The little dog licked his mistress's face rapturously.

"Come," the maid beckoned, a hushing finger to her lips, and set off up the main staircase. "No! don't put on the lights."

Valerie's hand dropped obediently from the hall light switch. She followed the maid to her own bedroom. It was unoccupied, of course. Richard slept in his dressing room when she was away.

"What on earth is going on?"

They tried the door to Richard's dressing room and found it was locked. The door was then opened, and Lady Barwick and the maid walked into the room turning on the light to see Sir Richard Barwick and the maid, Elisabeth, both standing in the middle of the room, Sir Richard had his shirt on and one sock but no other clothing. The bed had been slept in and there was a smear of lipstick on the pillow. Elisabeth was totally naked.

Elisabeth did not say anything but kept her head down and endeavoured to cover her body; she had dyed her hair blonde. Somehow, it infuriated Valerie more than anything. Jealousy.

CHAPTER TEN

Christmas at Thimbleby was cancelled that year

There was to be no children's party, the estate workers were informed. Valerie distributed the presents she had bought personally, calling at each sequestered cottage in turn.

'Will you be gone long, my Lady?" anxious-faced adults enquired.

"I can't say," Valerie invariably replied in a tone that conveyed bravely-strangled sobs. She would drink half a cup of tea, nibble a homemade biscuit, and depart squeezing hands meaningfully with a caress for sheep dog or child. She walked away, head slightly bowed with no looking back.

Sending her heartfelt regrets to the pantomime committee. Valerie urged them to continue rehearsals without her. She wished them all well for the performance

House guests were put off with the briefest of letters; invitations to county neighbours for the masked ball on Christmas Eve were withdrawn without explanation. At least two brand-new, professionally-made Nell Gwynn costumes were advertised for sale in local press. Which made it clear to keen observers of the local scene that Richard Barwick would be not be pawing his neighbours' bosoms at Thimbleby this festive season. Not in public anyway, Val had put her foot down. A break with tradition.

Valerie went about her work of destruction with grim efficiency, and as she saw the light go out of the faces around her, anger cauterised any sorrow she might have felt at inflicting pain on the innocent. They should see, all of them, how Thimbleby fared without her. It would be, she calculated, as it had been when she had first encountered the place. A wasteland populated by Richard's downtrodden serfs.

"I don't want to spend Christmas in a rotten old flat," Robert whined, thinking of his new pony.

"You'll do as you're told," his mother snapped.

In spite of Ernest's best efforts, gossip seeped from the servant's hall into the estate cottages and farmhouses to the village and beyond.

In Northallerton marketplace, ladies in silk head-squares with wicker baskets on their arms stopped to give their opinion. This time Richard Barwick had gone too far, poor Val.

Decamping to a borrowed flat in Stanhope Gardens, Valerie prepared to spend a London Christmas in siege conditions. She took Nanny and one of the maids. A depleted household but they would manage very well in the south-facing, roomy apartment.

She instructed the firm of Robertworth, Snodgrass and Didier to prepare her petition for divorce from Richard Barwick. They had chambers in Lincoln's Inn and Valerie was there most days once Christmas was over. The story of Clarke's career as cook, and her eventual death was very much liked, in the professional sense, of course. Witnesses to Valerie's physical torments were canvassed and half a dozen ex-maids were found to testify to Sir Richard's adultery.

On what grounds would Lady Barwick like to proceed? Adultery, cruelty or unreasonable behaviour. Preferable, too, not to make a more unsavoury affair of the thing than was strictly necessary. An open and shut case, it would be. No risk of a cross petition. Lady Barwick had been a faithful, supportive and indeed, submissive wife. She would look most appealing in the witness box too.

Valerie prevaricated. She was unsure how she wished to proceed. Could not all the evidence be presented?

"My dear Lady Barwick," Mr Robertworth said. "No doubt you feel an understandable desire to wreak vengeance on your husband but consider the children I beg you. It will do them no good to have their father's entire catalogue of misdeeds dragged out for public inspection.

145

What is more, the court is interested in awarding you a divorce on any permissible grounds not on hearing an exhaustive account of your grievances."

"I must know, Lady Barwick," said the exasperated senior partner when meetings were resumed. "What it is you wish to achieve."

"I want to go back to Thimbleby. It's my home."

"Then why do not you return to North Yorkshire and attempt a reconciliation? If you'll permit me to say so," the solicitor ventured with a dry cough and a glance at his pocket watch. "I think it unlikely you'll succeed. Your husband exhibits no taste whatever for domesticity, but your costs here with us are mounting, and all to no purpose. You really must decide what you want, or we cannot help you."

Valerie was dissatisfied. It was Thimbleby she wanted, not Richard. Thimbleby was the matrimonial home. She was an injured party, the innocent mother of children born in wedlock. She was entitled to Thimbleby.

Mr Robertworth disabused his client with brutal clarity.

"I'm afraid you must face the fact, Lady Barwick, that what you ask in respect of your husband's house is an impossibility. We are not speaking of a suburban villa here. The case of a landed estate, which has passed directly through several generations of the same family, will be viewed in a different light by the court. Your husband will be directed to provide you with a suitable alternative residence."

"You mean if I divorce Richard, I can't live at Thimbleby? And if I want to live at Thimbleby…"

"You must be reconciled to your husband," the lawyer finished for her. "Quite so, the choice is yours, Lady Barwick. Perhaps you would like to think about the implications at leisure."

Returning with fresh proposals to the offices of Robertworth, Snodgrass and Didier the next day, Valerie put her cards on the table.

"I should like to preserve the marriage if I can," she said. Mr Robertworth displayed no emotion at the volte face. "But I want a substantial settlement to safeguard my future and that of my children ... an independent, assured income."

The solicitor pursed his lips. It would be very difficult. Such a settlement should have been obtained before the marriage took place. She had been badly advised, very remiss.

"Has Sir Richard signified any anxiety for a reconciliation?"

Valerie was forced to admit that he had not. "His pride, you know."

"Indeed," the solicitor leaned his elbows on the desk and steepled his fingers. "Then our best plan is to proceed with a divorce action and stand out for a maintenance agreement of very substantial proportions, which we may ourselves be prepared to undercut at the last moment, with the offer of a reconciliation in exchange for a reasonable marriage settlement. We must hope the less-costly option will appeal to your husband. It's simple horse trading, I'm afraid."

"Blackmail, Mr Robertworth?" Valerie's hyacinth eyes opened wide.

"Leverage, Lady Barwick."

Valerie was delighted. Mr Robertworth was so terribly clever.

In the final analysis, Valerie would accept a settlement of fifty thousand pounds, the income arising to be hers during her lifetime. The capital was to revert to her children at her death. Sir Richard was also to purchase a property abroad in Lady Barwick's name for her exclusive use. For the Colonel part of the year, Lady Barwick would reside at Thimbleby Hall, in the county of North Yorkshire, and co-habit with her husband. The new Rolls Royce promised at the time of her marriage and never delivered, was also to be purchased and registered in Lady Barwick's name.

"You realise, of course, that if we succeed in this manoeuvre, you risk receiving precisely the same maltreatment of which you have already complained. The, er ... violence ... You are sure you consider your position in the County and this house worth ...?"

He had what he wanted now. A clear brief. He would put the opening moves of the campaign in hand. When the case was set down for hearing, he would let her know. It would be some time before he had anything of interest to report. Would not a short holiday be beneficial to Lady Barwick's nerves?

Weeks passed uneventfully. Robert went back to school. The services of a governess were obtained for Rozanne, Richard paid. The friends who had lent Valerie the flat began to hint that they would like her to vacate it or start paying rent.

Valerie began to worry. If she could not remain at Stanhope Gardens, where should she go? The pittance of a dress allowance that Richard gave her would not command a flat of adequate size, let alone a good address. Anything else was unthinkable. She might take the girls out to Kenya and visit her parents, but who would pay her fare?

"Why should I pay your blasted rent?" Richard growled on the telephone.

"You've got a perfectly good home here. By the way. I received your lousy petition this morning."

"Does that mean you want me to come back?" Valerie tested the waters.

"Please yourself. If you go ahead with this divorce thing, don't think you'll be screwing a fortune in maintenance out of me because I shan't pay."

Valerie sat down and drafted a letter to Richard reiterating the many griefs he had caused her. Yet, she wrote, nothing but nothing could ever erase from her soul the memory of the love that had been between them. How sad it was that it should come to this. They had everything, they ought to be happy. If only they could be again. However, she must be brave and strong for both their sakes, and the children's. Divorce was the only answer. She dared not, simply dared not live with him again. Perhaps in the fullness of time, her heart would mend but for the moment, it was quite broken. Valerie took a copy of the letter and sent it to Mr Robertworth. He was not pleased.

"When are we going back to Thimbleby, Mummie?" Rozanne enquired matter-of-factly.

"I wish I knew, darling, I wish I knew." Valerie wrung her hands tragically. The drama was underpinned by some genuine angst.

Valerie's imagination roved the corridors, rooms and galleries of her well-remembered domain. She had been away too long. There would be neglect, dirt everywhere, she was sure, standards would be falling away. She steeled herself for the continued war of nerves.

When she went back, it would be on her own terms.

Richard received Valerie's letter together with another from a more sinister source. A mass of thick parchment folded lengthways. Legal stuff, a wall of words. There were names, many of which he recognised. As far as Richard could make out it was somebody else's divorce.

His own solicitor in Barrow made matters clear to him. He was to be cited as co-respondent in a divorce action to be heard in the high court. There were cross petitions and counter petitions. Household names were involved. The case touched the fringes of the court. He himself was to be sued for enticement; in such a case, juries were apt to become excitable over the damages.

Richard snatched the papers and read the name. He covered his face with his hands. "Perversion in high places, Richard. Buggery, fetishism, whippings, my dear fellow … whippings! The press will have a field day. Dear, oh dear, your poor little girls."

"No, I'm sorry, you'll be lucky to escape with the shirt on your back and what with the kind of figure Valerie's solicitors are looking for …"

"I'll be a ruined man," Richard finished for him

The account Richard gave his wife of the entanglement on the telephone that night, was garbled. He protested his innocence.

Valerie sensed an advantageous trading position. It seemed she had more chips to bargain with than she had thought.

"You do seem to be in a pickle, darling. I really haven't the faintest idea what you're talking about."

"Listen darling, I've had the most pathetic wire today, from Ann MacMaster's husband. You remember them, they were at our wedding. Ann's my oldest friend, the poor girl's dying. A melanoma or something. Too ghastly. She wants me to go to her."

It was arranged. Rozanne would accompany her mother and stay with her grandparents in Muthaiga. Sandra would return with Nanny to Thimbleby along with the maid. Robert would come home at Easter to Thimbleby. Richard would be glad of the boy's company. The flat could be returned to its owners.

****

Ann MacMaster opened her eyes again and fixed them again on Valerie's face. Each time, she tried to hear the story in its entirety, but too often she drifted away before it was done. Whole patches of narrative were missing, but Val was so good, she repeated what she had said endlessly so that in the end, Ann had it all.

"Do you know, I had a boy once? Oh yes, miscarried at seven months. Richard was stone drunk as usual. It was New Year's Eve and I begged him to stay with our hosts. They invited us; we'd been to a dance. The snow was coming down so fast, but no, not Richard he said he was fit to drive.

When we got back to Thimbleby the hollow was full of snow. I told him to stop, that we couldn't get through, but he wouldn't listen. He plunged the car down the hill and the snow closed over the top of it, literally. We had to turn the engine off, of course. All I had on was a chiffon evening gown and a little fur wrap.

We were there in the dark for three hours trying to keep warm by lighting cigarettes. In the end, he managed to get a window open and push me through it. Of course, my shoes fell off. I couldn't see anything; the blizzard was so thick. I screamed as hard as I could till the man in the lodge heard. They got to me somehow and I had the baby in their bedroom all in a horrible, bloody rush.

150

They put it in the range oven like a lamb, but it died. Then he expected me to start all over again. The doctor told him it was out of the question. Not two days later he was sleeping with that girl I told you about."

Oh yes, Ann remembered that story, or one very like it. Last time the baby had been a girl, hadn't it? She must have got it wrong. She eyed the neglected ukulele where it lay on a chair. She wished Valerie would play once more, perhaps she was tired, poor Val, she'd had such a very hard time.

"So, you see darling, I'm not just going to tamely give and in and let him get away with it, I have a chance now."

Ann tried to raise herself on the pillows. It hurt too much but next time she faded out of consciousness, she might not come back again, and she wanted to speak, must tell Val …

The sound of Valerie's voice ran parallel with Ann's thoughts. She made a supreme effort.

"You must leave him, Val darling," the words, so loudly emphatic in Ann's head reached her lips like a sigh. "Don't you see? He's spending your life recklessly, using it up like money, but it's your life. He has no right to spend that. Help me, please."

"Shall I brush your hair?"

Ann nodded; even the softest, baby-bristle brush tore at her scalp like steel wire.

"Thank you, darling." Ann's thin chest exhaled in relief when the torturing brush was laid down. "Nobody is as gentle as you … except Jan."

Valerie concealed a grimace.

Jan hadn't been near his wife for hours. A cold man, or an emotional coward. Valerie was not sure which. 'The Flying Dutchman' Valerie dubbed him privately. His visits to his wife's sick room were hurried affairs. Then he would leave, roaring at the servants and stamping his boots on the stoop outside. It made Ann shudder.

"You have the choice, Val. Leave him now."

151

Ann died just five days after Valerie's arrival. She slipped away after luncheon as Valerie was telling her about Thimbleby, a description that covered every square foot in minute, lovingly possessive detail.

Noticing the glassiness in Ann's gaze, Valerie suspected her of inattention. Sighing, she picked up the ukulele and strummed, tinkling, tinny chords. A snatch or two from the test recording she had made herself. Ann never heard it. Eventually realising what had happened, Valerie closed Ann's eyes and called the servants. There was no more she could do.

When Jan was sent for, he found Valerie weeping large, lustrous tears, which proceeded down her uncontorted cheek in dignified procession. A lesser demonstration would have been insensitive. Valerie knew how to behave on every occasion.

Jan was touched. His wife's body lay covered and composed, awaiting the attention of the undertakers. Drawing back the sheet, Jan saw absence written on the face. The expression, so curiously like boredom, communicated nothing to him.

"What happened," the Dutchman asked awkwardly, "at the end? I should have been here ... I couldn't bear to... I owe you a debt."

"It was so beautiful," Valerie interrupted him smoothly. "I was playing the ukulele to her ... an old song we both used to sing when we were in the F.A.N.Y.S. together. She closed her eyes as if she was simply enjoying the music. There was a smile on her lips, and then it was as if she had fallen asleep. The last thing we talked about was you and the children. She said how much she loved you all."

The funeral was in Muthaiga. Afterwards, at the club, Jan asked Valerie if there was any keepsake; any personal thing of Ann's that she would like to take from their house. He mumbled something unintelligible about his gratitude to her. Loyalty, friendship, he owed the peace of Ann's final moments to her, that kind of thing. Valerie in her turn was touched. The big Dutchman wasn't hard hearted after all, just gauche.

Valerie said she would like the silver rose bowl that Ann had won for golf here at the club so many times that they had given it to her.

"No," Jan said, paling. "You cannot have it. I'm sorry. My children will naturally wish to ... I meant a photograph, a handkerchief ... Something of that kind."

Valerie waved the clumsy refusal away graciously. Jan had always been mean and really, there was nothing else of Ann's worth having. He had given her no jewellery to speak of.

"Poor Ann," Valerie wrote in her diary.

"She died in my arms and I have nothing to remember her by but the memory of her dear, dead face. I shall never play that tune again. My dearest, dearest friend."

In London, the momentum of legal processes gathered speed

Mr Robertworth wrote to Valerie and advised her to return. They had a date now, for the hearing of Lady Barwick's petition. And a bronzed complexion, Mr Robertworth ventured to remark, would do nothing to increase the sympathy of a jury which had no doubt, stretched its own corporate body on the chilly sands of Margate or Cleethorpes. The age of envy had arrived.

The imbroglio in which Richard found himself enmeshed also gained momentum. Never a day passed at Thimbleby without him receiving more communications from lawyers. As the weeks passed, Richard ceased to open or read these.

Sir Richard's latest mistress was not to Ernest's taste. A hard faced, hard drinking lady. Mrs Radcliffe, they called her, Denise. She slept with Sir Richard in her Ladyship's bed, and left ashtrays overflowing with greasy, lipsticked stubs on the night table. The maids complained.

From Richard's point of view, Denise at least, did not nag him. She was a woman of character and stamina. At forty years old, she could sink half a bottle of brandy and put up a hell of a performance in the sack.

After a couple of hours of that, she was up, into her clothes and away. She wasn't pretty or funny, but she knew what she wanted and took it without any sentimental whingeing about love. Richard was as fond of her as he had been of any woman, fonder. They satisfied each other's needs.

"Marry me," Richard said rashly.

"Oh yes? And what are you going to do about Valerie and this case, you fool. If you don't sort something out with her every door in London will be slammed in your face."

Richard thought about it, yet again. His club, Hurlingham, the MCC, all those places and institutions that were the cross-roads of his world. He would be reviled like a leper.

"I'm not sharing your exile, Richard," Denise went on attaching her suspenders calmly, a cigarette between her teeth. "If you want to strap a socking big black penis round your girlfriend's waist and get her to poke it up your bottom ... Well, jolly good luck to you, I say, but society doesn't like it."

"So, what do you expect me to do?" Richard asked her miserably. Denise was his type, his equal, in and out of bed. While he sported with her luxuriant, womanly flesh, he could lean on her manly character. He wanted her, they could be happy together.

"Make a deal, anything. Once you're off the hook you can divorce Val and I'll shove something up your backside to celebrate." Denise leaned over the bed to tweak the despairing baronet's testicles playfully. She dropped a long curl of ash onto Valerie's treasured peach satin quilt.

"I love you Denise," Richard said simply

'Then prove it."

Richard proved it. He got on a plane to Nairobi within a week. His wire to Valerie said he was coming to fetch his darling wife and little daughter home at whatever cost.

Valerie read the message correctly. Richard was ready to do business, how she loved him.

154

The scene of their reconciliation was played out on her parents' Muthaiga lawns. Sitting in the drawing room, her granddaughter on her knee, Alice Skelton applied a scrap of lace-edged cambric to her eyes. The upheaval of another divorce would have killed her, she was sure. Too terrible for the children. The sight of Valerie and Richard sitting in the middle distance with their heads so close together was a relief. It was what she had always wanted for Valerie, family life.

The Barwick's conversation blended the most tender avowals with some hard bargaining.

"I have never loved any other woman as I love you, Val," Richard swore.

Valerie dissolved into a refreshing flood of tears.

"Anything you want Val," Richard offered. "A divorce, I won't contest it."

"Oh no, not now, I want us to be happy together, a family."

Richard sighed deeply and thought of Denise. "It's what I want too, darling, so …"

Valerie dried her eyes at leisure. Richard was so slow. She would have to lay out her terms in horrible, tasteless detail. What on earth did one pay lawyers for?

There would be no divorce, Valerie told Richard. She would forgive him; she would stand by him in his hour of need. Richard would settle the sum of one hundred thousand pounds on her for life, just twice the figure Mr Robertworth had suggested would be feasible. The other details were unchanged.

"It's an awful lot of money." Richard made a subdued protest. For that amount of money, he could have been divorced from Valerie, he felt sure.

"Not really, darling. Remember, it goes to the children when I die, and in any case, it really is necessary. I simply can't put myself at your mercy ever again, but I know you need me so …"

"All you'll have to do is speak to the judge in chambers, quite private, and then the case will be dropped."

"I'll withdraw my petition when I get your signature on the Deed of Settlement."

155

Their embrace was long and lingering. Observing it from the house, Alice called her husband to witness the touching spectacle.

"Isn't that adorable, Bobby?"

Bobby Skelton grunted. He supposed Val knew what she was doing.

The Barwicks sailed home.

Whilst they were on the high seas, Richard's adulterous, enterprising girlfriend met with an accident. She caught a georgette evening skirt on the element of an electric fire. Within moments, she was engulfed in flames. When the flames were extinguished, it was clear that she would be grossly, irreparably disfigured.

"Horrific." Valerie noted kindly in her diary.

Notification of the 'withdrawal' arrived at Thimbleby the day after Richard had signed the document which would confer a private income and liberty of action on Valerie for life.

The danger passed. Richard could not wriggle out of his bargain, however. What was done, was done.

Thimbleby awoke to new life under Valerie's reviving touch. Fires roared in the grates, scenting the house with pine resin. Gilt-edged cards of invitation came to roost on the boudoir chimney piece once more. The mattress in Richard's dressing room on which traitors had lain was burned, and the fumigators called in again.

Tidying out her desk one day, Valerie reread her copy of the Deed of Settlement. Its sonorous, antique phrases pleased her. About to return to its pre-eminent place in the bureau drawers, Valerie spotted a phrase, the significance of which she had not noticed before. The reversion was to the children of the marriage. Robert was excluded. It didn't matter, she decided, folding the papers again briskly. Robert was going to inherit the estate. Who else was there? She really must persuade Richard to adopt him formally; he was a Barwick, in every sense that mattered.

Valerie dreamed in her boudoir while Richard fumed in his study.

An eternity of niceness stretched out before him. Valerie had booked him into an alcoholic's clinic. He longed for Denise's gravelly voice and tobacco-scented body, dammit, she smelled like a woman, comforting. Meetings were difficult. A tumble in someone else's bedroom at a party was the best they could manage nowadays. A rustle of taffeta and then Denise's tough, no nonsense underwear.

Denise now pressed Richard to be rid of Valerie.

"Divorce her," she commanded during one of their many, covert telephone conversations.

"How the hell can I?" Richard replied. "She has never done anything wrong."

"Then you will have to, won't you?"

CHAPTER ELEVEN

It was not long before Valerie identified her enemy. She stood her ground, fiercely guarding what she had won.

Denise returned to the charge repeatedly, believing that one day, Valerie would give up and move aside. She would see that Richard did not want her; she would cut her losses and withdraw. No woman with a drop of breeding of self-respect, could do anything else.

Denise's husband divorced her, and she took up residence in Heslington at Little Hall, which Richard openly helped her to buy. He did not forbear to say, whenever a pair of field glasses or shooting stick was lost, that he must have left the missing article over at Littlethorpe Manor.

Valerie had staying power. There was no outrage that Richard could commit that would she would not forgive, it dragged on for years. Every so often, there would be fresh starts and new beginnings. A number of these were staged at the place Valerie referred to as 'my home in Italy'. She did so from irritation that the modern apartment was not a classical villa. It was the property that Richard had been badgered into acquiring for Valerie as part of her settlement.

Perched on the rocky groin, which connects the thigh of Italy to France, Switzerland and Monte Carlo, it was convenient for visiting Rozanne and Sandra who were now at school at St George's School, Montreux.

That was another hard-won concession. What in God's name was wrong with Roedean School? Richard had demanded. Valerie had an answer for that.

Languages were badly taught in English schools, and she wanted Rozanne and Sandra to take after their mother and be fluent in half a dozen languages, and what was more, she hoped her daughters would make useful, international contacts in Switzerland. If the net were spread wide enough, she reasoned, there was no knowing whom they might marry. Richard gave in; they were his girls, after all.

Valerie's home in Italy was purchased in their first term at St George's School. Richard hated Ventimiglia, a scrubby Mediterranean town, overwhelmed by cranes and concrete blocks of flats, which leaned out rudely, over the sea.

For Valerie's own part, she had high hopes of longer-established residents most of whom knew somebody, who often dined with an equerry of Prince Rainier's. Invitations in the right quarter were issued and if they were refused the first time, they would be reissued on her next visit. Snubs were ignored; persistence would pay off in the end.

The pink palace on the hill in neighbouring Monte Carlo was visible from the apartment's balcony. It beckoned. There must be a route, a social route that led to its private, domestic quarters. Valerie craved the entrée there; she was entitled to it, she felt.

"I feel an almost … telepathic communication with Princess Grace when I'm here, you know," she would tell selected visitors to her broad terrace. "It's quite uncanny how much we have in common. We both gave up a career in films to marry, it's funny, isn't it," the thought would strike her with lightening suddenness. "That although her husband is a prince, actually, his little principality is far smaller than my husband's estate."

"We know so many of the same people, and of course, we both do so much work for charity, such similar lives we lead."

Those passages were for public consumption. Later, when the guests had taken their leave and even the cicadas had fallen silent, Valerie would kneel winsomely beside the basket chair in which Richard slumped to upbraid him about Denise.

159

"Don't you see, darling," she reasoned with him. "A miserable, lonely woman like that will do anything to get another woman's husband? She knows your weaknesses, knows how proud and sensitive I am. That is her plan, she thinks if the two of you go on humiliating me long enough, I shall leave, but, darling, I shall never do that, no matter what she tries to do to us. Thimbleby is my home and our children's rightful inheritance. Never forget that I love you. Do come to bed, darling."

At forty-one years old, Valerie conceived. "Our reunion baby," she told friends in North Yorkshire and in London. The friends were bemused. To which reunion did Val refer? She and Richard had had so many. Hadn't she left it rather late?

Valerie's fourth child was brought into the world with difficulty, only after she had spent many months on her back in the London Clinic. Her physicians disapproved of the pregnancy. The foetus tried to abort more than once. Valerie's will alone retained it in her slackened womb.

Every fashionable fortune teller in London came to her bedside. Crystal balls, palm readings, psychometry and tarot cards. Yes, the baby would be delivered safely. Charlatans to a man, the practitioners of these dark arts told Lady Barwick what she had paid to hear. It would be a boy, an heir at last, the very stars foretold it.

Richard waited for news at Thimbleby, cradled most nights in Denise's muscular embrace. When a girl was born, Richard departed for London with his mistress's sneer ringing in his ears.

"One hell of a fuss she makes over dropping a filly foal."

Weakened by her labour, Valerie rallied to protect the child from its father's wrath.

"I suppose you did your best," Richard acknowledged with grudging chivalry.

"I did my best? It's you who determines the sex of the child, Richard."

Richard gave his youngest daughter a cursory glance. Another set of school fees to find, another coming out dance to give, another wedding reception to pay for.

"I've nothing left to live for."

"There's Robert."

"Robert! God alone knows whose spawn he is."

Valerie started to protest this injustice as she always did but was shouted down as usual. A nurse came in and looked uncertainly from her patient to Richard. Richard glared at her balefully. "Clear off, can't I even talk to my wife?"

The nurse scurried away. Sister would have to deal with this.

"I'll tell you this much, Val, two years from now that young man will be twenty-one years old. You can give him a party and then he's out, out, do you hear me! Let him graft for a living. Thousands of pounds I've poured into his blasted education and bugger all to show for it. Might as well have made a bonfire of pound notes in the stable yard, the results would have been the same."

Robert was dyslexic before dyslexia was heard of. Eton would not take him, so he had gone elsewhere. He was Captain of Polo at Millfield. There was no kind of sport he did not play superbly, nor any kind of book he did not read without stress and strain. Valerie trembled for her son. An affectionate brother to his sisters, popular with the tenantry … he knew every inch of Thimbleby. There must be a place for him there. If he went to Cirencester, Valerie was sure she could get him a place between this contact and that.

Ten days later Valerie's own Rolls Royce was sent to fetch her and the baby home. A new nanny went with them. All the way up the Great North Road, she kept saying what a good baby the child was, she was, of course.

"Would Madam like to stop somewhere and feed baby?"

"No, Madam bloody well wouldn't," Valerie snarled. "Madam has done quite enough already, give her a bottle. Another thing, you call me 'My Lady'."

A lavish christening ceremony saw the world, the flesh and the devil renounced on baby Victoria's behalf. Champagne sealed this joyous pact with heaven, blurring the earthly disappointment.

Decorum, that good fairy who should attend every baptism, deserted the scene early. Richard wagged the London Clinic's long bill in his guests' faces.

"That's what it costs you these days to get a girl out of a woman my wife's age," he told them.

The godparents and other guests laughed nervously and eyed Valerie with compassion. She kept smiling. Dignity.

At school in Switzerland, Rozanne and Sandra heard the news. It was sad for Mummie but there would be no imperious boy to lay claim to all. And he would have been too young to be of much practical value, socially. A sister to share with was better really.

Flying home for the holidays, Rozanne and Sandra were excited. Baby Victoria Barwick could be given a warm welcome, she was no threat to the nursery pecking order at Thimbleby. Two thousand feet over Paris, her older sisters shook hands on the deal, it was correct juvenile form in those days.

During those same holidays, Lawrence Lorraine was summoned from Chelsea to paint a family portrait in which Valerie, the radiant mother, holding her lace-clad child, formed the centre piece. The artist knew his business, and a soft-focus technique knocked ten years off Valerie's age. Richard's double chin was minimised by his erect stance. Rozanne and Sandra in their puff sleeves and suitable, single strands of pearls looked destined to marry dukes, and Robert, their stepbrother, wore an air of noble, nineteen-year-old detachment.

"There you are," the artist commented blandly, wiping his brushes for the last time. "A typically English upper-class family at home. Contentment, confidence and continuity." Valerie was enchanted.

The County watched the duel with interest. At well-appointed breakfast tables, the state of the Barwick marriage had approximately the same news value as the cold war.

There was the night Denise had gone a tad too far and insulted Valerie to Richard's face.

Not that she didn't often do so, but Richard must have been feeling liverish because he dragged Denise across the room by her hair and put her, big woman though she was, over his knee. He pounded her broad, well-corseted beam with the flat of his hand until her cries of pleasure turned to pain. Then, if Denise's housekeeping woman could be trusted, he made her get on all fours, right there on the drawing-room floor, and he thrust his way up her rectum.

"Sucked him in like one of them there sea anemones, she did ... like on that underwater programme on the telly, did you see it? Madam never saw me, like," the good woman reflected. "Too taken up wi'it all, should'a seen her face — beetroot."

The sequel to that tale was supplied by a more respectable source, one of Valerie's own friends.

It seemed, as the story was pieced together later, that the night following his escapade with Denise, Richard had slept with Valerie and asked her to take his penis in her mouth.

"Oh no, Richard, no," she replied. "I don't know where it's been, do I?"

"She was so disgusted, she just spat and spat. Like a cat."

"Well, she would, wouldn't she?" the betrayer's interlocutor said musingly as she refreshed her visitor's cup. "It is of that precise animal of which your friend, Valerie, reminds me."

Was she not President of the British Legion? She was a tireless worker for the Conservative Party and for the RSPCA. Mrs Brooke's Hospital for Horses in Cairo had no more passionate supporter. Val had got Prince Philip's World Wildlife Fund off to a flying start in North Yorkshire, all good, sound stuff.

Her interests were widespread. She opened church bazaars and new housing estates for builders with equal grace. Good public relations, she said. Kosy Homes Oil Fired Central Heating had been delighted with her efforts.

"As a housewife myself," Valerie had piped sententiously "I know the importance of family life, and that is impossible to achieve without a really warm, clean home."

Perfect, the promoters agreed. Lady Barwick had the Royal touch; she was so good at saying nothing in a nice lot of easy-to-understand words.

The local newspapers liked her too. Took a good photograph, did Lady Barwick. First-rate copy with her animals and her title. At least twice a month there was a report or a feature.

"Blonde ex-film starlet, Lady Barwick is auctioning all her old clothes for charity."

That was an annual event now and very popular. They came down from Newcastle in coach loads. Two-year-old Belville Sassoon ball gowns could be had for a quarter of their original price. Valerie's friends joined in. For a day or two, Thimbleby's drawing rooms became the best rag-and-bone stall in the country. Even Richard enjoyed it ... and Denise could not burst her way in.

It didn't stop her sniping from a safe distance, however.

"Charity, my foot," she said to her own adherents. "Bollocks, Valerie Barwick and her so-called friends keep all the money for themselves."

Valerie wanted to sue. She issued a writ against Mr Robertworth's advice. Denise was only too delighted to receive it. Her solicitors claimed justification. Mr Robertworth intervened before things could get any worse or go further.

"Lady Barwick, I must say this is rather delicate ... Do you, in fact, retain any of the proceeds, expenses perhaps?"

In her rage, Valerie's pretty mouth ran away with her.

"Well, what if I do? Charity begins at home, you know ... I keep some of it, certainly."

She was advised to settle Mrs Radcliffe's hash by admitting as much to the press. Fortunately, Valerie did as she was bid.

Denise fumed while Valerie went to London to have her face lifted. She gave it out publicly that she was visiting a health hydro. Nobody, not even Richard was to know the reason for her 'rested' appearance when she should re-emerge.

The following year Richard and Valerie went to Kenya as usual. It was to be the last time.

Before Alice's death, Bobby had retired and had been planning to take his wife to live in South Africa by liquidating her considerable assets in Kenya. The Skeltons had hoped to realise enough to buy themselves a picturesque retirement estate in the Cape Colony. Orange groves or grapes, a toy business to tinker with.

Valerie supported this plan with enthusiasm. In fact, she developed the details. South African wine, for instance, was going up in the world, and a white Cape mansion standing among its own vineyards and pictured on a well-designed label would make a more glamorous inheritance than a plethora of bungalows and building sites.

The Skeltons, like their neighbours, did not voice the fears that now assailed the whole colony. It was business as usual ... but the tide in Africa had turned.

Gangs of black youths roamed the countryside drug crazed and blood lustful. In isolated farms like the one which Valerie had once inhabited with Roddy Ward, whole families met a sanguinary end under flailing pangas.

A 'State of Emergency' was declared and nobody wanted to invest in Kenya. For people like the Skeltons, who had not only lost all their money, but also their heart invested in land and houses there, it was impossible to comprehend that this no longer had value.

Unwittingly, Valerie had already allied herself with the collaborators. It saved her life.

One evening she and Richard were invited to dine with some friends of her parents, some seventeen miles north of Muthaiga. They set off in the moonlight, driving in the direction of the Kikuyu reservation.

"What the hell ..."

The car reared to a halt. Peering through the windscreen, Valerie could see a fallen tree trunk was blocking the road. Then something else cut the beam of the headlamps - movement.

"Oh my God," Valerie breathed. "Richard, do nothing and say nothing."

165

"Christ."

The car was surrounded by a group of silent men. In the dark, they seemed disembodied. Richard rolled up the window on his side abruptly.

"You fool," Valerie whispered. "Don't you understand? These people are Mau Mau. We mustn't look frightened."

There was a crash and broken glass fell into Richard's lap. The fragments winked in the dashboard lights. Richard started to panic.

"Shut up! You'll get us killed." Valerie spoke under her breath. She turned the diamonds on her finger inwards, into her palm. "Whatever they want, give it to them."

They wanted money, jewellery and firearms. Richard did not understand what they said. There were two revolvers in the glove box. Teeth bared, he started to reach for them.

"No! Leave this to me. I'll talk to them. Take off your watch."

Valerie handed over all the money and jewellery that she and Richard had between them. While she did so, she smiled a little, not too much, and talked quietly in Swahili.

"I am Bwana Skelton's daughter. You may know me. My name is Valerie Ward." She had no idea why she said that. A terrified confusion of mind. Intermittently, blades gleamed as they shifted pangas from hand to hand, examining the jewels.

"This your husband?" One of the men interrupted Valerie roughly. "Ward Sahib?"

Valerie glanced sideways at Richard. He sat rigid, face forward. Had he heard? It was too late now, anyway. What difference did it make?

"Yes, that is Ward Sahib."

There was a sudden scuffle outside the car. A pistol was shoved through the window, under Valerie's nose, an officer's side arm.

"This belong him?" the terrorist jerked his head at Richard.

Valerie felt the blood surge and ebb in her veins. The gun was Roddy's, the one she had made Kinsu take and hide all those years ago. There was no mistaking it; his initials were stamped on the stock. The hairs on her forearms bristled, she nodded.

166

"Ward Sahib good man," the black man declared, withdrawing the weapon abruptly. "He kill Erroll. Erroll wicked man. Bwana Skelton good man."

It all happened too quickly for Valerie to think how the story, untold by her, had spread. Tribal intuitions.

The men handed back the jewellery and other items Valerie had given them. She was careful to let her fingers touch theirs, naturally, show no fear. They kept the money.

"We need guns. You got guns?"

"No," Valerie said. "Why should we need guns? We're on your side."

It seemed to satisfy them, and the group shambled off to move the tree trunk aside.

"Start the car," Valerie ordered Richard. "Move forward very slowly, wave, smile, they're our friends."

As the car crawled past the men, they raised their flailing pangas and shook them in salute, inches away from Richard's face. Valerie turned the diamonds round on her finger again. She smiled and bowed, tasting acid on her tongue. It was unpleasant, never mind, there was a tube of Polo mints in the glove box along with the guns.

"Silly of us to come on this road after dark," she remarked simply.

Richard was grateful for his life. He neither knew nor cared what Valerie had said to the thugs.

"I don't know a word of their lingo … lucky you'd got a few words under your belt, darling."

Valerie was not having that. Richard ought to remember, that when it came to Swahili, she was more than fluent, she was bilingual, she had spoken this language from childhood, which is what impressed the men so much.

Richard was in no mood for argument. If Val wanted to be thought fluent in Serbo-Croat, at that moment, she could be as far as he was concerned.

167

Over dinner and later in bed, he babbled out his wife's praises. Without her, he would have been a dead man. He owed everything to her. Like any man spared, he was in the mood to make offerings. A superstitious reflex, Valerie had observed the phenomenon in him before.

"There's something you could do for me, Richard," she said, massaging cuticle cream into her nails.

"Darling, anything. If it weren't for you ..."

"Give up Denise."

He agreed. Adrenalin and whiskey made him careless. Getting into bed, Valerie turned the bedside light out. She said a pre-emptive good night to Richard, kissed him and turned over on her side.

When she got home, Valerie thought she would write Mrs Radcliffe a strongly-worded letter, then that would be the end of that.

For a while, Richard was more discreet.

He met Denise in hotel rooms in London accompanied her to race meetings in Paris. The French scandal magazines carried the odd picture of them together, but Valerie never saw these. Her husband's absences could be accounted for. In reality, the pattern was unchanged.

Valerie felt all that remained, was to make things clear to Denise. The task, Valerie considered, could be shirked no longer. She settled to the work in her boudoir one morning after breakfast, soon after Richard's Bentley was out of sight.

Valerie's letter to Denise was injudicious

On her return from Deauville, Denise read the letter in growing disbelief. Howls of laughter alternated with expletives and oaths. Who did Valerie Barwick think she was? A common little adventuress? If she knew anything about it!

A ridiculous person, with her face-lift, her Rolls Royce, her home in Italy and her nodding acquaintance with the Duke of Edinburgh. The World Wildlife Fund, she always managed to slip that into the conversation somehow.

Disdaining to respond Denise circulated Valerie's letter widely. It was shown to this crony and that. Snorts of whiskey accompanied the snorts of laughter. Delicious fun, Denise imposed a condition on her confidantes.

Naturally, every syllabic of the letter was soon common property. It was rumoured that somebody, somewhere had a photocopy; priceless.

At first, the sniggers brushed Richard only lightly. Some woman's nonsense. They persisted, however, until Richard could not go into a bar or his own estate office without there being a sudden cessation in the conversation. Typists' lips held rigidly horizontal, were belied by mirthful sparkling eyes.

"What the hell are you titterin' at? Pull yourself together or pick up your cards."

Richard was not accustomed to being laughed at by his own employees.

It came to a head at a ball given in aid of the Distressed Gentlefolks Association; Lady Barwick was on the committee.

Denise was a member, so many people were, she found a farming neighbour to take her. He wouldn't want to do anything when he got there but drink himself senseless. No damned capacity at all. Richard would be squiring Valerie - officially.

Encountering Denise in the supper room, Valerie treated her to a superior smile. She nodded graciously. There could be no harm in that, now that their relative positions were fully understood. Denise turned her back.

The evening passed happily enough. Richard was attentive and danced with her several times. Valerie was glad to see he ignored Denise entirely. He was missing temporarily during the son et lumiere but reappeared at her side saying he'd had a hell of a job finding the gents.

There was more dancing, more champagne and couples wandering under the stars in the castle's manicured grounds. It had been a heavenly ball, everyone agreed.

By the time their calculations were done, the last waltz had been played and there was a bracing scent of scrambled eggs and bacon coming from the marquee.

"Coffee or Buck's Fizz, Madam?" offered one of the hired waiters.

"Oh … neither just yet, if you don't mind," Valerie said, raking the tented space with her eyes. "I must just go and find my husband … he doesn't know where I am."

"Please don't Val." It was Sandy Milne and his wife.

"No, he'll come back in a moment. Have some of these Eggs Benedict; they're truly scrumptious. We must have done awfully well tonight."

Reluctantly, Valerie allowed herself to be distracted. People engaged her in conversation, calling waiters to replenish her plate and fill her coffee cup. How did she do it? All that dancing and not a hair out of place. What a pretty tiara, they said aloud. Damn Richard. What a swine he was. Valerie's friends seethed inwardly. Whose bed was he pumping away on now?

An hour passed before Valerie saw her husband again. He was framed in the entrance to the marquee. There was a murderous expression on his face. Valerie caught a glimpse of Denise Radcliffe just behind him. She seemed to dodge to one side of him and waggle her fingers, then she disappeared. Hideous woman. She had been pestering Richard. No wonder he was angry, she spoiled everything.

Driving home, Richard was morose. Valerie prattled about the success of the function.

"I'm sorry I had to leave you alone for a while darling. That horrid woman got her talons into you again, didn't she? Next time I'll ask whether she's going to a thing or not. If she is, we won't go ourselves. Don't worry, once people know our attitude they'll understand and not invite her, or tickets will be sold out, something like that."

It was broad daylight when they turned into the lodge gates and Thimbleby lay bathed in early-morning sunlight at the bottom of the hollow.

170

"Gosh. I'm glad to be home," Valerie yawned. "Aren't you, darling?"

"Get upstairs," Richard caught hold of her elbow and squeezed it painfully.

"Richard, you're hurting me! What's the matter?"

"Do as I say, or do I have to carry you up?" Richard spoke between gritted teeth.

Numbly, Valerie obeyed. She kept turning her head to look at her husband as he followed her up the staircase closely. Some kind of dreadful mistake ...

"Now get in there."

Richard shoved her through the door of her bedroom and closed it behind him. He produced a letter, Valerie's to Denise, from the inside pocket of his tailcoat.

"What's this?"

Valerie looked at the torn envelope helplessly. It could have been any letter written by her on the Thimbleby's quarto-sized paper.

"I'll tell you. It's a stupid, illiterate, screed written by you to Denise."

Valerie snatched angrily at the letter in Richard's hand. He held it out of her reach.

"She's not such a fool as to be hurt by this sort of rubbish but I am. You've made yourself look a fool Valerie. Worse, you've made me look a fool."

"How dare you? That's private."

"Private? Do you know who's talking about this sick-making junk? Everyone."

Valerie looked at him for a long moment and then turned with a casual shrug of her shoulders. She swayed her hips to make her skirts hiss softly. A beautiful, seductive sound.

"Come here!" He lunged at her shoulder and pulled her back. "You move when I tell you to ... Denise has more sense in her little finger than you'll ever have. I'm fed up to the back teeth with your posturings and..."

"Surely, Richard," Valerie began, "I'm entitled to..."

171

She saw the side of Richard's hand come down as if were a falling axe. It described an arc in the air. Very slowly, as it seemed. There was no time to move.

The hand chopped beneath her jaw. For a split second, Valerie thought her head was bouncing up from her shoulders. There was a punch then. It switched out the daylight. Stars whirling in her head, green and red prickles in a purplish night. Her lip felt thick and ugly. Sticking out from her teeth, like a beak. Another blow on the side of her head dislodged the tiara. She heard its muted thud on the carpet. When her eyes focussed momentarily, she saw dark red, wet spots on her dress. She fainted and regained consciousness more than once. The nearest thing to her eye was the pattern on the carpet, tufty bits of blue. Now and again, she caught a flash as Richard's patent shoe swung into her ribs.

Valerie was unconscious when her maid found her.

"I may have broken a rib, Molly. Get me to bed …"

Molly Hathaway put her ear close to Valerie's mouth. It was difficult to make out what she said.

Don't bother the doctor. It's all right. I just … I just fell."

Molly misunderstood her orders. She sent for Sandy Milne. When he appeared at the foot of her bed. Valerie shunned him.

"Go away. Sandy. I don't need…"

Doctor Milne brushed these feeble objections aside. With Molly's help he gave Valerie's battered body a thorough examination. No bones broken that he could find. She might have a cracked rib. He peered into her eyes with a pencil light; by a miracle, both her retinas were still attached. Valerie Barwick was much stronger than she looked.

"Thank you, Molly," the doctor dismissed the maid. "You can go now while I have a word with your mistress. I'm going to give her some painkillers and sleeping tablets if she needs them. I'll give you the prescription before I go."

"What happened, Val?" He sat down on the bed as soon as the maid had gone. "Who did this? It was Richard, wasn't it?"

"No, nobody. I fell, bumped my face or something."

"Oh, come on, Val. This is me you're talking to."

172

"Get off my bed, Doctor Milne," Valerie's voice was faint but freezing. "I told you, I fell."

The doctor left, a maelstrom of emotions churning inside him. He smarted at Valerie's treatment of him; Richard Barwick should be arrested for what he had done … was Valerie a coward to protect him so? Or simply the most gallant woman he had ever met?

Richard left Thimbleby the same day. Suitcases and hatboxes were to be taken to Little Hall.

Downstairs it was the same in the gunroom and the study. Everything that Richard used daily was being piled into a shooting brake. Under the direction of the butler, the white-faced servants fetched and carried. Humidors, files full of papers, guns in cases or canvas bags, a silver collar box that had been left in her Ladyship's bedroom, and an old riding mac. It was lost and had to be found. Two cases of claret from the cellar. Shortly after two o'clock, Richard had gone.

The house was hollow with his absence. Echoing. Untidy with the litter of hurried departure.

A day or two later, Valerie was up and about. She walked cautiously trying not to limp. The swellings looked worse, if anything, so she kept to her bedroom and boudoir. Even Nanny was not allowed near, only Molly.

Looking at the thing dispassionately, Valerie believed that by far the worst feature of her situation was embarrassment. That, like her bruises, would fade. Meanwhile, she had the thing she had always wanted. Thimbleby Hall. She had got it to herself as of right. Richard had moved out of his own free will. Deserted her. She would never have to put up with his unclean love making again. Denise was welcome to him.

Of course, she cried. Shock and anger. She didn't mind crying. The tears were washing her clean, calming her down.

Nothing really would change. Things would go on as before, without Richard. He had made his choice, so be it. He would have to make some arrangements about housekeeping money.

She was wrong.

Within ten days, Valerie was informed by Richard's solicitors that she had a period of ten months in which to leave Thimbleby Hall with her children. She might take her personal belongings, that was all. Sir Richard would pay her rent on a suitable flat in London pending divorce proceedings. It was presumed that Lady Barwick would wish to petition the courts.

"He can't do this," Valerie stated confidently over the telephone to Mr Robertworth. "I have a right to be here, he left me, and I don't have to divorce him, do I? Not if I don't choose to."

"Lady Barwick," the solicitor broke in on Valerie's monologue desperately. "I'm afraid he can give you notice to quit. As I explained before, if you are not living as man and wife."

"But I'm willing to ... I saved his life, and he beat me up so badly."

"I did try to warn you Lady Barwick, if you remember? The law is not quite the same for Lord and Lady Bloggs as it is for Mr and Mrs Bloggs of Acacia Avenue, Penge."

"But that's terribly unfair," Valerie wailed with unconscious irony.

"Possibly. It's all over now. Anyway, thank heavens we managed to get that settlement for you. I daresay it's not worth as much now as it used to be."

Valerie came as near to emotional collapse on that occasion as any other in her life. Mr Robertworth was very patient.

"To expect me to leave Thimbleby after eighteen years ... after all the sacrifices I've made. How can I tell the children that their own father is turning them out of their home? Poor little Victoria, why ever did I bring her into the world? I won't give him a divorce ... I refuse ... You realise I'm forty-three?"

"I'm so sorry, Lady Barwick," Mr Robertworth spoke firmly to stem his client's rising tide of hysteria. "You must confront the facts. Face up to things as they are. It's time for you to make a new life for yourself. Let me urge you to have a little courage, you're still young."

Valerie dropped the telephone, slicing the lawyer's voice off cleanly.

CHAPTER TWELVE

Valerie made the last stand. She refused to leave, but as the precious remaining weeks went by, her clutch hold on the cliff edge of the old existence slipped, inch by sickening inch. An abyss of uncertainty yawned at her feet and Valerie thought less of it *a* then she had done in the past.

She gave orders in the house, which were countermanded by terse notes to the butler, issued from the estate office. Silver normally left on display in the dining room was to be locked away in the pantry safe. Richard's signature could not be ignored.

"Does he think I'm going to steal anything?" Valerie asked Ernest bitterly.

"I'm sure I don't know, my Lady," Ernest replied tactfully as he carried the salt cellars that were used every day, the chafing dishes and candelabra away. "Will your Ladyship be wanting anything fetched from the wine cellar today?"

Valerie waved her hand dismissively. Why should she want anything? She generally took a glass of wine with her supper when she was alone, but no fuss was made about that.

Ernest bit his lip as he watched her go. Sir Richard had ordered a complete inventory of the wine stocks and then the cellar keys, all three copies, were to be deposited at the estate office. Mean, that was the only word for it. Ernest determined to look out for a few odds and ends for kitchen consumption, and a case of champagne, Her Ladyship's favourite: he'd do it on his own authority. Loyalty still counted for something.

As head gardener, Pollit received orders not to fill Lady Barwick's requisitions for either flowers, fruit or vegetables until those of Mrs Radcliffe at Littlethorpe Manor had been attended to. Mortified, Pollit kept the diktat to himself, there was enough and to spare for both ladies.

So there was, until the day Denise asked for two dozen of the nectarines that ripened on the south wall early in the season. Downright greedy Pollit called it. There was barely eighteen ready to harvest and here was Cook's note wanting a half dozen for Lady Barwick.

Valerie walked over to the garden herself when the cook complained there were no nectarines.

"Come on, Mr Pollit," Valerie wheedled sweetly. "Surely we've got three at least. One for Miss Victoria, one for Nanny and one for me. I know it's early but ..." It was at that moment that Valerie caught sight of a trug, laden with the crimson and white fruits.

"Mrs Radcliffe's, my lady," Pollit admitted shamefaced. "I'm sorry, but it's Sir Richard's orders."

The little man did his best to place his own body between Valerie and a view of Denise herself over by the glasshouses, cutting the last of the Delphiniums to the ground. It was no use, Valerie saw her.

"What are you doing here, Mrs Radcliffe?" Valerie strode over to her husband's mistress. She was white, trembling with impotent fury. "How dare you? Those are my flowers."

"That's a moot point," Denise replied easily, secateurs in hand. "You can have a few, if you want."

Valerie spun on her heel, choking on bile. Richard should hear of this.

Still, she made no move to vacate the Hall and spent long hours at her desk. From September, daily letters were delivered to Little Hall by hand. Reproaches, pleadings, reminders of the good times. Pollit's lad took them on his bicycle until Richard fired a gun shot at him from his bedroom window.

"Bugger off! Or I'll do more than pepper your backside for you. Keep out of my frigging sight or I'll slice your nuts off and have them on fucking toast."

After that, Valerie resorted to postage stamps. It was all to no avail. Richard was implacable.

Whether Valerie divorced him or not, he and Denise would move into Thimbleby Hall in October. Richard wrote in a note from the estate office.

If Valerie were not gone by that time, every trace of her presence removed, then she would be forcibly ejected, and her possessions thrown out on the drive. Nanny and a maid could accompany her if she wished, for the time being, Richard would pay their wages. Valerie could please herself.

Rozanne who had left school now, came to help her mother pack. The nursery was the worst thing. The discarded toys that might have been kept for another generation were thrown away or given to orphanages. There would be no room for them in a flat. Victoria watched amazed as her safe, miniature world was turned upside down. It was difficult to understand that things that had always been there, always loved, were now designated 'old' and 'unwanted'.

"You're a big girl now," Nanny urged her, patiently extracting a stuffed panda from Victoria's passionate, defensive embrace. "You won't be wanting these old things when you go to your smart new school and there are plenty of little girls who'll be right glad of them."

Small girls know from earliest days what it's like to lose a child. The knowledge comes with the first lost doll. Victoria watched helplessly while the panda was entombed in a tea chest with others of her older sister's teddy bears, doll's tea services and picture books. She felt an agony of bereavement.

Dick drove Valerie and her small daughter away from Thimbleby in her own Rolls Royce early one October morning. The leaves in the parkland were turning at the onset of the nineteenth autumn since Valerie had first seen them as a bride. She kept her head up, eyes fixed firmly to the front. There was a right way to go into exile. No faltering or long, last looks. Kicking off her shoes, when the gates were out of sight, Valerie stockinged toe caressed the smooth calf exterior of the jewel case at her feet. The Barwick tiara was inside. She was entitled to it. Insurance for the future.

Ahead lay a flat in Princes Gate, SW7 and Valerie's new life.

From the first, there were money troubles. Richard's remittances were irregular and never enough. The income from Valerie's settlement would not meet the rent of the flat, clothes, food, wages and school fees. And there would soon have to be a coming out party of some sort given for Rozanne. A cocktail party, probably. Funds wouldn't stretch to a ball.

"Your only hope of securing an income adequate to your needs is to divorce Sir Richard," Mr Robertworth insisted, "Alternatively, you could cut your expenses."

"What do you mean?

"Well, Lady Barwick, there are a number of ways," explained the solicitor patiently. "You could move to a less costly part of London ... say Hampstead or Highbury. Very pleasant there, I'm told. You could take Sandra away from St George's and send her to school here in London, or The Lycee perhaps. A nanny is reasonable, but a personal maid? You might even consider getting a job. Nowadays ..."

Valerie was outraged. She had a job, her charity work. Wasn't she already in the throes of arranging a most massive show business event for the Duke of Edinburgh's World Wildlife Fund? It was going to be the most tremendous success ...

"Ahem," the solicitor cleared his throat. "I was thinking in terms of gainful employment."

It was cruel, Mr Robertworth nodded solemnly. Financial retrenchment was not a manoeuvre acceptable to Lady Barwick; it would involve a loss of face. Remarriage, however, was not outside the bounds of possibility. He mentioned the fact in passing. Divorce would be a pre-requisite. A workmanlike preparation for the inevitable romance, which would soon come Lady Barwick's way.

This was language Valerie could understand. Yes, she must do as she had done before and seek a new husband. Curiously, she found she had little enthusiasm for the project.

In the meantime, Mr Robertworth was to prepare her petition for divorce and arrange for a fair settlement. A lump sum and annual income. The lump sum she would keep in any event, the annual income would be paid to her children should Valerie remarry. That way she would lose nothing. Everyone, these days, had to find ways of keeping abreast of inflation.

Once again, Mr Robertworth set to work with a sigh. The exercise might at least release some funds from which his own outstanding bills could be paid. Lady Barwick seemed incapable of grasping the unpleasant reality that some laboured for her.

A day after her interview with Mr Robertworth, Valerie went for a fitting to Norman Hartnell, for a dress for the World Wildlife cocktail party at Buckingham Palace. It was not really what she would have liked for such an occasion. Dior would have been better, but economies were necessary. As it was, she was to have a short gown of white jersey silk completely encrusted with opalescent sequins. When she moved, she would appear, as the couturier's vendeuse put it, as a flame of white light in the crowd. It would be perfect too, for the cabaret supper at the Talk of the Town after the palace.

Two hundred and fifty pounds the dress would cost, which was reasonable, Valerie thought when you considered that most of the tickets she was selling personally were priced at five hundred pounds.

Valerie pinned great hopes on this chance. She might land a crowned head, or something close. The purchasers of the five hundred-pound tickets were to be presented to no fewer than seventeen monarchs from all over the world and selected members of the British Royal family. Valerie was to liaise with the palace staff and help with the protocol. Prince Philip was sure to make a fuss of her. After all, she had arranged it all at his own request, though it had come at three removes.

Lady Barwick and her motley crew had served His Royal Highness's laughable purpose. Outside on the forecourt, some of those who had paid five hundred pounds to be so graciously snubbed, wondered why they had done it.

There was Walter Hey, a Lancashire brewer, who muttered he didn't think a right lot to it. Could he give Lady Barwick a lift? Valerie regarded him with contempt. A country bumpkin who said what he thought. Charity work was very levelling. One rubbed shoulders with all sorts. How did these people get the money?

"No thank you," Valerie replied with hauteur. "My own car is coming."

The footman singled her out from the crowd as the white Rolls drew up with its temporary chauffeur at the wheel. Ten shillings an hour and he couldn't stop it making that frightful noise. Clouds of embarrassing, smelly smoke as well, what on earth could it be? One was so utterly helpless without a man.

"Wants a new exhaust, does that," commented the Lancashire brewer succinctly. "Cost you a pretty penny, an'all. You'd be better off trading the old bus in for a new one."

Valerie glared. How very, very vulgar some people were.

At the end of the day, the whole affair including the dinner and cabaret where a galaxy of show business celebrities had given their services free, a sum of just three hundred and sixty pounds was raised. A wonderful contribution to the Fund's newly announced one-million-pound target. She did not ask herself where all those five hundred-pound cheques had gone. She knew everyone had expenses.

The committee decided not to announce the results of the efforts to everyone who had so generously contributed. Bob Hope, for example, might wonder why his airfare and hotel bills represented so much more than the money made for the animals.

Not every event in Valerie's social calendar financed itself so smoothly. Bills piled up while Richard's lawyers continued to quibble. His huge fortune it seemed, was now considerably reduced in bulk. It was capital, not income, the Barwicks had been spending so freely over the last few years.

"Then he must sell Thimbleby," Valerie said vengefully. "I'm entitled to support."

Mr Robertworth agreed with her and handed her a valuation of the house. Just eight thousand pounds.

"But that's ridiculous," Valerie protested. "Thimbleby has seventy-five rooms."

"Oh, quite, quite, Lady Barwick. But you see, large houses are little thought of these days. The running costs … the staff."

"I'm not satisfied," Valerie said. "What about the timber in the parkland?"

More searching enquires were made while Valerie bought toothpaste on tick in the Brompton Road. At Harrods childrenswear department, they said Victoria could not have any new shoes. Lady Barwick's account was sadly overdue.

It was in the midst of this pecuniary crisis that Valerie met Tom Hanbury.

The felicitous accident of their meeting was the result of much discussion between her friends.

It was the fear of Valerie's carefully-moisturised cheeks, lifted and stretched over those self-same bones that led to the rapid selection of Tom Hanbury. A free-ranging man about town, Tom was on the hunt for a woman. Let him find Val on the end of his lance. "Take her mind off things … They were made for each other."

Diaries were consulted, who could give a dinner party and how soon? The quicker the introductions were made the better.

The campaign was an immediate success. Valerie swept into a first-floor drawing room, a whirlwind of scarlet georgette. Tom, tall and handsome, rose to greet her. His hand was dry and warm. His eye met hers and it was decided between them instantly, without words. Valerie could not look long enough into his beautiful, boyish face. Valerie shivered involuntarily; here was a man she could love.

She sat next to him at dinner, breathing in his powerful presence. He ate, talked and laughed while Valerie seemed transfixed. He exuded the predator's elusive musk from every pore. A tiger, burning bright. She knew nothing about him and yet, in her lower abdomen, desire uncurled and awoke.

When the ladies rose, they separated her from him quite gently, like someone who is mad. Tom looked down into her eyes, devouring her with his own. They must be a whole half hour apart, he seemed to say, then they would be free.

Powdering her nose in the bedroom, Valerie asked no questions except the repeated urgent murmur. "Who is he?"

They could give her no answer that satisfied her hostess and the rest. Addressees and biographies were meaningless. She had probed his nature with the never ends. No one had ever known him better than she. His name was just an alias, a handle that mortals could hold. Tom Hanbury was a god come down to earth. Valerie sat immobile before the looking glass, the lipstick idle in her hand. Overshadowed by a creature from on high.

Behind her back, the other ladies winked and pursed their lips discreetly. The evening had produced results. They began to tell Valerie the things she ought to know, reserving certain details, she would find out, soon enough.

Tom it seemed was very well fixed. He was cousin to a Northamptonshire squire and often rode to hounds there. Work? No, he didn't work. He was a man of independent means. During the week, he lived in London and travelled to every race meeting within reach. Horses were the love of his life. Did he have a wife? Oh yes, he did. Nobody important. She didn't share his interests. Such a pity that, didn't Valerie think?

Valerie ought to have questioned more and might have done so, had she not fallen so dangerously deep in love. Tom gave her a lift home after dinner. They were silent in the car.

"When can I see you again," he asked huskily at her door. "Tomorrow?"

It was tomorrow, the day following the day after that. They spent a great deal of time staring unwinkingly into each other's eyes. There was talk about the youth of their spirits and the rest of their lives. They had found each other, they said over and over again. Inside a week, they were making love in the afternoons at Tom's bachelor flat.

Valerie had never known such bliss. No other arms compared to his. No other body had spoken so eloquently to hers. She sang out like a blackbird at the moment of his coming. Four times in three hours, on that first, unforgettable day. Valerie hungered for his every approach. There could never be enough of this. Tom never hurt her, rushed her, disgusted her or bored her. When he had done, he cupped her breasts in his palms. They were like a young girl's he said, created for a young man's pleasure. She would never grow old, he said. Nor would he while she remained at his side.

They would stay together forever, immortal, while around them, ordinary people dimmed and grew old. They laughed with the pitiless superiority of lovers, at greying hair, thickening waists and stiffening joints.

Nested in the crook of Tom's arm, Valerie would caress his sleeping manhood until it sprang all at once, back into vibrant life. The want of eternal youth, they called it. There would be another twenty minutes of unspeakable heaven.

"I love you," he whispered hypnotically. "There has not been, is not now, will never be anyone but you."

"Oh Tom, oh Tom, oh Tom!"

And then this glorious person would rise and fetch champagne back to bed. Vintage Veuve Cliquot, because life, even their life, was too short to drink ordinary stuff.

Valerie loved to go with him to the great classic races and others that only enthusiasts cared for. Beneath tweed cap, grey topper or trilby, Tom's features registered so many emotions to enrapture Valerie's infatuated glance. In six minutes or less, he was jubilant, enraged, hopeful, despairing … crackling and flashing with life.

The day that a cheque drawn on his current account was refused by a bookie, Valerie was not there to see it. The horse won, and Tom couldn't conceal his fury. He tore up the race card and scattered the fragments at Valerie's feet.

"There goes your ring, darling … the pink diamond you wanted."

Valerie gasped, heart leaping behind her ribs. Tom wanted to marry her. She wanted, oh so desperately to marry him and the pink diamond solitaire in Bloom's window, he had thought of buying it for her. But the odds on that horse had been short. It gave her pause.

"Darling, it was far too much money to bet on a horse."

"It was nothing. Never mind, there's tomorrow. The three thirty at Sandown Park."

Tom was a serious gambler and in very low water too. When he won, he spent all the money he had. The ecstasy lasted until the last penny had gone. Then he borrowed to bet again. Tailor, shirt maker, shoemaker and wine merchant waited for their money. Turf accountants took priority with Tom. He was hopelessly hooked.

Valerie hid the truth from herself as long as she could, loving each crowing note of his triumphs, sympathising with his failures and losses. She lent him money increasingly. It was not always returned now, but this didn't matter, it would make no difference once they were married.

In the background of Valerie's life, other things happened. Occurrences that were scarcely noticed at the time. She got her divorce from Richard. He would allow her a couple of thousand a year but no lump sum. She should be able to manage on the income from her marriage settlement and the maintenance payment. The court would not force him to do more. Why didn't Valerie flog that place of hers in Italy?

Rozanne did a film test for Franco Zefferelli. They were looking for a Juliet. Her face was not the chosen one. Valerie hid her disappointment and sent her to classes to improve her French. After all that money spent at St George's School, it should have been good. Typing and shorthand rounded off Rozanne's accomplishments. She had better get a job in an Embassy and marry as well as she could.

Robert had married already, left the spring manufacturer and was driving a bulldozer on the A59. He liked the open air and learning about construction from the ground up. Polo? No, he played no polo now. Valerie strangled her worries about him. Something would turn up. If only she could come by some money to leave him. Still, there was plenty of time.

Dennis Dangan died of a heart attack in London. A friend sent Valerie the newspaper cutting. It was a wicked way to break the news, Valerie thought, releasing perfectly pear-shaped tears. Of course, Roddy had already gone years ago, carried off by cancer. It was a good thing in a way, because now the Erroll killing was safe, a permanent mystery.

A week later, Njinsky ran his last race at Le Bourget. Valerie went with Tom. It was more than a race this time. That was the excuse. It was a last fanfare for a hero, and everyone wanted the great horse to win. He lost. Tom cried, Valerie cried, the winning horse's jockey cried. A flood of tears met a tidal wave of champagne.

The Bentley was sold to pay the debt. There was only one way to salvage the wreck. Valerie scraped a few thousand together to let Tom try again.

"Oh, darling, I don't want to accept this from you. Couldn't you pawn old Barwick's tiara again?"

No. Valerie couldn't. Richard had fought over the jewel's return. There had been court orders and summonses. It seemed Lady Barwick, (that was Denise), wanted to wear it on her rusty red curls. Richard had stopped Valerie's monthly cheques until she sent the Barwick tiara back. She had died a thousand deaths until Tom managed to win enough to rescue the thing from the clutches of a Finchley Jew!

With a show of shame and reluctance, Tom took Valerie's money, backed an outsider at thirty-to-one, and won. That was fortunate, as Sandra's school fees had arrived. However, it couldn't go on.

186

It never occurred to Valerie to suggest he get a job, no more than it crossed Tom's mind to get one. Tom Hanbury was a free spirit. A gentleman. He made his living by gambling and sponging. He knew no other way.

Valerie too, had her living to make in her own particular way. Tom Hanbury, she saw clearly at last, had been a three-year extravagance and he would have to go. Their last scenes were not easy. Neither really wanted the split. For Valerie it was a matter of survival. She had nothing left to give.

She left him finally outside The Ritz. Looking over her shoulder briefly, she saw him standing there on the pavement, white faced and forlorn. Valerie had to force her legs to walk down Piccadilly. Her feet landed on the pavement like lead, one after the other.

Now in her forty-ninth year, Valerie began to panic. She still had such a long way to go. Victoria was only eight. The cost of everything was rising. The value of her share portfolio was slipping sideways or sliding. Standards had to be maintained. She must marry again and soon.

It was Sandra's last term at St. George's. Valerie decided to go and collect her. A few days in a small, chic hotel in Montreux would allow opportunities to survey an interesting scene. There would be other parents flying in from every direction … Connections to be made and revived. Aristotle Onassis had a niece there. Unfortunately, he'd married Jackie Kennedy in the same year that Valerie had fallen in love with Tom. Another chance thrown away.

Arriving in Montreux, Valerie did all the usual necessary things. Teamed up with old faces in the hope of meeting new ones, dropped names that would inspire confidence, professed herself incredibly busy.

There was so much to do, she was taking Sandra straight to her home in Italy at the end of term and the child hadn't a rag to wear. So many friends in the area wanted to see her, so Valerie was trying to get around them all in a day or two.

Valerie retreated from Montreux empty-handed. She took Sandra to Ventimiglia and had the rest of her children join her. The children were delighted to have Valerie to themselves for once. She gave them no inkling of her worries. Sandra would have to be sent to some kind of finishing establishment with typing thrown in, in September. In a couple of years, Victoria would start at St George's School. How was it all to be afforded?

Returning to London in the last week of August, Valerie went through her post. Among the bills and impersonal, charity event invitations, was a ticket for a Monday Club dinner. Valerie was a valiant support of right-wing causes, a believer in private enterprise and self-reliance. She would like to go to the dinner but how could she without a partner? She telephoned the friend who had sent the ticket. Priscilla Prescott.

There were a few moments chat about the Season Valerie had missed, her delightful, recuperative rest at her home in Italy ... and Tom. The subject could not be wholly avoided.

"Don't you worry about a partner for the Monday Club, darling," the friend encouraged. "I have somebody who very much wants to meet you. He's going with us in our party. Walter Hey ... you might remember him. He was at that shindig three years ago at Buckingham Palace. Extremely rich," then Priscilla added on a girlish, gurgling note. "He's not quite so good company when he's sober."

Robert and Valerie

Valerie with her father (Bobby) at the
Osmotherley Show, North Yorkshire

Barwick family photo - 1964

Tom Handbury

Valerie and Victoria with Jute, the Great Dane

Family photo, 1988. Left to right: Victoria, Valerie, Sandra,
Philip Bradburn and his sister Mary (back row)

Barwick family portrait

Valerie's 1947 Silver Wraith Rolls Royce

Robert Barwick-Ward

Sharow Cross

Valerie Barwick – the later years

The Skelton Vault (Mausoleum)
Sheffield Cemetery

Thorpe Underwood Hall

Thimbleby Hall in 1953

Portrait of Valerie

PART THREE
Walter Hey and Sharow Cross

CHAPTER THIRTEEN

"So, what do you think I should do, darling?"

Robert shifted uneasily in the brocade armchair. He stared out of the ground floor flat window onto Cadogan Square's private gardens, where the tall plain trees were veiled in a green, springtime mist. It was all a million miles away from the artisan's terraced cottage he occupied with Laura in Aldborough just off the A59. His mother's question seemed bizarre. What had her standard of living, so far above his own, got to do with him?

"Well come along, Robert," Valerie glanced at her watch and rang the bell beside the chimney piece briskly. "I must have your opinion, you're my only son, Walter Hey has proposed to me fourteen times. He may not ask again."

The purpose of this meeting, for which Robert had been obliged to take a day's precious holiday, was to determine whether or not Walter Hey, a Lancashire brewer and bachelor was an eligible solution to his mother's otherwise insurmountable problems. To suggest a reduction in her expenses would be futile.

Walter cut an unimpressive figure despite tailoring that was a credit to the engineering skills of Saville Row. God alone knew what fleshly core supported that super structure of shoulder padding, weighting and interlining. A large nose dominated an otherwise unremarkable physiology. He looked like a duck.

"Richard only lets me have a thousand a year for Victoria. That's for everything, school fees, airfares, Nanny, food, clothes, holidays ..." Valerie began with the litany of grievances, which her three eldest children already knew by heart.

"It's an impossible situation for me. And poor, dear Walter, he's so hopelessly in love with me, I feel quite badly about having allowed it to happen, but I do sometimes wonder if my conscience isn't a little too sensitive." Valerie cocked her head on one side appealingly, "I mean, do you really think it's my responsibility?"

Opening his mouth to reply to his mother's last question with the expected compliment, Robert was forestalled by the appearance of a smartly-uniformed maid. She bore a silver salver, sherry glasses and a silver-mounted decanter. A dish with a few little salty biscuits supplied by Messrs Fortnum and Mason. No matter what the subterranean upheavals in Valerie's life, the surface rituals remained the same.

"You know Walter is so keen on the idea of having a ready-made family. The three of you are grown up now but it would be delightful for him to have Victoria at home with us in the holidays…"

While his mother talked, Robert wondered how much Colonel Hey had seen of Victoria. Very little, he imagined. It was much more likely that his fondness had expressed itself in a willingness to pay his prospective stepdaughter's school fees in Switzerland where she was shortly to attend.

"Do you like him, mother?" Robert asked dutifully.

"Well, of course I like him, darling. He's such a charming, generous man. It's just that he's so much older than me. I mean, nearly sixty-three …"

Robert knew exactly how to interpret those words. When Valerie said someone was charming and generous, it simply meant she had become dependent upon them for the luxuries of her life, if not the necessities. That she should mention the age gap between herself and her suitor was an unusual feature.

"My father was eighteen years older than you."

"Oh, it wasn't at all the same. Walter is old in his ways, if you know what I mean. You realise, he's never been married before, now don't you think that's just the slightest bit odd darling?"

Robert shrugged. "Perhaps he never found the right person to marry before."

"That's just what I say, darling. It's so obvious, isn't it? I don't know why Priscilla has to go around saying all these awful things about him. I mean, if they're true, why on earth did she introduce us?"

"What awful things?" Robert helped himself to more sherry, irritably.

"Well, she says he drinks a lot."

"For God's sake, mother! So far as I know, you've never lived with anyone who didn't drink ... and drink pretty well to excess. What are you talking about? Look, I've got a train to catch ..."

"Damn your train!" Valerie crashed her glass down on the piano case angrily. "Isn't my future, your sister's future much more important than any stupid train? I'm quite sure Laura can manage on her own for few more hours if she has to. Is it too much to ask that I should be able to discuss our family affairs occasionally with my only son?"

Robert subsided. It was always the same. Somehow, his mother, glittering amongst her sumptuous possessions would manage to convey that she was helpless and alone in the world, neglected by ungrateful children.

"I'm sorry, mother. So, what are these rumours you say Priscilla's spreading?"

"They were saying that Walter Hey was impotent ... or some sort of pervert."

"Well he does live with that rather odd cousin of his, the same age and a bachelor, too."

"No, I'm quite sure that Walter is just a very discerning man, a very moral man who has never been able to separate sex in his mind from love and marriage. He must be in absolute agony. What do you think it would be like, Robert, for me to initiate a sixty-three-year-old virgin? Tell me, you're a man."

Robert flushed darkly. This was not a matter over which he felt he could advise his mother.

191

"Let's face it, if you don't marry this poor sod, the only position you'll be left with is one in a soup-kitchen queue, so why wrap it up? At the very least you'd like me to say I approve of this marriage, so you'll have somebody to blame when it goes wrong. Because nothing, nothing can ever be your fault. Isn't that it, mother? Well I'm sorry you'll have to square it with yourself. I've acted as sounding board for long enough, don't expect me to do the pimping."

"Get out! Get out! Just go."

She entered her drawing room to open the morning's post, to discover it was a bill from Colefax and Fowler's interior decorating service; it also contained a County Court summons. The carpets and curtains in the Belgrave Square flat were still unpaid for. Valerie hid the document in her desk where it joined several others of the same kind. It would never do to let the servants see such things. They would be upset for her, perhaps begin to worry about themselves, quite unnecessarily, of course.

With her brain properly oxygenated, Valerie dialled Walter Hey's office number in Leeds. He went to the brewery most days when he wasn't in London. Valerie wrinkled her nose in distaste. Of course, if you had to be in a trade, brewing was quite respectable. It wouldn't matter at all if Walter didn't insist on going there personally and peering into vats and things. So smelly, perhaps he wore an overall in the brewhouse. Valerie averted her mind's eye from the dreadful, humiliating thought. A man without a title lost caste so easily. He really would have to learn to take a great deal more care.

Walter's direct line was busy. The switchboard operator put Lady Barwick through to Colonel Hey's secretary, Miss Hartley. Valerie cursed under her breath. She and Hartley loathed each other cordially.

There were times when they seemed to be locked in some sort of undignified wrestling match for the attention, if not actually the unprepossessing person of Walter Hey. Valerie recognised the symptoms as jealousy. The poor old thing was defending the only man she had, her boss. It was as pathetic as it was ludicrous.

"Oh Walter! It's so good just to hear your voice. I've had this horrid thing through the post. I just can't understand it. Some awful people seem to think I haven't paid them and they're threatening to take me to court. It's all such a muddle and I need your advice so desperately. One is such easy prey for these people when they know you're on your own, they'll try anything on."

"Whoa, whoa …" Walter halted Valerie in mid-flood. "My dear girl, there's no need to upset yourself. Why don't you ask your solicitor? He's the chap to go to."

"I can't Walter! He gets so cross with me because he thinks I'm really rather stupid. He explains things in such a complicated way and sends me a huge bill just for speaking to him on the telephone," Valerie lied smoothly. "I have so much more confidence in you."

Valerie's voice broke here. A carefully organised discordance, not too prolonged. On the whole, Valerie had observed, women generally went wrong with tears because they applied them to situations too liberally. A light touch was best.

"Now, now," Walter consoled. "Why don't you go and have a nice lie down. Get that maid of yours to cosy you up in bed with some whiskey and hot water and I'll be down first thing in the morning. I'll take you out to lunch and we'll sort the whole thing out. The Ritz, eh?"

With suitable expressions of heartfelt gratitude, Valerie rang off. Help was on the way.

Walter was certain to propose again tomorrow, and she would accept. There was absolutely no alternative. Her immediate debts would be settled, removing the spectre of public disgrace. She would have to manage the business of a marriage settlement on her own since Robert was being so beastly.

Propped up on her lace-edged pillows, Valerie leafed through *Vogue*, her mind only half occupied with the magazine's content. There was no possibility of them living in that ridiculous house. To start life again as a married woman, she would need a proper country house.

193

Walter must buy one, and an estate. If they were put in her name, that would go some way to amending the mistakes of the past. This time she would control everything. Nobody could argue with landed property, and his name. He had quite a respectable middle name, Lancaster, wasn't it? Yes, Lancaster-Hey. Why not? Much better, Mrs Lancaster-Hey.

A double-barrelled name covered a multitude of sins.

Valerie became Mrs Walter Hey at Chelsea Register Office in the late summer of 1972 after several months' hard negotiation.

She and Walter were to title themselves Colonel and Mrs Lancaster-Hey. Walter had refused to change his name by deed poll but had submitted to the informal aggrandisement without too much reluctance.

Somewhere amid the twists and turns of Valerie's slippery logic Walter gave in. If people who'd known him all his life laughed at him, well, so be it. If you married into the aristocracy, you had to put up with things like that, and Lady Valerie Barwick was an aristocrat.

A small reception was held at Claridge's in London.

As Walter's pride grew, his courage diminished, by the time his wedding morning dawned, he was positively timorous. If it hadn't been for his best man, Henry Ryecroft administering a few stiff whiskies, Walter might well have run out at the fence and sneaked home to his nice suburban semi-detached house, his quiet, affectionate cousin and a peaceful life in the office with good old Hartley.

Walter reached into his inside pocket obediently, searching for his notes. His first, conventional speech had gone off quite well. The thought of delivering this other one, which Valerie had drafted in fact, filled him with apprehension.

Valerie smiled encouragingly at her husband. His nose looked larger and redder than ever. Too much champagne for lunch and God knows what else besides before the ceremony. Still, he seemed sober.

"And now I come to the business side of our union," Walter announced heavily, rising unsteadily to his feet as a waiter wheeled the last laden trolley from the private room.

Walter glanced across at Valerie nervously. She was a hard woman to please. Harder than poor old Hartley by a long chalk.

She had been kept out of these arrangements, excluded from the Colonel's business for the first time in over thirty years. It was the family, of course. They were afraid that the Colonel might have married her, and why not? Miss Hartley was deeply hurt. She would never have come to the wedding if it hadn't been for her loyalty to the Colonel, but he had pleaded with her.

As far as Miss Hartley could see, the new Mrs Hey, for that was her name now, however much she liked to mess it around, had only one genuine friend of her own here. That thin, monkey-faced woman on the opposite side of the table in the black straw matador hat, now there was somebody Miss Hartley felt she could talk to. Lady Priscilla Prescott. She looked just as horrified by the whole nauseating affair as Miss Hartley was herself, they must have a chat in the Ladies' later

"As you all know," Walter began manfully.

"My wife is a country lover," Walter continued. "And as I am to retire shortly, she has taken me in hand and acquired for our joint occupation the property known as Thorpe Underwood Hall, together with two hundred acres of prime farmland. The house was purchased for a sum of seventy-five thousand pounds, which my dear wife tells me is a bargain. It forms part of my wedding present to her. That is to say, her name alone appears on the deeds. I have retained the farmland in my own name," Walter added in a small spurt of rebellion. Beads of sweat appeared on his sloping brow.

Lady Priscilla and Miss Hartley eyed each other. Part of his wedding present!

"And, I am settling a quarter of a million pounds on Valerie in Grand Metropolitan shares. My brokers advise me that these should show substantial growth in the coming years."

Nobody heard Walter's prosing about earnings per share and the rest. They were too busy gasping and calculating. Valerie would have nearly twenty thousand pounds a year on top of what her trust fund from Richard produced, tax paid. Walter caught up with his audience and made it all abundantly clear.

Valerie's daughters looked pleased if mildly embarrassed at this public display of wealth, poor Mummie. Walter wasn't quite a gentleman, but he was lovely and rich – jolly good.

It was not over yet. There was a brand-new Rolls Royce Corniche for Valerie, too.

"Oh, darling!" Valerie exclaimed throwing up her hands. "What a perfectly lovely surprise. You do spoil me."

A commissionaire announced the arrival of the honeymoon conveyance at the door. Valerie's new Rolls Royce; she and Walter were to travel up to Yorkshire in directly.

"Walter? Where is my darling husband?" Valerie searched the little crowd in the lobby in vain. Walter was not to be seen. So stupid of him. One could not 'go away', so to speak, on one's own.

Valerie filled a little time kissing her daughters on both checks. "Mmm, darlings, I know I'm going to be so happy." She extended her hands to others, particularly Priscilla to show off the new diamond solitaire. One diamond was much like another, quite frankly, Valerie thought, but this ring was even more impressive than the last. Richard's three stones looked very well on her right hand, though. A pity really, that she'd sold Roddy's.

"Valerie," it was Henry Ryecroft pushing his way through, consternation on his plain, dependable features. "Ah! There you are. Look, why don't you take the car and go on ahead of us."

"My dear Henry … ahead of you?"

"Yes. It's Walter. Got a bit of a tummy upset. He doesn't want to hold you up … I'll bring him along in my car. We shan't be half an hour behind you, okay? See you at Thorpe Underwood."

Valerie was obliged to leave her wedding party alone. She rose to the occasion magnificently. When the great, shining car slid silently away from the kerb, Priscilla and Miss Hartley choked in unison as Valerie waved exactly like the Queen.

Passing through the gates of Thorpe Underwood Hall at half past nine that evening, Valerie contemplated her new house with renewed satisfaction. Moonlight became it a nice, compact little mansion

It was Victorian, of course but most people would take it for the genuine Jacobean Manor it had been designed to imitate. Valerie certainly had. Sturdy stone lintels and mullions stood out from the intricate pink brickwork, the place was a satisfying riot of oriels, gables, twisted chimney stacks and mansards. Not a surface undecorated, not a simple elevation anywhere. Quality lights twinkled from all the diamond-paned windows in welcome and the studded outer door stood open.

"May I offer my felicitations, Mrs Hey," the newly-recruited butler bowed Valerie into the hall.

"Lancaster-Hey," Valerie corrected him smartly. "That is my husband's name. Lancaster-Hey."

"As Madam wishes."

How very odd to be called plain Madam again, after all these years.

Valerie had been right to choose this house. The transom mullion window was entrancing, as was the baronial fireplace with its huge dog irons. The stone escutcheon was a challenge. Was Walter entitled to any armorial bearings? It could be fixed a small payment to the College of Heralds. The parquet floor could use some more polish. Of course, she would not have the staff here that she was accustomed to.

It was a full four hours before the crunch of tyres was heard on the gravel outside. Valerie was dozing in the armchair beside the fire when the sweep of headlights awoke her.

"The Colonel has arrived, Madam," the butler informed as he glided through the hall on his way to the front door.

"I'm afraid he's been celebrating, Valerie dear." Henry supported the drooping Colonel. "Not much good to you tonight, I fear."

Valerie took one look at her bridegroom.

"Get him upstairs at once in his dressing room," Henry Ryecroft flinched. He had the fleeting impression that Valerie thought he was some kind of domestic servant, and she gave the same intonation to the words dressing room as she would to dog kennel.

Walter's best man and his butler got him to bed.

The truth was that Henry had had one hell of a job to get Walter into his car to bring him north at all. Shaking with terror at what he had done and the tests that still faced him. Walter had made one drunken attempt to escape, been apprehended halfway out of Claridge's gents' lavatory window, been brought back, calmed down, given another drink, taken back to the bog to throw up, had insisted on drinking more. They finally left London as Valerie had arrived at Thorpe Underwood.

Henry had done his best. The honour of Hey's Lancashire Ales and its board of family directors was at stake. Walter's marital ambitions might yet cost them all very dear.

Valerie said goodnight to Henry and retired to rest alone. She luxuriated in her righteous anger and the large empty space beside her. There had been a reprieve, but for how long? In the morning, a sensible looking woman in a pink nylon overall brought Valerie her breakfast on her own special tray.

Walter never entered her room. Once she was dressed, Valerie stepped out onto the corridor to find a pile of soiled sheets lying on the carpet outside his dressing room. They stank of urine.

"I don't know what we're going to do with his mattress, I'm sure," she heard a voice say further along the corridor, in the linen room.

"Nowt we can do, is there? 'spect we'll have to get one of them there rubber sheets if he's going to make a regular caper of this. Does Madam know, do you think?"

CHAPTER FOURTEEN

During the fortnight that followed, Walter was driven the twenty-odd miles to Leeds each day, returning at seven o'clock in time to change for dinner. Valerie had ceased to expect that her marriage of convenience would be consummated.

"Caught a hell of a cold in London. Don't want to give it you, my dear. Sleep in m'dressing room if that's all right with you."

The 'cold', Valerie was sure now, would prove to be permanent. Priscilla had been right. Perhaps it was just as well. Valerie found she could acknowledge to herself now that she had never really cared, one way or the other, it had been of secondary importance.

The bed-wetting incident was never mentioned between them. A 'one-off' lapse, Valerie assumed, caused by drink and drink alone. Resolutely, she edited that pile of acrid smelling linen out of her memory. No one who mattered knew about it and with the habitual mental hygiene of a lifetime. Mrs Lancaster-Hey chose to ignore it.

Every evening the routine was the same, the table talk of such mind-numbing dullness that Valerie learned to prefer silence. Dinner, unleavened by laughter or anecdote, took fifteen minutes to consume. After the entree was removed, Walter ferreted a gold toothpick from the recesses of his dinner jacket, a garment he wore under protest at home, shielding the operation prissily with his hand.

After dinner, they sat for a while in the library drinking coffee as Valerie flapped the pages of glossy magazines and Walter rustled those of the *Daily Telegraph*, the oracle which supplied him with all his opinions. There were sporadic comments regarding Walter's plans for retirement.

The clerical excellence of Hartley was discussed and the movement of shares. Grand Metropolitan were holding up well. Walter had bought a substantial block himself, double Valerie's holding.

"Do you really think we should have all these eggs in one basket Walter?" Valerie asked.

"Don't you worry, m'dear," was all the reply she could get. "Dug you out of your hole, didn't I? My brokers know what they're doing, I see to that."

The evenings at Thorpe Underwood Hall crawled by, uninteresting pages in an unreadable novel.

"I'll go up then," she said on the fourteenth night of their marriage. It was only a quarter past nine. "It's surprising how tired one gets doing nothing."

The irony of this was lost on Walter.

"That's right, dear. I shan't be far behind you."

"You know, Val," he grabbed at her hand unexpectedly, detaining her. "I think you and I are doing pretty well. Can't say how glad I am we took the plunge."

Escaping, Valerie lifted the skirts of her evening gown and ran up the shallow staircase two at a time for the sheer pleasure of vigorous movement. Tomorrow, she decided, she would walk, walk as far as her legs would carry her. On and on, across the ploughland until she was muddy, exhausted and alive again.

She was lying in bed, her diary propped up on her knees, when she heard Walter's footsteps pass on the corridor. Her heart missed a beat when a few moments later he opened the internal door, which separated his dressing room from her bedroom. She sat bolt upright.

"Walter!"

He was dressed in thick, striped pyjamas, a woollen check dressing gown and a pair of disreputable slippers. A tuft of grey hair stuck up over his left ear. An old man.

"Chilly tonight," he commented, crossing to her bedside.

200

Valerie watched numbly as he fumbled with the knotted dressing gown cord and got in beside her. She shrank away, moving to the far side of the bed, her eyes round.

"Well, lie down, then. You'll catch your death in that flimsy thing. Ready?"

Ready for what?

Walter switched off the lamp and there was silence except for the rustle of sheets and pillows being adjusted. Below in the hall, the long case clock signalled the hour. Ten o'clock. An owl hooted and a scream announced the demise of a rabbit caught in a fox's jaws. Here at Thorpe Underwood Hall, it was the dead of night.

"Goodnight, Walter," Valerie's voice contained everything of finality that she could muster.

Suddenly, Walter's face was thrust into hers as he lunged across the bed. His big nose was cold, and his lips moved like worms on her mouth, mobile and thin. Valerie pressed her head back into the pillows, her arms rigid at her side with fists clenched. Horror rippled over her skin.

"Goodnight, dear," he retreated abruptly. Valerie heard a rattle on the bedside table and then another. His teeth, she hadn't known about that.

At dawn, Valerie fell into an exhausted doze. She was woken, as she sometimes had been in early childhood by a delightful, spreading warmth. It grew clammy and Valerie realised she was wet. A sharp sour smell filled her nostrils

"You filthy, filthy old man!"

Springing from the bed, Valerie swept the curtains back from the window and looked down at her bedraggled crêpe de Chine. The lace hem was sodden. "Get up!" she screamed at Walter ripping the bedclothes from his recumbent form. Then she replaced them quickly seeing that his pyjama trousers had sagged open at the fly. Walter's private parts, flaccid and mottled, like a hank of white puddings, spilled onto the saffron-stained bottom sheet.

Walter opened his eyes innocently, like a child waking.

"You've wet the bed! You repulsive, vile, revolting old man. You've wet my bed. Get out! Get out this minute!"

Valerie stripped the nightgown from herself, touching it only between finger and thumb caring nothing that Walter should see her, she let it drop to the ground and kicked it to the far corner of the room.

"Oh, I say my dear," Walter mumbled sibilantly. "This is most unseemly."

"Put your bloody teeth in," Valerie spat at him, struggling into her robe. "What's the matter? Haven't you seen a healthy woman's body before?"

"I'm going to have a bath," Valerie picked up Walter's slippers and hurled them onto the bed. "By the time I get back, I want you out of here. Do you hear me? The bundled-up checked woollen dressing gown followed the slippers, landing on Walter's head. "Just never come near me again! You make me sick!"

Widowhood was all Valerie had to look forward to. At least it would come soon. Content with that thought she prepared to replace the shattered veneer, which covered the imposture of her marriage.

Mending the fences with Walter was easier by far than Valerie could have dreamed.

"That's all right, my dear," he said, stiffly. "Knew we'd have some adjustments to make. Bit dickey in the waterworks department for a while, now. Sort of thing happens to a fellow at my age. Thought you'd know. All over now, anyway. Marriage well and truly consummated. Eh? What?"

From that little speech Valerie deduced that Walter would not impose his night-time, physical presence on her again and that he considered a kiss in bed constituted the ultimate fleshly communion between a man and a woman.

"Oh, darling Walter! How kind and understanding you are so much older and wiser than me. What a very silly girl I've been. Let's do something to celebrate, show the world how happy we are."

Walter smirked complacently and agreed to allow Valerie to give a ball. Their friends would be hurt if not invited to visit the newly-wedded couple in their home as soon as decently possible. Clearing this social obligation off in one fell swoop would be more economical in the end.

Valerie and Walter spent Christmas alone. It was the dreariest festive season Valerie could remember.

But Walter would allow her to invite no one. He carved the goose himself to the butler's shuddering disdain and wore a silly paper hat.

"This is the life, eh Val? Just the two of us for our first Christmas together. Don't want any rubber-necking nosey parkers out for what they can get mucking things up, do we? Not on your life. Have Henry Ryecroft and old Hartley round for drinks tomorrow and that's all the company we'll be wanting isn't it?"

By half past ten on Christmas night Thorpe Underwood Hall was dark except for a light in the butler's pantry. He was having a little party.

Valerie felt a twinge of envy. The working classes had so much freedom no responsibilities. She had to lie here alone, next door to a nasty incontinent old man. Lately she'd found some sort of 'grown-up' disposable night-time nappies for him. The stupid old buffer refused to wear them.

With no presentiment of what was in store, Valerie watched Miss Hartley neatly hatted and gloved alight from Henry Ryecroft's car on Boxing Day with only a mild feeling of impatience. Hartley was about to find herself right out of her depth. Never mind, with Walter retiring, it would not be necessary to entertain her again. Next year after the ball, everything would be quite different.

"Well, I must say this is all very nice," Miss Hartley twittered, stepping over the threshold. "Quite oldie worldie, if you know what I mean. Oh! Bristol Cream," she seized the glass of dark brown syrup.

"My favourite, the Colonel always keeps it for my Christmas treat, don't you Colonel?"

203

"That's right, Hartley," Walter beamed. "Old habits die hard. Here's to your new home."

Everybody, including Valerie drank.

"Are you moving to the coast then, Miss Hartley," Valerie enquired, thinking Walter's toast referred to some retirement bungalow in Wetherby. "Or is it somewhere in the Lake District."

Miss Hartley blushed and made a gobbling sound in her throat

"Oh dear, Mrs Hey, how very awkward this is," Hartley simpered. "Didn't the Colonel tell you?"

"Lancaster-Hey! Tell me what, Walter?" Valerie's glance was glacial. "What can Miss Hartley mean?"

Henry Ryecroft looked away.

"Hartley's selling her little flat and moving in with us m'dear. More convenient."

"But why, Walter? You're retired, you don't need a secretary. Oh yes, a few things, but I can type you know and keep files."

"Thirty years, she's been with me. I'll not see her put out to grass on a pittance."

"Then for God's sake, Walter," Valerie screeched. "Why didn't you marry the withered old bat?"

Walter looked uncomfortable.

"Needed someone to care for me in my old age. Priscilla Prescott said you were a practical woman."

Valerie's lips withdrew from her teeth in a snarl.

"It was a fair exchange," Walter shouted, red with colour. "There you were, with bills you could never pay, expensive tastes, needing security."

"Then why the hell didn't you shack up with that mealy-mouthed old virgin? She's so stupid, she would have been cheap!"

"Because, my society lady, Miss Hartley is a woman with brains. She works with her head. I could never ask her to."

"Aha!" Valerie flashed. "So that typist is an intellectual, now is she? What does that make me, may I ask?"

"My wife. I have no wish to burden you with my business affairs. I understood that you wished to be protected from unpleasantness of that kind m'dear," Walter trumped her, rocking from heel to toe. "Now, no more need be said about this. It would be a pity, wouldn't it, to have to cancel your dance? Let us try to pull together."

It was always like that with Walter. He operated a kind of emotional coitus interruptus, tasting Valerie's anger but denying any orgasm of hate.

Valerie lost no time in identifying a small suite of attic rooms in the house, which could be turned into a maidenly apartment for the secretary. She decorated them herself, enjoying the clean, invigorating smell of the paint and relishing the creative occupation, which kept her apart from Walter.

Miss Hartley's little suite was ready, a sitting room, a bathroom, a bedroom and an ingeniously compact kitchenette. The sitting room even had its own tiny little Edwardian open grate. The whole thing was cosy, and cretonney.

"If she doesn't like it," Valerie declared, showing her handiwork off to Walter. "Then she's got no bloody taste."

Miss Hartley felt a surge of mad excitement rush through her veins. Here she was at last, under the same roof as the Colonel! She and Mrs Hey were much of an age, not three years in it, well, maybe five. They were rivals. Why not admit it? Miss Hartley turned to the looking glass and pulled wisps of grey hair from her bun. The effect, she decided sensibly, was sluttish not seductive. Imitation would get her nowhere. Sterling qualities, not superficial attractions, would win the prince in the end. Had he not fallen in with her suggestion that she should live here with boyish delight?

She was to dine downstairs the first night. Miss Hartley primped the lace ruffle of her best evening blouse and wiggled her mother's coral ear drops to feel them bounce on her neck. She might be old Hartley, but she wasn't dead yet!

"My," Walter greeted his secretary's appearance at the foot of the stairs kindly. "I'd no idea. Hartley, that you were such a high stepper."

Hartley bridled, her face mottling with pleasure. Emerging from the drawing room in her new emerald velvet gown, Valerie met the older woman's eye. What she read there was an undisguised challenge.

Of the ball invitations sent out by Valerie, more than two thirds were accepted. All of Walter's South Yorkshire friends, the 'Pie and Peas Brigade' Valerie privately dubbed them, forgetting her own father's origins. Fortunately, their numbers would be outweighed by the County and the London contingent.

Valerie's old friends needed no motive for coming beyond the satisfaction of avid curiosity about Valerie's new man, and the splendours with which he had reputedly bought her, of course. Some of them put it as crudely as that. Others merely agreed that if Val were giving a hop of any sort, it would be a good thrash. There'd be nothing spared in the way of booze, scoff and flash.

Hartley obtained caterers' estimates, dealt with the marquee and flower people. She was very efficient. Valerie canvassed her local friends to give dinner parties and put up some of the London guests for the night. Thorpe Underwood Hall she modestly laughed was nothing more than an overgrown cottage.

"You really are the most wonderful Lady-in-Waiting, Miss Hartley," Valerie said, signing a letter and thinking it a pity she'd not yet dealt with the matter of Walter's crest. "I don't know what I should do without you."

Hartley eyes narrowed behind her new golf-ball typewriter. Insufferable woman, who did she think she was?

The ball itself was a complete success. A balmy evening in early May wafted the scent of bluebells from the woods. The new moon was shining brightly in the sky, the carriage sweep side of the house twinkled its diamond-paned welcome from every window, whilst to the rear, a candy-striped yellow and white marquee spread itself over terrace and lawns.

Inside this improvised ball room were forty-three tables with cream damask cloths, garnished with roses, carnations and jasmine; each with its circle of six spindly gilt chairs. The lights were low and rosy; the band began with some easy, toe-tapping stuff.

"I ordered five whole salmon in aspic and I see only three. Do be certain to count the Colonel's silver ware, we must be aware of the security risks."

For once, Valerie minded none of it. Walter looked quite decent in his white tie and tails. They suited his curious duck shape better than anything else. At dinner just now, he'd been almost entertaining. Well, his own friends had laughed. Funny stories about brewing, stuff about shares.

Rozanne and Sandra were there with their husbands exuding wholesome prosperity, and Robert, resigned, reconciled and mild mannered as usual. He hadn't said 'Oh Mother' once. He was going to take charge of the band, their repertoire, morale and refreshments.

There were plenty to embrace Valerie with warmth, and sincerity. One could have too much of her but by jove, she was funny. Where had she been hiding herself since the wedding?

"You've got to hand it to old Val, she does keep on going."

"Funny, isn't it … I've never liked her so much."

Nobody could quite bring themselves to discuss Walter in detail. As far as anyone could see he behaved himself perfectly properly, there was just something there or rather not there.

Obscurely, women found themselves hating the moment when their hands had lain briefly in his. Men found Walter's plain Lancastrian act didn't add up. A two-faced sort of twerp. Never mind, this was a thumping good 'do'. Had Val met her match? Well, hardly match, more of a Waterloo.

Supper was in full swing, the buffets were crowded with happy, excited people forking up luxurious tit bits, plotting to corner the last of the lobster when a telephone rang.

Nobody took the slightest notice of course, except Hartley, who bustled off to deal with the call in the study. Who on earth would be ringing at this hour of the night?

It was Henry Ryecroft who was wanted.

tail?

Henry was found lurking at the tall end of the pudding queue swopping fishing statistics with a well-muscled lady in puce.

"I'm sorry, do excuse me," Hartley was all of a dither. "Mr Ryecroft, would you come?"

Henry absorbed what the senior partner of Blair, Gowrie and Heath had to tell him slowly. They were Walter's brokers, and his.

"I'm sorry to load this onto you, Henry but you're in the clear and someone's got to break it to Walter. I can't just do it on the telephone … a man of his age. Try and find out what he wants me to do. Bail out, take the first loss? You'll know how to handle it."

Leaving the study, Henry was wrapped in deep thought. He encountered his friend in the hall standing with his hands in his pocket, tails lapped up over his forearms. Valerie was with him saying something or other. The bad news couldn't wait. Henry just blurted it out.

"Grand Metropolitan's crashing, Walter. That was George on the phone."

Valerie and Walter turned blank faces towards him. More at one in that moment than ever before, their ears rejected the truth.

"Sorry old man. Do you want to sell and get out … or hang on and see if they rally?"

Knots of people milling around fell silent by degrees, sensing crisis.

Walter farted. A series of truncated, jazz trumpet sounds. He crumpled to the ground in slow motion, his face all twisted and strange.

Valerie stood like a statue, unable to move.

"I say. The man's fainted."

"Is he all right?" somebody cooed.

"Don't be a fool," another shouted. "For God's sake, someone get a doctor, is there one here?"

There was, as it happened, Sandy Milne. He wasn't immediately found and in the meantime Hartley and Henry Ryecroft rather foolishly got Walter to his feet. Scarcely conscious, his body stiff as a board on one side and like a rag doll on the other.

His trousers were wet, there was a terrible stench and looking down Valerie saw something very unpleasant had spattered over Walter's left sock. Oozy and brown.

"Get him onto the sofa," Dr Milne took one look when he came on the scene. "Bring some blankets ... Valerie, is there some brandy?"

Walter was taken away in an ambulance with in what seemed like minutes only. He had had a stroke. Everyone had to go home.

CHAPTER FIFTEEN

"A cup of bouillon, Madam?"

The steward hovered balletically beside Valerie's deck chair, the tray of cups held at shoulder height on his splayed fingertips. Valerie shook her head in dumb refusal.

"For sir, perhaps?"

Valerie glanced at her husband's swaddled outline, laid out on the promenade deck chaise longue. His felt hat was tipped forward and he appeared to be sleeping. Again, laying her forefinger to her lips, Valerie shook her head. Any time that Walter spent asleep was a God given respite. The RMS *Windsor Castle* was four days out of Southampton and as yet, there had been no pleasure in the cruise.

Swaying expertly with the slight roll of the ship, the steward was about to move onto the next group of passengers when Walter's leather gloved hand shot out demandingly from beneath the travelling rug.

"Oh Walter, no," Valerie begged him quietly. "You know it will only make you ..."

"Doctor says it makes no damned difference what I have. Give me some bloody bouillon." His speech was still faintly slurred.

The steward placed the beaker in Walter's outstretched hand with a perceptible shrug. He flicked his blonde forelock and moved on.

"Trying to starve me now, are you lady?" Walter grumbled as he slurped a mouthful of soup. "Suppose you think that with half your settlement gone, the best thing you can do is kill me off sharpish and cash in under my will. Well, I'll tell you this much, m'dear you've a way to go yet, there's plenty of life in me yet."

Walter was doubly incontinent now after his stroke, specialists from London and Glasgow had been called in. Colonel Lancaster-Hey, they told Valerie had made as satisfactory a recovery as could be hoped for at this early stage.

He had regained a good deal of motor function in the stricken half of his body. His speech was remarkable. The incontinence well, that would probably be permanent. It was a question of management forethought and basic nursing. Why not get a male nurse in? At any rate, take a holiday that might do the patient some good.

The voyage to South Africa had been the result. Walter would not hear of a male nurse, however.

Walter lived stubbornly on. Back at Thorpe Underwood, Miss Hartley had attained a kind of moral ascendancy. For every hospital visit that Valerie had made to her husband, Hartley had made two.

"I'm just off, now," she would say smugly while Walter's own chauffeur and Daimler waited outside. "Have you any message for the Colonel? Shall I say you'll go tomorrow?"

Hartley scarcely bothered now with the formality of names or titles. She addressed her employer's wife as 'you'.

Left alone in the house Valerie answered the letters of sympathy, which came after the ball in place of the hoped-for flood of invitation cards. There were some, of course. Friends who invited her to get away for a while. But they didn't realise that she dared not leave her post. If she turned her back, Valerie guessed, Hartley would try something or other. That sort of thing had happened before with Richard at Thimbleby ... Denise. Maidservant, professional employee or neighbour, it made no difference. Men turned to the first woman who was lying in wait. Valerie had learned her lesson, she thought.

"Here, take it," Walter said peremptorily. "I've had enough."

Taking the cup, Valerie noted that very little had been drunk. That was typical of Walter now. Most of his demands were mere gestures of will. It was as if he feared that if his needs were not seen to be constant, they would soon be neglected.

"That daughter of yours, she'll have to leave her posh school in Switzerland," Walter jibed meanly. "At the end of this year. Can't go paying fees like that anymore."

"Surely, Walter ..."

"No," he clamped his thin lips together. "You spend The Barwick Trust fund money, if that's what you want. That's what it's for. She can go to Harrogate Ladies College. It's good enough for most folks, it'll do for her."

Valerie rested her forehead in her hand it was just one more blow among many. The Barwick Trust did not produce ten thousand pounds a year, only five or so. That was Valerie's own income, her only lifeline. Already, Walter's coven of advisors had tried to wrest it away from her in the aftermath of the Grand Metropolitan crash. But they couldn't do that. Luckily, Mr Robertworth had been quick to point it out. The Barwick money was sacrosanct for what it was worth. But the rest, bits and pieces of stocks and investments they'd all been swallowed up in the rationalisation of Walter's portfolio. Oh, why had she ever signed that letter?

Staring unseeingly at the Atlantic breakers, warming now from grey to turquoise as the *S.S. Val* steamed towards South Africa, Valerie wished she had not been panicked into surrendering her little bit of independence. They hadn't given her time to think to consult Mr Robertworth, or anything.

Only two days after Walter had been taken to hospital there had been a Hey family meeting, in the Leeds office at Hey's Lancashire Ales. A sea of unfamiliar faces round the board room table. Walter's solicitors, family members, accountants ... Hartley, of course.

A letter written in Valerie's name had been placed before her. She had barely understood it at the time. It seemed to suggest that from now on all her affairs would be managed jointly with Walter's by the same brokers and bankers. Just a consolidation, they said more sensible. Well it may have been true, but Valerie had felt threatened, beleaguered by strangers.

"Come along now, Aunt Val," a ferret faced Hey nephew harassed her. "My uncle was very generous to you. I think you might show your appreciation by co-operating with family arrangements now. Nobody's trying to take anything from you."

"But shouldn't I consult my own advisors first? My family ..." Valerie's feeble protest had been swept away on a tide of scorn. They were family now, whether she liked it or not. Didn't she trust them? Or was what Hartley said true? Of course, if it was ...

Abashed at the insinuations, Valerie signed. Rumbles of satisfaction replaced the hostile bayings when it was done. They all went out to luncheon then at the seedy Station Hotel. Nobody spoke to Valerie much. They leaned across her and behind her, throwing remarks to each other. Hartley it was clear, was more highly regarded than she.

Driving home to Thorpe Underwood with the secretary in the back seat of the Rolls beside her, Valerie had trembled with rage. It was two months later that she had decided to take up the consultant neurologist's suggestion of a holiday. Walter must be taken beyond reach of Hartley's pernicious influence. What honey-flavoured poison had she already dropped in her husband's ear. Valerie dreaded to think. Divorce? No, Walter had no grounds.

"Finished, Madam?" The steward, returning with a tray of empty bouillon cups, broke through Valerie's reverie. "How's the Colonel today?"

"A little better, I think," Valerie lied meaninglessly. Walter had disgraced them at the Captain's cocktail party on the second night out. Wet his trousers and got stupidly, aggressively drunk. By now, the whole ship knew.

"Look, Madam," the steward offered now. "If you fancy a turn round the deck, I'll keep an eye on the Colonel for you."

Valerie was grateful, Walter had fallen asleep again. Spittle bubbled at the corner of his mouth. On this nightmare voyage, any minute of freedom was precious.

Not liking to walk alone past the knots of fellow passengers lining the deck, Valerie went below to their state room. Sympathetic murmurs were more than she could endure. It was no good trying to make friends, Walter would only spoil everything.

He couldn't be trusted in company. The smallest amount of alcohol made him drunk, his bowels exploded without warning. She'd suggested a colostomy bag to his consultant, but Walter had made such a fuss.

The first-class state room was spacious and neat. Bowls of flowers and baskets of fruit stood around, Bon Voyage gifts from Valerie's friends. Most of them hadn't the remotest idea how bad it all was. Priscilla Prescott's card said she was sure Valerie would make a valiant nurse and that under his wife's loving care, Walter would soon be himself again. The bitch. Valerie had torn the card in two as soon as she read it.

Seeing the bundle of fresh laundry on Walter's bed, Valerie began to undo the cellophane parcel. Then she realised the shirts, vests, pants and pyjamas were still soiled. Crusted fragments of faeces clung to them and dried urine stains discoloured the fabric. A frosty odour rose from the garments, Valerie pressed the bell by her bed.

The cabin steward answered her call after a few moments popping his head round the door.

"Yes, Madam. What can I get you?"

"Well, nothing actually," Valerie replied. "It's these clothes of my husband's, the laundry has sent them back unwashed by mistake ..."

"No mistake, I'm afraid, Ma'am," the steward winced. "I think you'll find there is a note ..."

There was, attached to the cellophane. Valerie had ignored it assuming the piece of paper to be a carbon copy of her list.

"The ship's laundry is not able to accept passengers' fouled underwear, facilities limit us to processing garments soiled by normal wear only."

"Oh!" Valerie glanced up from the note.

"Sorry, Madam will there be anything else?"

"Well, perhaps the ship's sick bay ..."

"Sorry Madam," the steward repeated, "Emergencies only. If you're sure there's nothing else I can do."

"Perhaps you would," Valerie scuffled quickly in her handbag for a five-pound note. "I mean, it's just a few things ..."

"No," the steward said flatly, the professional smile fading. "I've been fifteen years at sea and I've never been asked to deal with anything like it."

"But what can I do?" Valerie wailed. "My husband is ill ..."

"There are 'launderette' facilities available in the Second-Class accommodation abaft of B and C decks, Madam. That's all I can suggest now."

The door was closed swiftly as the steward beat his retreat. Valerie was left alone with the thud of the engines and Walter's pile of dirty clothes. She sat down and wept.

After spending the afternoon washing and ironing, Valerie returned to her state room to find another note waiting. This time it was propped up on her dressing table. A square card enclosed in a thick white envelope. An invitation. It wasn't.

Instead, there was a message from the Chief Purser. The Captain presented his compliments to Colonel and Mrs Lancaster-Hey but understood that the Colonel was unwell. That being the case, he presumed that they would be unable to dine at his table tonight as planned. The Purser had suggested the substitution or two other passengers in their place. The Captain hoped very much to have the pleasure of entertaining the Lancaster-Heys at some later stage during the voyage when the Colonel was fully recovered.

Valerie acted immediately and she contacted the Purser by telephone. There was nothing to prevent her from dining at the Captain's table alone. The Colonel would have a tray in the state room.

"How very unfortunate," the Purser reacted smoothly. "I do wish we'd known before. I regret to tell you that the seating plan for tonight is fixed, some other time perhaps."

Valerie crashed the telephone down savagely. How dared they? Didn't they know who she was? Really was?

****

Sooner or later, there comes a time when any child realises their parent is old. Valerie saw that her father had entered the last phase of his life.

In his eighties now, he was smaller than she remembered him. Early widowhood, exile and financial misfortune had shrivelled Bobby Skelton. Living in modest comfort in a Durban suburb, he played a little golf now and then and went to the club. His face was tanned but pathetically thin, wreathed by jowls of empty skin. The stocky body had withered to frailty. He had neither appetite nor energy for much news.

His welcome to Walter Lancaster-Hey was courteous but distant. It was as if he was trying to work out what part this person played in his daughter's life. There had been so many men. Whether Val was happy or not, was no longer a matter of concern for him. She'd always known how to go about things and managed to keep her head above water.

When all the grandchildren had been asked after, Robert's poverty-stricken plight glossed over, the conversation between Valerie and her father was more or less at an end. Such sparse common ground as there was between Walter and his father-in - law was dutifully trodden. A ride along the seafront, a meal or two in restaurants up the coast eaten. Those amusements exhausted, Valerie was glad enough to get away, the effort of watching Walter, controlling his drinking, foreseeing his bowel movements, suffering his temper tantrums was too much of a strain. There was nowhere she could take him without fear of social disgrace.

After a trip north to Johannesburg and two nights in a hotel there, the Lancaster-Heys turned south and took passage home on a ship leaving from Cape Town.

To Valerie's surprise, Bobby had friends drive him down to wave them goodbye. As tugs nosed the ship off from the quay, there were tears in Valerie's eyes. It was a long time since she had wished her father away from the jetty on the banks of Lake Victoria. How little she had valued him then. This time it was her turn to wonder if she would ever see him again.

"I took to your father," Walter remarked as they ate the informal embarkation night supper. "No airy-fairy nonsense about him. Makes me wonder where you got yours, m'dear."

They docked in time for their first wedding anniversary. Reminded of this by Valerie, Walter proposed to buy her a handbag. She'd got enough jewels he said. Valerie celebrated the event by saying it had been the longest year of her life.

"Want a divorce, m'dear?" Walter countered in spite of the fact that his chauffeur who had come to meet the boat at Southampton was listening, "You won't get much you know, just the house I reckon since I was fool enough to give it you."

Valerie dared not say anything else. What could she do at her age, alone in the world with a twelve-year-old daughter? An annulment would be no better. She had slipped too many notes in with those ball invitations, hinting she and Walter were enjoying a blissful physical relationship. At the time, Valerie had persuaded herself, those notes had been no more than an unselfish reassurance to close friends who cared about her. Nothing to do with pride.

"Why, Mrs Hey," Hartley greeted her at the door of Thorpe Underwood Hall. "I swear you've lost over a stone in weight!"

Indeed, Valerie had lost a substantial amount of weight. For nearly two months, there had been scarcely a meal not interrupted by Walter's wants and with all his laundry work to do and the worry, her flesh had reduced, her face become pinched.

Seeing herself reflected in Hartley's insolent sneer, Valerie hated what she had become. The secretary's triumph, she inwardly vowed, would be of short duration. She would get back her strength and fight every inch of the way to survive.

She would be beautiful until the day that she died, long after these, her tormentors had gone.

She was barely unpacked before the butler sought an early interview with Valerie. His tale of woe occupied a full hour. He had had some things to put up with in life, he claimed, but now he was nearly at breaking point.

"It's Miss Hartley, Madam. I wasn't aware she had any brief to supervise the household in your absence."

"She hasn't. That's your job."

"So, I believed, Madam. But Miss Hartley thinks differently. She's never off my back for a minute. This is dirty ... that is untidy. She nit-picks at cook ... insists her vegetables must be steamed ... questions the tradesmen's books ... told one of the maids her shoes were tarty ... her word, Madam, not mine."

The list of Hartley's attempts at self-assertion went on and on. One maid had already gone and was not yet replaced. Valerie had her work cut out for the next few weeks to reorder her forces and make peace in her household again. Walter would not hear of Hartley leaving.

"But Walter, she's not needed now. Let's face it, you're not fit for any kind of work ... the household accounts are really my responsibility or ought to be."

"No!" Walter roared. "If you know so much about bookkeeping, lady, you'd have not got yourself into such a fine mess when I met you."

In the weeks that followed, Valerie took up her charity work again. She no longer played a leading part, but nobody, it was generally agreed had a stronger stomach than most for the gut-wrenching RSPCA tales and sickening photographic evidence of cruelty. Mrs Lancaster-Hey had courage. Fund raisers and organisers at local level idolised her. Vain and self-important she might be ... but look what she achieved.

For Valerie, it was terrible work with some purpose that counterpointed the desolation at home. Hartley didn't see the point of it all when there were so many humans to care for.

218

There was an interlude in which Valerie took Walter to Switzerland to collect Victoria from school and then went on to the apartment in Italy. Valerie drove all the way herself, anything for a change of scene. Unfortunately, the Rolls broke down over the Alps.

"Why did you marry him, Mummie?" Victoria asked after a particularly humiliating performance in a restaurant just over the Italian border in France. "If I've got to go to school in England, I'd rather live with Daddy than you."

"Well, I'm afraid he won't have you," Valerie was too tired to find excuses for Richard. "So, you'll have to put up with me and Walter. You're old enough to face facts. That disgusting old man as you call him, is all that stands between you and a comprehensive school. Do you know what they do in places like that, to people like you? You wouldn't last ten minutes. Now come on, help me get him to the loo."

If Victoria cherished any belief that a battering at plebeian hands behind some bicycle shed would be preferable to sharing a roof with her mother's new husband, she wisely kept it to herself. Her mother, whom she scarcely knew thanks to the buffer provided by nannies and schools, was very near the edge.

When the January term started at Harrogate College after a miserable Christmas, Valerie was glad to have Victoria safely installed in a healthier place than Thorpe Underwood Hall. She missed the child sometimes, however. Victoria at least, was her own flesh and blood.

There had been some argument about Victoria boarding.

"She can go every day in your car," Walter stormed. "I'm damned if I'll pay extra fees when you've got two bloody Rolls Royces to ferry her there and I keep a chauffeur."

Valerie brought every scrap of her old thespian talent into play.

"Walter, this is no place for a child. It's full of old people. Miss Hartley, you and I, and we're not well, are we? And you need your rest, I can't care for you as I should and attend to the needs of a

219

child. Children must have company and friends to stay. My dear, they do make a noise even in a big house like this and you'd tire of her being around all the time."

The rough and ready combination of flattery with threat cajoled Walter into agreeing to Victoria's boarding fees.

Not long after, Valerie was helping the grim-faced maids to strip Walter's bed after a noticeably unpleasant 'accident' when the butler told her there was a telephone call for her from Durban.

Hurrying into her own bedroom and lifting the extension there, Valerie did not hear her father's voice as expected. The Afrikaans almoner of a public hospital told her Mr Skelton had been admitted with double pneumonia. He had only one lung and frankly, wasn't expected to stay the course. Could she please come at once? She was the next of kin, wasn't she?

"Can I speak to my father?" Valerie asked, penetrated by a stabbing guilt. Oh, why had she left him there? She should have brought him home.

"Not possible," came the reply. "I'm afraid Mr Skelton is far too ill. Please try and get here in time. He has been asking for you."

With a lump in her throat, Valerie promised immediately. Of course, she would come as soon as a direct flight could be booked.

As soon as the overseas call was ended, she rang Hartley on the house telephone and told her to obtain one outward first class air ticket, routed through Manchester, Heathrow and on to Durban. It did not occur to her to ask her husband's permission.

Hartley referred her instructions to Walter. Had the Colonel been made aware of his wife's imminent departure for South Africa? Hartley gave no excuse for this treacherous officiousness, nor did she need one.

"Mrs Hey," she trilled. "Mrs Lancaster-Hey ... Are you there? The Colonel would like to see you downstairs in the library."

"Is anything wrong?" Valerie stepped out of her room with a preoccupied frown.

"Oh, I think you'll have to wait and see what the Colonel says," the secretary dimpled obscenely as Valerie pushed past her. "I really couldn't think of interfering between husband and wife."

Walter had no such scruples and demanded his secretary's presence as a witness to what then transpired in the library.

"What's all this Hartley tells me about you going to South Africa?"

Angrily, Valerie stated her case. Her father lay dying, as his only child she must go to him without delay.

"And what of your duty to the Colonel?" Hartley broke in.

"Now, now, Hartley," Walter reproved her. "Let me attend to this. I can't have you gallivanting back off to South Africa Valerie, m'dear, I'm a sick man myself and I need you here. A husband comes before a father I reckon, you'd better bear in mind who supports you and the child."

These considerations were never far from Valerie's mind, but filial compassion combined with testatory expectations made her impatient of argument. Walter, Valerie told him, outraged natural feeling. He was a heartless, selfish old man.

"You have the servants and Miss Hartley to look after you, Walter, nor are you dying. I'm going to my father and no power on earth will stop me, certainly not yours."

Valerie slammed out of the room, her blood boiling with righteous indignation. She ordered the car, packed and telephoned British Airways herself. No other conceivable plan of action was possible.

Valerie arrived in Durban to find that her father had weathered the crisis. Little short of a miracle, the hospital staff called it. Having prepared a speech centred on blessed release, Valerie felt a nerve-jangling annoyance as she spoke instead of her heartfelt relief. Her beloved father was not to be taken from her just yet.

She began to regret her impulsive departure: no thought of self-interest had entered her head, only the most desperate anxiety had impelled her to leave so abruptly. She must ring Walter tonight take back what she'd said. Breathe deeply and think!

"We can't have you in here, Daddy," Valerie appraised the long ward and its occupants in one glance. "Too depressing for words. We'll find you a nice private convalescent home."

"You don't change, Val," Bobby chuckled feebly. "You want me to peg out at a fashionable address."

"What absolute nonsense you do talk, Daddy. But you see, Walter's ill himself at the moment. I must go home quite soon and then I'll be back to see you again."

But Valerie's sudden realisation that she had left her position at home exposed to plunder came too late. Walter Hey had already acted. He changed his will in Hartley's favour. Should his secretary survive him, she would be richer by half a million pounds. All the former bequests intended for Valerie were cancelled.

Was Colonel Hey's wife aware of the changes, asked the lawyer who took the instructions.

"No, she is not," Walter stated irascibly. "Her Ladyship's sucked enough of my blood as it is. God knows, she's not given value for money."

CHAPTER SIXTEEN

Her father, having settled with cussed determination to the business of recovery in Durban's Rhodes Clinic, Valerie was obliged to leave South Africa with her primary objectives incomplete. Daddy was still very much alive. Neither funeral director nor estate agent would be required.

Privately, Bobby Skelton longed to go home to his roots, but there could be no trading of truth for affection or roof. His daughter, he had made it very publicly plain, could take him or leave him on those terms.

Valerie operated her power of decision in favour of leaving this parental encumbrance to the benevolence of the Natal climate. It was what any doctor would recommend for invalid lungs, she declared.

"You'll have checked up I don't doubt," Bobby, who was eating his lunch at the time, answered her easily. The transparent ploy hurt him, but he gave no sign of it.

"And the medical facilities here are second to none."

"'S right, love," Bobby helped himself to another glass of the Clinic's domestic white wine with a bittersweet smile. "They do you a grand death, right here in Durban."

"Don't be silly, Daddy," Valerie pinkened. "Gerontologists say that people of your age do best among their friends and things that they are used to."

"That's enough of that," Bobby's eyes hardened momentarily. "I don't want any half-baked lectures from you. You've your own life to live. I'll not stand in your way. Go on with you now."

Valerie left the clinic, shaking the drops of accusation from her like an indignant cat with wet fur. She would return the same evening after supper and again on the following day to take leave.

Things would be properly done no matter how painful. Each day, she reminded herself, might yet be the last. A clear conscience, Valerie instinctively knew, would be the only comfortable mourning attire.

Valerie had an asthma attack at the airport. Oh, why did Daddy have to be so horribly, commonly blunt? That characteristic of his, to which she had devoted some lines in his draft obituary, would have been a most endearing memory. A slice of family lore to be laughed over in comfort once the actuality had been transmuted by death into legend.

Strapped in for take-off, Valerie was already thinking that nature was unkind to let old people outlive their own dignity. The hospital had done her father no favours in bringing him back from the dead. Really, it was too cruel when you thought he'd only have to face the same things again. There must be so many families in the same agonising situation.

These lofty, purifying thought soothed Valerie's nerves as far as Terminal Three at Heathrow where it was necessary to think again about Walter. An end to his misery seemed very far off. Why were evil people always so strong? Comparisons with old Clarke, Thimbleby's cook, were inevitable. Valerie brought herself up shortly. One did not marry cooks, let alone have them for parents, they didn't leave wills and one was not manacled to them for life. Valerie was confused.

She sat down for a moment on an orange plastic chair. She knew what the trouble was. Not enough oxygen in her blood. An air hostess came running along the glass corridor.

"Mrs Lancaster-Hey, your dressing case, you left it. Are you alright?"

A handful of airline staff crowded rounder her, looming like cliffs and stifling her breath. They chattered like monkeys in the Thompson's Falls treetops, and for a few moments, Valerie was back there, up, up in the clear Mount Kenya air. The light was going dim. A bad attack, worse than before.

"My bronchodilator," she gasped out, "It's in the case, get it."

Somebody did while others talked of fetching the airport doctor.

"No, no," Valerie breathed gratefully through the device, opening her air passages into her lungs. "No, I'm alright. It's nothing, just asthma. Please leave me alone."

Valerie stood up and walked a few faltering steps. Her chest felt easier now, so silly to give into weakness. The uniformed people drifted away to other concerns.

Attempting to pull her suitcase from the arrival's concourse carousel, Valerie gave up in despair. They were too heavy.

"It's Valerie Barwick, isn't it?" A man's voice came from behind her. She turned, half recognising him, a face seen somewhere, sometime in the past. "Let me help you with those."

"Oh, thank you. You're so kind. I'm afraid I don't ..."

"Did you hear Tom Hanbury had died?" the man said swinging the bag effortlessly onto a trolley. "He married, you know, not good though, not after you."

Valerie staggered slightly. The clean cedar smell of Tom's skin swept through her olfactory memory, pushing the echoing, airport sounds to the margin. Dead.

"Gosh, I'm sorry," the man looked over his shoulder at Valerie. Her face had an opal pallor. "How unforgivably clumsy of me to tell you like that. Do you know, I wasn't even sure it was you?"

The man flushed. Valerie's appearance had shocked him.

"It's perfectly all right," Valerie felt for her inhaler. "Not your fault." She felt dizzy and sick.

"Is anyone meeting you? So, you're married. Happy?"

"Oh, very," Valerie said automatically. "My car should be outside."

Her voluntary porter cast an admiring glance over the Rolls and its casually saluting chauffeur. She'd always had style, had Val Barwick.

"May I give you a lift?"

"No, thanks awfully, my chauffeur's coming to fetch me. Ah, there he is now."

She waved and blew her admirer a kiss.

Valerie got into the back of the Rolls numbly. Other people were carrying on living and loving without her. As the car moved forward, Valerie screamed inwardly.

Why had she been left behind with the Jeyes Fluid and Smith Nephew incontinence products? There was no justice in life, none at all. Only the dignity of silence and duty. In the end, Valerie gritted her teeth, she would get her reward.

A persistent cough racked her most of the way up the A1.

Valerie took to her bed for three days. Walter's GP came and uttered platitudes about a mild attack of pneumonia exacerbated by asthma. He prescribed an expectorant, rest and the avoidance of stress.

"Doctor, there's hair coming out on my brush."

"Well, you have to expect that at your age."

"What the hell do you mean," Valerie blazed at him. "I'm not yet fifty-four."

"Exactly so, Mrs Hey," the doctor replied snapping closed the locks on his bag. Removing himself from the room, the doctor went downstairs to Walter and accepted a measure of whiskey.

"Middle-aged women," he pontificated, roasting his buttocks before the fire. "If they have ever been attractive, are usually unable to face the fact that nature has done with them. Their reproductive life over, few of them are able to contemplate a future in which they must make themselves useful in a practical way to win approval from those around them."

Sound judgment. Walter's thin lips puckered in judicious endorsement. He nodded and signalled the doctor to continue.

"Resentment is often presented as purely psychosomatic illnesses like your wife's asthma. Some women will sink into inertia. But hyperactive types like your wife may well embark on a restless round of travel and visits. I gather she's just back from South Africa?"

Walter sniffed virtuously. "Some alarmist nonsense about her father's health. I let her go."

226

"Agitated depression, my dear fellow, that's what it is. Movement for the sake of it. They'll do anything to distract themselves from the unpalatable process of accepting sexual demotion. In working women, it takes the form of pestering visits to neighbours. With a lady like Mrs Hey ..."

"Air tickets and hundreds of pounds," Walter finished for him. "She'd better frame. I've had about enough."

"I can only advocate patience. It's a trial, Walter, that comes to all married men."

"Have you read her ladyship her fortune then?" Walter enquired nastily as he saw his physician to the door.

"Indeed, I have not. These are emotional adjustments which you must make by yourselves. I've told you the facts. It's up to you to be understanding but firm."

Walter shirked it. He didn't doubt the truth and justice of what had been said. It came very close to Hartley's opinion, but what was the point of any discussion? Valerie did not love him. He had punished her secretly, made the only personal adjustment he felt was due of which he was capable. Whilst his wife malingered in her room, Hartley could dine with him every night. So much better.

Getting wind of this dangerous practice from the maid who brought her supper on a tray, Valerie thrust the meal aside. Weak and wobbly as she felt, she completed a grande toilette and descended the staircase at half past eight.

Hartley was halfway through the neat dissection of a fillet of sole when Valerie flung open the dining room door. The secretary was sitting at the short end of the table nearest the door. Valerie's place.

"Ah, Miss Hartley," she declaimed hectically. "How very kind of you to bear my husband company. It will no longer be necessary," She turned to the butler, "Carry the rest of Miss Hartley's food up to her sitting room. My husband and I would like to be alone."

"Just sit down and be quiet, my dear," Walter said with a nervous titter.

The butler hesitated. Mrs Lancaster-Hey owned the house, the Colonel paid his wages. Which of the two, had the best right to his obedience? In the same instant, Valerie swept to the sideboard, grasped the open bottle of Sancerre, poured some of its contents into a fresh glass and bowled it overarm at Hartley.

It hit her smack on the forehead. Wine dripped down her face. Valerie laughed.

Walter's fork was still suspended in mid-air, half-masticated food churned in his open mouth.

"Shut your mouth, Walter," Valerie said quite calmly. "Let's keep as much of you sealed up as we can. Now Miss Hartley. You've had your wine, be good enough to retire."

Valerie got away with her scene but paid for it with an attack of extreme breathlessness. The butler had to help her upstairs and find her inhaler. When he returned to the dining room, his master was sitting transfixed in a pile of his own excrement.

"I'm very sorry, sir, I'm unable to help you. It's not my place."

"I know that, lad. Get my wife."

"Mrs Lancaster-Hey is in no condition."

"Rubbish, she's putting it on. I have that on medical authority. Fetch Miss Hartley, then."

Hartley ministered to Walter's needs very tenderly. It was an odd kind of sublimated devotion. The fact that Walter could have cleansed himself meant nothing to either of them.

"Oh Hartley, how long do I have to go on?"

"Why don't you speak to your lawyers?" Hartley patted Johnson's Baby Powder over her employer's naked fundament gently. She'd done it a few times while Mrs Hey was away.

"It won't wash, Hartley. If I divorce her, she'll take me for every penny I've got."

"Never mind, Eddikins," Hartley looked up from her work with a lupine smile. "She will deliver herself into our hands in the end, just you wait."

Walter was not alone in taking medical advice on his spouse's condition. As soon as Valerie was rested, she sought a private interview with her husband's specialist. He was to be seen at his consulting rooms in King Street, Manchester.

"Does my patient know you are here?"

Valerie admitted that Walter was not aware of this consultation.

"But I must know what to expect, Mr Smith," Valerie appealed. "I don't want to upset him, but how long has he got? Walter seems unwilling to talk of the future, but I am his wife, I must make plans for his comfort. I'm frightened, you see, and I suspect he is …"

It was perfectly reasonable. Terminal cases were difficult for relatives. Colonel Lancaster-Hey, however, the neurologist hasted to reassure, was not quite in that category; Valerie registered becoming relief at this news while her heart sank unseen. How long? The specialist's additional remarks made better listening.

"I think you had better tell me whatever you can … So that I'm ready to do my part when the time comes."

"Let me be frank, Mrs Lancaster-Hey. Your husband's stroke was a mild one. Were he never to have another, he might last for years. The truth is this; he is more than likely to have another and then another. The first occurrence is generally the start of a series of increasing severity experienced at narrowing intervals."

The specialist used a lot of long words, but Valerie got the gist of it.

"I've known patients survive up to five strokes but it's generally the third or fourth that gets them."

It was not quite enough. Valerie wanted to know when Walter's next stroke might be anticipated. Mr Smith shrugged, turning down the corners of his mouth. That, he was unable to say. Good diet, the elimination of alcohol and nicotine … a supportive family circle … The specialist paused before swinging around on his heel with an engaging smile.

"And the incontinence, Mr Smith? Can anything be done?"

229

The medical man paused in perambulations and pursed his lips. This was awkward ground. A colleague of his who had examined Hey claimed to have observed some perverse stresses of the rectal walls and sphincter, attributable, he believed, to intense homosexual activity, though probably not of recent date.

It was just conceivable that Hey's loss of normal function there might have been something to do with it. At any rate, there was nothing to be done. Nor was it a thing to be discussed with the patient's wife.

"I thought that had improved lately."

"It had, a little," Valerie acknowledged. "We are able to plan, to anticipate a movement, but not always, it is socially inconvenient," she added sharply, momentarily forgetting her role.

"This is really not my department, Mrs Lancaster-Hey, but will you allow me to speculate a little?"

"Please do, Mr Smith. I'm at the end of my tether."

"Yes, yes, I'm sure. Now let's see. You and Colonel Lancaster-Hey have not been married long. As I understand it, he was deficient in urinary function when you were first married ... the bowel thing came later. It may have. I could be wrong, of course, but the thing may have a partially psychotic basis. It may be that your husband has sub-consciously reverted to infantile behaviour to attract attention, emotional reassurance."

Love and Colonel Lancaster-Hey? The incredulity registered clearly this time on Valerie's face.

She could not render her thanks or make her goodbyes fast enough. She would think about everything she had been told. Her chest was starting to constrict.

Not altogether surprised by his visitor's sudden haste, Mr Smith gave some last-minute advice regarding the prolongation of Walter's life. He recoiled hardly at all from the spear points in Valerie's eyes. Such hostility to a sick partner was common enough. He should have realised. Mrs Lancaster-Hey had come for one purpose only ... to discover the date of her widowhood, and he had failed her. A sordid transaction.

"And if I may say so," the specialist concluded. "You should pay some attention to your own health. With respect, Mrs Lancaster-Hey, you appear seriously under-nourished, run off your feet with the Colonel, I know."

He was interrupted by Valerie's coughing which turned into a bout of wheeziness.

"Oh dear, oh dear."

After a session with the inhaler, Valerie pronounced herself perfectly fit and ready to leave. Mr Smith was alarmed. He walked Valerie down to her car himself, handing her the card of a very good chest specialist. Asthma should not be taken too lightly, he said, suspecting she may have something worse.

"Well," said the practice receptionist when the specialist paused in her office. "That one's not long for this world."

"She's not the patient. Her husband, Colonel Lancaster-Hey is."

"Oh, him."

"Yes him. I reckon," confided the specialist indiscreetly, "that those two are locked in a deadly contest for survival."

"A quid says the Colonel wins," the receptionist remarked sportingly as she made an entry in her professional charges ledger.

"Oh no, you'll lose your money. I put mine on the lady, did you see her eyes?"

"Yes," the girl looked thoughtful. "Very beautiful for a woman of her age. Like summer skies."

"Hmm. Or industrial sapphires."

"What's at the bottom of it, do you think, Mr Smith?"

"Oh, I don't know. Cash, I imagine. A will, maybe. One gets to know the signs."

Days became weeks which were swallowed by months. Walter showed no sign of weakening.

Interweaving currents of hatred throttled the atmosphere in the house.

Both partners attributed the other's symptoms to a deep-seated selfishness. The deadlock was total, sealed with a vacuum through which no human sympathy could leak. Thorpe Underwood Hall was a closed frontier where patrolling footsteps softly menaced. There were occasional bursts of servants' chatter as the green baize door swung open and shut. A sound of dishes clattering in the kitchen was like small arms fire reporting from a separate front. Weapons in the family rooms, usually mute, were invariably loaded.

Hartley haunted the shadowed parts of the place. Every day, Valerie heard her conversing with Walter somewhere out of sight. She scurried in the wainscots like an infestation of mice ... flapped battily in the roof voids. At night, her typewriter could be heard clicking at a distance. Hartley was writing a detective novel, Walter said.

"She'll have you down as the victim, me as the murderess and herself as Miss Marple I suppose," Valerie remarked carelessly.

"I couldn't tell you the source of her inspiration m'dear," Walter replied archly. "Your notion tells us more about you than Miss Hartley."

"Oh, for God's sake, Walter, I'm not going to poison you."

Such exchanges were the currency in which the master and mistress of Thorpe Underwood Hall most commonly dealt.

The formal routine of the house continued under the butler's management. Grim faced, he presided over the relentless march of meals which marked off the hours. Once or twice, he threatened to leave, as other staff had done, but each time it happened, his wages were raised. Walter had no wish for new faces.

Little was seen of Victoria. If she was not at school, she was frequently making some prolonged visit to her married sisters or school friends. Valerie encouraged it. All the hospitality her daughter had enjoyed at this difficult time, she wrote to Victoria at school, would be returned a thousand-fold once things improved.

"She means when he's dead," Victoria commented to one of her sisters.

232

"It's disgusting. I don't really have anywhere to live. I get palmed off on one of you two or have to farm myself out to girls at school. Do you know, I took somebody home one weekend and we both had to help her cart the old faggot to the lavatory. Never again."

Occasionally visitors from London or abroad proposed themselves tentatively for a short stay. It was generally known that Val was not very well, and of course, her husband had that stroke. Valerie implored them to come, she was lonely.

There were times now when she talked to herself, fearful that the power of speech had deserted her, she and Walter sat in silence so much.

One evening saw Valerie ordering Walter to remove the deposit of white scum which gathered in creases at the corner of his mouth. Nervous irritation, pitiable embarrassment at her husband's infirmity. Whichever her friends called it, they could not find her manner with him attractive, nor his with her.

Another disastrous evening, Walter was drunk and would not be guided into decorous conversational channels. Valerie apologised to her guests and left the room. The women followed her at a nod from her husband.

"Oh, my dear. I'm so sorry! Why don't you leave him? You know you can come to us."

"I just can't afford to," Valerie sobbed.

Refusing to accept defeat, Valerie made another attempt, this time it was some racing friends and a show business couple as well. A larger party than had gathered at Thorpe Underwood since the ball, between them, they knew the greater part of their hostess's history. Much too much was said about Kenya, MGM films and Tom Hanbury. Valerie frolicked in the garden of recollection brought into bloom by her friends. It was all, 'Do you remember ...' And 'I'll never forget ...'

The conversation excluded Walter who grew sulky and snappish by turns and then drunk.

He started on a rambling monologue about taxation matters, wagging his index finger didactically whilst his wife's guests paid him polite but apprehensive attention.

Afraid that something unfortunate would soon happen, Valerie tried to coax her husband out of the library and up to bed. He shook her off roughly declining the help of one of her male guests, Valerie called for the butler to help get his master to his own room but on the way there, voided the content of his bowels into his trousers.

"Walter, you spiteful old man! You could have waited; I know you could. You did that deliberately to spoil things for me. You do it to get attention. You're horrible."

The butler would do nothing other than complete the short journey to the dressing room where he left Walter with Valerie. Hartley was away for the night and neither of the maids could be asked for assistance. Valerie was prepared to do everything herself, but Walter would not allow it. Every time she tried to get near him, he lunged at her with his fists.

"Get your grasping hands off me, lady, I'll tend to myself."

Valerie re-joined her guests in the library, apologised and tried to enjoy what was left of her party. In the morning, the maid who took Walter's breakfast to his room dropped the tray with a crash. Valerie leaped out of bed to see what had happened. She opened her own bedroom door.

"Don't go in there, Madam," the woman was retching.

Valerie fastened the sash of her robe and looked past the litter of broken china into the room. The smell said it all. Even so, there was a certain appalling fascination in the scene. A massacre. Walter had only half undressed himself. Too drunk probably, to complete the task, he had slid down a wall leaving thick yellowish streaks on the wallpaper. He lay slumped in a heap by the skirting board. He had realised his own danger sufficiently to throw out his teeth. The plates grinned up from the carpet. Walter had vomited. His eyes were open, defiant and angry. Valerie closed the door.

Fighting off an asthma attack, she made her way to the kitchen quarters. The uproar there penetrated the green baize door. It continued unabated when Valerie made her presence known.

The cook turned from the gas stove and delivered a speech on the proliferation of bacteria, hands on hips, she was going too. "I feel dirty in this 'ouse."

"That's enough now," the butler interposed. "I regret Madam," he looked Valerie straight in the eye, "that it is no longer within my power to hold the staff together. Neither I nor they have any hospital training. I must tender my own resignation. I have secured another position."

He remained in the house long enough to help Valerie revive the appearance of guest's breakfast trays which lay neglected on the kitchen table. The rest walked out within the same hour. Hartley had not yet returned from her visit.

Until each guest was informed that Colonel Lancaster-Hey was unwell and that in consequence, as Higgins put it, Madam would deem their early departure a favour, Valerie left Walter where he was.

Valerie contacted Walter's GP, who was also, ostensibly hers. She rang Sandy Milne. They hadn't spoken in ages. She was afraid he might have retired.

"Oh Sandy, please come. I need someone on my side. Walter's doctor just thinks I'm hysterical, menopausal. You could come privately, couldn't you? That would be all right … Sandy, please!"

Doctor Milne's general practice had given up taking private patients. They had proved uneconomic, too much bedside manner for too little pay, but Valerie's voice was cracked with desperation. She was close to tears one minute and struggling for breath the next.

"Okay, okay," he soothed. "We'll fudge something. I'll come. Be there in half an hour."

He was on the scene quicker than Walter's own doctor.

The butler showed Doctor Milne up to the first-floor landing and the door of his erstwhile employer's dressing room. It was the last service he performed in the house having refused to work his notice.

Valerie was found surrounded by bowls and buckets containing various disinfectants. She had managed to strip the soiled clothing from Walter and heave him onto the bed that she had covered with a rubber sheet.

The operations, so far, had been conducted in complete silence. Walter regarded his wife's perspiring face with a reptilian stare. He made sure that in her efforts to manipulate him, she bore the full dead weight of his body. Valerie leaned over him in concentration, her teeth clamped down hard on her lower lip.

Her breathing, Sandy Milne saw immediately, was rapid and shallow. If he had not known her so well and for so long, he would have doubted that it was her.

Further discussion at this point was interrupted by the coincidental, simultaneous arrival of Walter's own GP and Hartley in a taxi.

Sandy Milne introduced himself to his professional colleague and intercepted Hopkin's intended progress up the staircase.

"I must go to him."

"Mrs Lancaster-Hey has already done all that is necessary, I assure you. What they both need now is rest. There is no danger. Not to the Colonel at any rate."

Doctor Milne eyed the other man meaningfully.

"May we have a word?"

The medical men were closed together in the library for approximately twenty minutes. They managed to cloak their partisan views on the business in hand with well-tried, professional phrases of concern.

It was pointed out by Doctor Milne that the Thorpe Underwood staff had resigned as a body. Even the butler was packing his bags.

Valerie herself could not be left to nurse her husband on her own. Her stature, it was admitted, was diminutive but normal at five foot one. On the other hand, her weight, which he assessed at six stone, was most emphatically not.

Walter's doctor was routed. Under Milne's eye, he contacted a nursing home on the outskirts of Morecambe. The management had a vacant room available. Walter was taken away the same day. Infuriated by the pre-emption, Hartley elbowed the chauffeur aside and covered Walter's knees with the travelling rug herself. She was weeping.

"Don't take on so, Hartley," Walter said. It was the first time he'd spoken all day. "It's only temporary. I'll be back."

Ascending to her apartment ... her garret, as Hartley now openly called it; she telephoned Henry Ryecroft and every accessible member of the Hey family. They were deployed throughout the more expensive suburbs of the small Lancaster conurbation.

Valerie, suffering from shortness of breath, visited her own doctor.

"I can take it, you know," Valerie leaned forward in her chair.

"I don't doubt it for a minute, Mrs Lancaster-Hey. Fundamentally, you have a constitution of iron," and, he thought privately, the courage of a lion. It was a miracle she was still walking about.

"But?"

"You have emphysema ... an irreversible disease of the lungs."

"Can it be cured?" Valerie asked tensely.

"No, as I said, it's irreversible ... but controllable."

"And how will it end?"

The specialist looked over the top of his bifocals into Valerie's steady gaze. Doctor Milne's referral letter had been necessarily bland but additional details given on the telephone described an astonishing background.

Rapid development of the disease studied self-neglect ... except as the specialist noted, in the sartorial area ... and most culpable ignorance of the signs by her usual medical attendant. The patient was probably stressed by an unhappy marriage.

Valerie repeated her question, determined to have the answer.

"The disease, you understand, is progressive.... In the end, Mrs Lancaster-Hey, you will die of asphyxiation or drowning, at this stage, we cannot tell which."

Valerie's laugh chilled the specialist's blood. She simply did not believe him. She would get treatment in America, she said, her husband would pay.

Going home to the dark, empty house in her Rolls, Valerie vowed, that she would live long enough to be happy again. Nothing and no one should cheat her. Long ago on the Nile, she had decided exactly how she would die.

CHAPTER SEVENTEEN

Walter's peremptory removal soon caused a storm of protest from the Hey camp. Hartley's abilities as agent provocateur saw to that.

Cousins in varying degrees, nephews, great-nieces and remoter connections telephoned their complaints or came in person to register displeasure. Valerie received all comers in state, seated in the drawing room, the least dusty room in the servant-less house.

Peering down from the dormer window of her room, Hartley could see the Hey's deputations arrive. Over a period of days, they came singly and in groups. Rovers and Jags approached from the long drive, passing through the tall courtyard gate posts portentously, coming to rest like ships of war slowing ahead to fire their guns broadside.

They rang the bell without immediate result, thundered the iron knocker on the oaken timber to no apparent purpose. Hartley fretted and fumed lest these envoys of justice depart unheard. In a battle of mere coarse-grained nerves, Valerie Hey, Hartley conceded, would always carry the palm. The acceptance of this minor defeat was outweighed by the pleasure of having her rival rebuked.

Valerie took her time, ordering Hartley to direct her visitors to wait in the library and show them into the drawing room when she was ready. The audiences called for a complete change of dress. Her morning fluff of face powder and flick of mascara wouldn't do either. A fully-enamelled mask was an essential defence when parleying with enemies.

Valerie's lip curled as she worked. Frequent rests between one phase of the operation and the next slowed her down. She must not appear breathless to them.

Once enthroned in a commanding position, back to the light with her inhalers to hand, Valerie rang the service bell to signify that she was at now quite at leisure.

"Well now, what's the meaning of this?" The disgruntled men in town coats and ladies in excellent quality, slightly-out-of-date furs stumped across the Chinese washed carpets. "You've gone and put Walter in a home it appears. We're expecting an explanation. Why weren't we consulted? It's bloody cold in here. Why's there no fire?"

Valerie neither apologised nor explained. Anger at her own state of health forbade her to draw attention to it. None of the Hey faction noticed anyway. Walter's wife, in Hartley's surmise, was a hypochondriac plain and simple. Her opinion had been trusted so long by the board of Lancashire Ales, it was not now to be questioned. This Valerie woman was a dud.

"I thought it best at the time," Valerie stated imposingly, head high, knees together, beringed hands clasped loosely on her lap. "When my husband and I agree that it will be convenient, he will return home. Until then, he will remain where he is. That is our mutual decision."

The barefaced lie took the remaining wind out their sails. It was unrewarding work getting in between married couples. Here was Hartley shouting the odds on the one hand and Valerie looking a picture of injured innocence with her damned supercilious smile on the other. Walter was whingeing and whining at a daily cost to himself of fifty-five pounds, or was it guineas?

Valerie's self-control shook the Hey contingent. One by one, they retired hurt to Morecambe, Heysham and Grange-over-Sands. Speech at a safe distance seemed best so they rang up to say what they had dared not utter in her presence.

"You know what you've done, don't you? You've effectively deserted him, Valerie, and that's grounds for divorce ... If he takes our advice." There was plenty said on that score. Even the terrifying suggestion that Walter might be able to sue her for support was made. The tide of judicial opinion was turning against idle women.

"That is nonsense, as I'm sure you know," Valerie parried the thrust. "All I have is this house ... the Barwick Trust Income and ..."

"Aye, well don't imagine the courts will think any of it sacred if it comes to t'stick and lift, so, think on. You've battened on him long enough."

No sooner was that harangue terminated than a female Hey harpy rang to scream abuse. Hartley fielded the call gleefully, put it through to the morning room and listened intently to the fun. She always did. Monitoring calls, she named this activity.

"You only married him for his money ... you avaricious bitch ... You've made such a mullock of your affairs in the past you've nothing to leave those kids of yours ... and what's Walter got for his money, I'd like to know."

"I never," Valerie responded with surface tranquillity, "talk about money, except to my nearest and dearest on those rare and unpleasant occasions when it is necessary. Naturally, Walter and I are at one on this subject as on all others."

Hartley's heart twisted inside her with loathing. She replaced the receiver in her office stealthily and prayed to the Reformed Methodist God that the gates of hell be kept standing open for Valerie Hey - liar!

For Valerie this obduracy under fire was a holding operation only. Something would have to be done. The situation looked grave. She realised that somehow or other she must recruit a new staff and engage a male nurse if only Walter could be persuaded. Four years with him could not be thrown away now. He must be brought home. Slow, deliberate breathing brought clarity to the brain.

Advertisements were drafted and placed in *The Lady*. Cheerful housemaids replied in painstaking handwriting, claiming they liked the countryside and knew how to 'get into the corners'.

A couple of supposedly unflappable butlers applied and an 'indomitable' cook who referred in green biro to her preference for plain but tempting fare.

Valerie asked herself idly how the two could be reconciled but agreed to see her, nonetheless. What counted now was docile temperament, not flair.

Most urgent amongst the appointments was the search for a congenial male nurse.

"Well, as your quack seems convinced you're fit for nothing, we'd better have one it seems," Walter agreed petulantly. It would not do to admit that Hartley was all the attendance he desired. Walter longed for Hartley's visits. They held hands and talked about the good, wholesome old days at Hey's Lancashire Ales. She came on the days when Valerie did not.

Brian Sharples was the only applicant with relevant experience, as Valerie delicately put it. Sharples slapped his knee in appreciation. Relevant! He liked that. Mrs Lancaster-Hey had a way with words. Mind you, it was funny old way to talk about turds. He could see they'd all get along like a house on fire. Or, he paused for effect, how's about an incinerator? Did Mrs Lancaster-Hey get it? Loved a good joke, he did. Brian Sharples's high-pitched laugh honked like a peahen in season.

Walter made no kind of difficulty over Valerie's choice.

"I daresay the lad will do as well as another," he remarked languidly after Sharples had left the nursing home in a taxi paid for by Walter to catch his train home to Blackburn. "You can get off now if you want. Hartley will be here soon. We've some papers to go over," he added as an afterthought. For decency's sake.

Valerie's lips contacted Walter's brow briefly. As she closed the door of his room, she touched her handkerchief to her mouth and grimaced. Then she threw the scrap of lace-edged lawn into the first fire bucket she encountered on her way out of the building.

At the same moment, Walter wiped his forehead with his fingers, staring angrily at their tips.

****

"Telegram," the postman handed the cheap yellow envelope to Miss Hartley. "For Mrs Lancaster-Hey."

"Oh, thank you so much," Hartley replied. "I'll give it to her at once."

Valerie was still at the nursing home following the introduction of Sharples to the Colonel. Or more likely, she was on her way back. Hartley mind raced. It seemed of vital importance to know the content of this telegram before the taxi came to take her to Harrogate bus station for the trip into Leeds. Keeping one step ahead ... that's what the Colonel had always depended on her for in the past.

Opening an envelope of coarse material like this could be done without detection but it was a painstaking, time-consuming task. An interruption would be extremely awkward ... for technical reasons. There was no guarantee that Mrs Lancaster-Hey would not walk into the house even before the taxi arrived. She had a key, naturally. Hartley considered these facts and shot the iron bolts behind the front door. She dealt similarly with exits and entrances in the rear quarters of the house, telegram in hand. Such measures would cause a convenient delay in the event of disturbance.

Whatever information was contained in this telegram, the Colonel ... Eddikins ... had a right to know. Hartley was convinced of that.

At last the glue dissolved. The flap of the envelope came unstuck of its own accord. This was where the skill came in. The telegram must be extracted whilst the envelope remained suspended in the steam. Shrouded in steam. Hartley made out the misty words. It was not, at first sight, very spectacular news.

"Your father very ill. Complete relapse. Your presence urgently required."

The sender's name meant nothing to Hartley. It was unimportant anyway. So, Mrs Lancaster-Hey would be hurrying off abroad again. Fancy that.

The taxi arrived just nicely on time. Hartley was ready and waiting in the hall where the telegram was propped up on the table against a brass jardinière. So perfectly natural it looked, no one would guess it had been tampered with at all. It gave Hartley an extra fillip when they met Valerie's Rolls turning in at the main gate off the road. Such exquisite timing, quite like a novel.

"Slow down, if you please," she ordered the driver. "I just want a word with Mrs Lancaster-Hey."

The two women rolled down the windows in the rear seats of their respective conveyances.

"Yes, Miss Hartley?" Valerie arched her eyebrows coldly. "What is it? You'll be glad to know that my husband was pleased with Mr Sharples."

"A telegram came. It's on the hall table. I do hope it isn't bad news."

One hundred and ten minutes later Walter and Hartley were laying their plans. They had a glass of sherry to celebrate. No, they agreed. Brian Sharples was not a nice man. He had, in Yorkshire parlance, a great deal too much of, and thanks to Hartley receiving a telephone call from South Africa in Valerie's absence ... (the smallest of little white, undiscoverable fibs designed by Hartley to protect the Colonel from the least suspicion of guilt) ... they would have plenty of time to make alternative arrangements. It was all, Hartley gushed, very romantic. Walter dreamed that night of his mother.

****

Valerie's chest specialist havered and wavered over whether or not she should respond to the call to her father's side. Was there not someone else who could go? A grown-up grandchild, perhaps. No, they all had responsibilities and her son, Robert, could certainly not take several weeks off work. Valerie stamped on the suggestion smartly. Bobby Skelton was very fond of his grandson.

244

Old people got funny sometimes and started altering their wills on unreasonable pretexts. Left their money unfairly. Skipped a generation capriciously. They got the wrong end of the stick so easily. Valerie herself was the only child of her parents' marriage. She must be there, she insisted, with a catch in her voice, to close her father's eyes at the last. He'd a right to expect it.

After a medical check-up and an extra prescription of steroids, she was sent off with her specialist's qualified blessing in forty-eight hours.

Walter was told on the telephone.

Valerie had gained a little weight lately, had the breathlessness under better control, the dry sunshine climate of South Africa might well do her good. A change of scene was often beneficial, the specialist said, although, of course, her mission was sad. She was to carry a sealed letter from him with her. It was addressed to the clinical staff attending her father. On no account was Mrs Lancaster-Hey to be subjected to any needless distress. The name of her condition alone, the specialist judged, would be enough to inform interested parties that she was dying herself though the rate of pulmonary destruction had slowed. A minor miracle, the specialist thought of his patient's strong mind over the sorry devastation of the lung tissue hidden behind her ribs.

In the same Durban hospital as before and later the same private clinic, Bobby repeated his earlier triumph over death. The Skeltons, he observed, were made of pretty stern stuff.

Worn out by the journey and a range of contrasting emotions, Valerie found herself offering her father a home. What, she asked herself bitterly, was one more set of symptoms among so many? For a time at least, Thorpe Underwood Hall would become a hospital for the terminally ill. After all, she had Brian Sharples. Let him work harder for his four thousand a year and all found. She would be able to look after herself.

Having made the decision, she booked a call through to Walter at the Morecambe nursing home.

"I just can't do this again Walter … drop everything at a moment's notice … My father's so frail now but it could go on and on."

"Please yourself m'dear," Walter replied. "As far as I'm concerned, your father's welcome at Thorpe Underwood Hall."

That was an odd way for him to refer to Valerie's house. He usually just called it the Hall. Valerie's mind logged the detail and stored it away. Walter sounded rather chipper … in the early expectation of going home, she supposed.

"Now the new servants report on Monday morning by twelve," she told him. "Could you make sure Hartley is there to settle them in … I laid out sheets on the beds … They ought to be aired."

"Yes, yes," Walter drawled, "All arranged. Don't you worry about anything. Hartley's got everything in hand."

"And Mr Sharples comes on the same afternoon. Once he's installed, Walter there's no reason why you shouldn't go home."

"That's right, m'dear," Walter agreed affably. "No reason at all."

"I'm afraid I shall have to stay here to put Daddy's house on the market."

"No need to rush, we shall manage quite nicely without you."

When Valerie put the telephone down, she felt a momentary uneasiness. There was something not quite right here. She shrugged off the feeling and set to making an inventory of the bungalow's contents. Some might be sold with the house; others would have to be freighted. Among the carpets and curtains, the sterling silver and survivors of her mother's trousseau linen, Walter's voice kept straying back to her mind. The last thing that he said. We shall manage quite nicely without you. The words carried a presage of doom.

Bobby, discharged from the clinic, was tucked up in bed. Should she take him a cup of tea? No, he must be sleeping. The place was eerily silent. Where had she been and in what situation when she had last heard words like the ones that Walter had spoken. It was absurd, of course. People often said things like that. Why shouldn't they? They didn't mean anything by it.

No resolution came until the morning. When it did so, it struck her with force. Richard! Hadn't he said exactly the same sort of things to her on the telephone in London when she'd gone down there to find a replacement cook for Clarke. She'd got back to find him in bed with ... What exactly were Walter and Hartley ... it had to be Hartley ... up to? Something. There was no time to be lost.

Valerie began with breathing exercises, her morning inhalant of steroids and a business-like toilette. Plane tickets must be booked, the estate agent seen, and an international removal firm selected. Bobby objected to all the haste.

Bobby insisted that there were friends he must visit, friends who should be entertained, asked to drinks at the very least. A farewell party of some sort must be given.

Saying nothing of her worries ... they might be ill founded in any case, Valerie allowed her accelerated programme to be extended by a few days.

She issued invitations quickly and gave a cocktail party for her father. It had to be early, five o'clock, before the curfew banished the servants outside the white town. Pressing the hands of his departing guests, there were tears in Bobby's eyes. All the brave talk of coming back on a visit covered the truth. These people he would not meet again, this side of heaven.

****

To Valerie's combined relief and astonishment, her own car was there at Heathrow to meet herself and her father.

"But how on earth did you know?" Valerie questioned the chauffeur. "I tried to get in touch with my husband but there was never any reply."

The chauffeur was, as always, taciturn. He was Walter's man.

"Miss Hartley, Madam. She got hold of British Airways and asked when you and the gentleman were booked. Dead efficient she is."

"But I might not have come back on British Airways."

247

"No. Madam. You might not, but you did."

The man was disinclined to say more.

"Has anything been wrong with the telephones at home?" Valerie tried a different tack.

"At Thorpe Underwood? No, Madam. Not that I know of."

"Leave t'poor fellow alone," Bobby intervened. "He's enough on, driving this ruddy great tank."

Bobby slept in the car all the way home. Valerie was left to her thoughts. There were no lights to be seen in the house when the Rolls bowled along the drive at dusk. A feeling of dread clutched at Valerie's heart. If they knew she was coming, why hadn't some sort of welcome been laid on? The new butler would hear about this and shortly. The place looked completely dead. What was all this about? Some kind of economy drive on electricity. Trust Walter, at least his Daimler was parked outside.

The chauffeur helped both his passengers from the stationary car and took the luggage from the boot. Still no lights. They must have heard the car arrive. There was a nip of early frost in the air.

"I've the key here somewhere," the chauffeur searched in his pocket.

"What do you mean?" Valerie asked him quietly. "Where are the servants? Where is my husband? Isn't Miss Hartley here?"

The chauffeur said he didn't know and carried their bags inside. The place was cold. It had an uninhabited smell. Valerie could see her breath steam faintly in the air.

"Fetch the butler … to me here, now, this minute."

But Valerie was talking to an empty space. Behind her, the door creaked on its hinges and the headlights of the Daimler shone through the window. Valerie ran outside, leaving her father standing there.

"Just a minute. Where the hell do you think you're going? Where is everyone? Turn that engine off at once!"

The chauffeur did so and wound down the driver's seat window. The Colonel was giving him a good tip for handling this.

"I've my instructions, Madam. I was to leave you and the gentleman at the Hall here, and the Rolls. Then I was to drive the Daimler back to … Well, I'm not to say."

"How dare you! How dare you defy me."

"It's the Colonel as pays my wages. Ma'am."

Valerie stepped back as the Daimler's wheels span on the gravel. In a moment, its taillights were red dots in the distance.

"What's up, Val?" Bobby stepped out of the house. "What's wrong?"

"It looks as though that stinking bastard's left me, that's what."

"By heck, Val," Bobby chuckled sourly. "You get yourself into some right fixes, don't you?"

They ate baked beans in the kitchen and Valerie made up her father's bed herself. He was soon ready for it. Thank God. If he had said 'By heck', just once more, Valerie thought, she might have strangled him. It didn't help to know that he was doing it on purpose and laughing at her.

She had a bad attack of asthma that night. Too bad to enable her to summon help. The inhalers seemed to do no good. She lifted the telephone once but found she couldn't speak. In the end she managed to get her pillows propped so that she could sit upright in bed. If she lay down, she would suffocate.

For an immeasurable space of time she hovered in the cold, star-bitten sky over the house. She could see clear down the chimney stack to where her body lay in bed. There were visitors crowding around her. Roddy, Ann MacMaster, Dennis Dangan, her mother, Tom Hanbury and others. They were saying she should come with them now, taking her hands in their own, down-feathered palms. No feeling but softness. A seductive lack of sensation. So easy to go now …

No! Valerie's heart beat again. The funnelled view of her room broadened as the pain resumed and the visitors left, looking over their shoulders.

She would have to drive herself to the specialist in Preston tomorrow, Valerie thought. There was literally nobody here. It was hard to take in; as hard as a breath of air.

Valerie's specialist came to see her as it happened. Bobby insisted that he did. His daughter, he barked down the telephone with more than a little of his old fire, was 'fit for nowt'.

The specialist went through the motions with stethoscope and questions. He already knew that the disease had reached its next stage.

He made out a range of new prescriptions and rang a large hospital who would supply a pair of oxygen tanks. Valerie would have to sleep with these in her room, she was warned, for the rest of her life.

"How very alluring," she commented crossly. "Will I have things strapped over my face all night?"

No, it was carefully explained. There would be no need for that, not for a while.

"But you must top up your oxygen level without fail, every time before you go to sleep. And the same before you take exercise … and you should take a little of a moderate kind."

"Oh, so, my life's not over yet, then?" Valerie snapped.

He asked where her husband was, and Valerie waved her hand dismissively. He was at a meeting of some sort somewhere. Would her chauffeur take the new prescriptions into Northallerton and get them filled? Unhappily, Valerie replied, the chauffeur was driving Walter today.

Giving Bobby a lift into Northallerton, the specialist tried to find out what, if anything, had happened.

"Search me," Bobby turned off the questions lightly. "I'm nowt but a visitor." But he added sincerely "I'll tell you something for nothing if you like. That place gives me t'creeps. Whatever's gone on there, is stuck in't bloody walls."

The gas tank men having come and gone, Valerie wondered what to do next. She rang the nursing home and asked to speak to Walter.

The switchboard put her through to the Matron who told her that Colonel Lancaster-Hey had discharged himself and gone away with Miss Hartley. No, he had left no forwarding address, other than Thorpe Underwood Hall. He had paid the outstanding charges on the nail.

Valerie slammed the telephone down and dialled Henry Ryecroft's office number in Leeds.

"Now then," he said, after some inaudible, background discussion. "What can I do for you?" His tone was wary.

"Oh, dearest Henry, I am so worried. When I got home last night with Daddy, I was sure Walter would be here, and now the nursing home say he left them. Do you think I should contact the police? Where can he be?"

Henry Ryecroft stonewalled. He hadn't spoken with Walter for nearly a week. Well, well, he couldn't make any suggestions. If he had left with Hartley, as the nursing home claimed, he couldn't come to much harm, could he? No, Henry wouldn't go troubling the police. Walter would let her know where he was when he wanted her to know …

"Look, Henry," Valerie interrupted sharply. "Has he left me or not? Do you know?"

"Er … I really couldn't say, my dear. Your husband hasn't confided in me. I'm sorry to rush, but I've a meeting."

It was Brian Sharples who blew the gaffe on Walter and Hartley. He rang after Valerie and Bobby had consumed some doubtful-looking frozen sausages and instant mashed potato from a cupboard in the kitchen. Valerie leaped to the telephone when it rang.

"Thorpe Underwood Hall, Valerie Lancaster-Hey speaking."

"And about time too," Sharples sniffed. "I've been trying every day. What's all this about me not being wanted now. I'm due some sort of compensation."

Sharples raved on at length. He'd been visited by Miss Hartley at his Blackburn home and told his appointment was cancelled.

"She just rolled up like Mary Poppins, said the Colonel hadn't any need for a nurse and he wasn't going back to Thorpe Underwood. She gave me this envelope with a cheque inside for a measly twenty-five quid. What's the good of that to me? I turned down a job abroad for you and the Colonel."

"Mr Sharples, I'm so sorry this happened. I was called away on urgent business. I suspect the Colonel had no real idea of what he was doing. Miss Hartley, well, it hardly matters now, is a hard, manipulative little woman who's after the Colonel's money.

She has a very great and dangerous influence over him. I'm extremely worried. This could well be a matter for the police. Now tell me, did she tell you where they were going?"

"Yes, as a matter of fact, she did," Sharples replied. "She came all over coy, said she and the Colonel were taking up residence in a pleasant villa in Grange-over-Sands, full of it she was, went gabbling on about sea air and select society."

"The address Mr Sharples, did she mention the address?"

Sharples wasn't sure. No, he was almost sure no address had been given, and even if it were to come back to him, in a manner of speaking, he wasn't certain he should give it away, it wasn't professional etiquette.

In the end, Valerie offered to post a cheque for a hundred pounds which she would cancel unless Sharples came up with Walter's precise whereabouts in two days' time. If he should recall the address by then, he would get another similar sum for his trouble. Sharples said he knew that he and Mrs Lancaster-Hey would always have seen eye to eye. He was sure his memory would serve him, given a little time to work.

"Get anywhere?" Bobby asked casually mopping tomato ketchup from his plate with the last forkful of potato. Val wasn't much of a caterer.

"Grange-over-Sands. The pathetic little man has run away with Hartley to the genteel seaside. Not Nice, not Venice, not Torquay, but Grange-over-Sands. About as much glamour as Hartley can take, I imagine."

"Haven't been to Grange for donkey's years. Nice little town. Is there anything for afters?"

"Oh Daddy, do shut up!"

Father and daughter retired to rest.

Bobby found his way to Hartley's deserted apartment during a restless exploration. Opening a panelled door which looked as though it led through to another room, he found it concealed a cupboard. Inside, a steel rail carried a number of empty wire coat hangers.

Seeing a shoe box on the floor with pages protruding from it, Bobby bent down to retrieve it. The sheaf of papers seemed to be a discarded manuscript. It was Hartley's novel, *The Loyal Sword of Love* by Gertrude Hartley.

Laughing quietly to himself, Bobby plugged in the electric fire and settled down to read this masterpiece in Hartley's lately-abandoned chair.

It was a dark tale, a melodrama concerning a ménage a trois set at the turn of the century. Even so, it was hardly difficult to identify the principals with the recent, present day inhabitants of Thorpe Underwood Hall. The characterisation was spirited if crude. The wealthy gentlemen of high virtue and simple tastes, the dazzling, titled, fortune-hunting widow with her calculating wiles, and the ever-faithful governess, plain and poor, who conceals her passion until the moment that she murders her rival with a bank messenger's truncheon. (Bobby had noted one of these hanging in the hall as an ornament.) Gertrude Hartley had made much of crimson blood matted in blonde hair. She had lingered too, over splinters of white bone and grey splashes of brain. It was strongish stuff and very well spelled into the bargain.

By the time the daylight had faded from the dormer windowpanes. Bobby felt it was as well for Val, that Hartley had found an outlet for her feelings. That his daughter had been in serious danger, her father was suddenly aware. She was exactly the sort of person that other people murdered.

He shivered and gathered the papers together back into the shoebox. He went downstairs and began to feed the typescript into the Aga's firebox, a score of pages at a time.

Whilst her father had been reading, Valerie had been writing. The diary so long neglected was taken up again. The Lancaster-Hey marriage must now be given shape.

The end had not come as Valerie willed and planned it. There was to be no tidy package of shroud, coffin, fetching widow's weeds and a comfortingly-large bequest.

She would have recourse to the divorce courts once again, of course. Walter must certainly pay for his behaviour. Valerie was wounded to the quick that Hartley had supplanted her. Such wickedness, she would tell Mr Robertworth, cried out for retribution, he would naturally agree. The customary lump sum and annual income would do.

Robert was summoned at two in the morning to hear of his mother's contingency plans. "You must come, darling. I know I'm going to have a severe asthma attack. Laura can come as well if she wants."

CHAPTER EIGHTEEN

Thorpe Underwood Hall was sold for little more than its purchase price. Valerie could not afford to keep it.

At first, she had intended to sell off the outbuildings: stables, a pretty dovecote, coach houses and disused barns clustered near the rear of the house. They were ideal for conversion to manageable, 'bijoux' homes. The estate agent was optimistic. Courtyard developments were all the rage. Had she seen the plans for something similar at Rudding Park? But that was North Yorkshire for you, very go ahead.

Thorpe Underwood would make an equally attractive scheme and the Hall itself would give the smaller units cachet. Outline planning permission shouldn't be a problem. Once granted, the site should be valuable. The proceeds would certainly enable Mrs Lancaster-Hey to remain in her own house. Oh yes, the round pond must be included in the common areas, it was a strong selling feature. There would be a loss of privacy, of course, but then, neighbours were no bad thing when you were getting on in life, were they?

"I mean, it must be difficult for you, out here, alone with a gentleman of Mr Skelton's advanced years," the estate agent amended quickly, seeing the frost crystals sparkle in Valerie's eyes. "There's a planning meeting next month, shall we handle the application for you, Mrs Lancaster-Hey?"

Valerie agreed reluctantly. There would be no harm in that, at least. She would be committed to nothing irrevocable. It was too dispiriting to think of other people's children running wild here.

What if they used the round pond to paddle in and left toys, plastic things in crude primary colours all over the lawns and paths? Bicycles and roller skates. Ugh! And the noise.

255

There was really no alternative. Valerie's private income amounted to no more than seven thousand pounds a year and Thorpe Underwood Hall cost nearly twice that to run, even on a shoestring. Until the divorce was sorted out, she would have to be careful. She had done the sums over and over again.

The Rolls Corniche that Walter had given her had already gone to a flashy little man with a ginger beard in advertising. His small red hands were hot and hard when he shook Valerie's. Incredibly, he called himself Piers England. He had kicked the tyres with his awful mock crocodile shoes and said if he'd known it was silver grey, he wouldn't have bothered coming all the way over from Leeds. Silver grey Corniches were nose to tail down West Park in Harrogate these days. He had wanted two thousand off for cash.

Valerie could not afford to argue. The Aga alone cost ten pounds a week to run and the last quarter's gas bill had been presented three times. They were threatening to cut off the supply. Valerie's BUPA subscription was due, some stupid man had called and asked to see her colour television licence. Logically, a property like Thorpe Underwood should be able to maintain itself. It had been so mean minded of Walter to keep the farmland for himself. It really made the gift of the house itself almost valueless, so Valerie told Bobby, Robert and his second wife, Laura. They listened in restive, embarrassed silence. To contradict Valerie these days meant risking an asthma attack and wild recriminations. She had suffered fools gladly all her life, she said, and would have continued to do so if her health had only permitted it. Surely, her own family could show some consideration.

For months Valerie delayed. Builders' men would make the place look messy. Cement mixers and scaffolding. The thought of people coming to live so close was disagreeable. This was Victoria's home, she argued with Bobby. She ought to have the benefit of it, at least until her twenty-first birthday party.

Valerie proved as impermeable to her father's insult as she was to reason. The urge to spend money had banked up behind the damn of frustrated energy. It could no longer be contained. Needing to affect her environment, Valerie's mind had fixed on a random purpose. The misjudged project was forced ahead, rammed like a wrongly-shaped jigsaw puzzle piece into a set of surrounding circumstances into which it did not fit.

Valerie spent the better part of ten thousand pounds on building a tennis court at Thorpe Underwood Hall that would have been the envy of the Hurlingham Club. The money was available only because after some argument, Walter released the small parcels of shares not connected with the Barwick Trust, which she had handed over to him after the Grand Metropolitan collapse. Deaf to the all-contrary advice, Valerie sold her gilt-edged and blue-chip stocks. The tennis court, she said was an improvement to her property. A solid investment.

Bobby stood daily on the site and watched his daughter's folly taking shape. On the tennis court's matchless surface, a sloth would have been fleet of foot and from it, a rock could have bounced. It was constructed over land that formed part of the outline courtyard development scheme.

The estate agents didn't know. Valerie's bank manager looked on in alarm, scenting the onset of a kind of financial hysteria that sometimes affects women of a certain type in late middle age. A structural fault in a column of figures foretelling speedy disintegration. Helpless, and equally concerned, Bobby telephoned his grandson.

"I don't know what she thinks she's up to, lad. You'd better come and have a look."

Robert did. He came with Laura, who was pregnant. Valerie ushered them out of the house to view the marvel.

"How nice," was all Laura could think of to say.

"I don't understand why you've done it mother," Robert said. "You were going to sell this land."

257

A developer who was eager to buy the Thorpe Underwood Hall site was introduced by the estate agents. It was a good offer. Valerie dithered. Could the tennis court area be excluded from the sale? Could a new plan be drawn to ensure that the subsidiary dwellings were confined to a distance of two hundred yards from the main house? The sale went off. Later Valerie said she had been badly advised. The local estate agents were ignorant and provincial, lazy or not up to sophisticated negotiations.

Storm damage in the autumn proved the last straw. The repair bill could not be met without making further inroads into the remaining small amount of capital that was free of the Barwick Trust provisions. Valerie called in a firm of London estate agents. They would want 2% commission, a half per cent up on local rates.

Over a glass of gin and tonic, the London man laughed off the whole idea of the courtyard scheme. Mrs Lancaster-Hey, Valerie, as he was quickly invited to call her, had had a lucky escape. Did she realise, that had she ever wished to sell the Hall itself at a later date, it would have hung on the market forever? Houses like these were white elephants without their ancillary buildings. By the merest and most fortunate chance, his firm had a customer for a decent little mansion house in the North of England. Thorpe Underwood was a pretty spot. He might be interested. How soon might he view the property?

A few days later, a monosyllabic man with a tape measure, theodolite and hydrometer came and went with a frown on his pale, clever face. He had no wish apparently to incommode Mrs Lancaster-Hey.

Consequently, they were not introduced. Nonetheless, the London estate agents communicated his offer of ninety thousand pounds for the entire property.

Contracts were exchanged, and the sale completed. In fact, it was one of the partners of Broderick, Gooch and Grieves who had acquired the property in opposition to all honest rules of practice. Thorpe Underwood Hall, it was reported back to London, had definite development potential.

Valerie signed the conveyance, convinced that her London agents had served her well. Mayfair vowels could not deceive.

Thoughtfully, these same estate agents sent her the lavishly-printed particulars of a brand-new apartment building only recently completed at Beech Grove Court in the centre of Harrogate. It was already, trumpeted the copy, the best address in North Yorkshire, and, Valerie had already heard enough about the fashionable attractions of that county to think a move there desirable from every point of view. Charity organisations, Valerie had it on reliable authority, abounded in Harrogate, along with antiques and tourism. It was a local industry. That meant social opportunities and possibly, financial flexibility.

Dotted thickly on every available surface, porcelain and silver objects looked pained. Like middle-class refugees trying to be glad they are still alive in the midst of socialist revolution. Valerie rearranged vases, candlesticks, boxes, bowls and figurines repeatedly. Try as she might, the penthouse stubbornly refused to acquire a baronial aspect. The warehouse atmosphere prevailed.

Portraits variously and inaccurately described by Valerie, to Gainsborough, Reynolds and Romney, lined the flat walls edge-to-edge. They celebrated in oils the very style of femininity that Miss Hartley's despised Royal Doulton figures expressed in clay. Valerie saw no connection between the two. She was proud of her pictures.

They were all an authenticated masterpiece in her opinion. No family member, and certainly no friend was allowed to question their provenance.

To do so was to be instantly struck from Valerie's visiting list. She was not to be doubted where art was concerned, she was an expert.

Valerie was unhappy in Harrogate. She put it down to the Hey faction spreading vicious lies about her. The Lancashire border had proved no barrier to poison. If only she could catch one of them at it, she would sue for damages. They might be quite substantial.

It was a pity, she told Robert, that dear Mr Robertworth had always been such a stick-in-the-mud about libel actions. A safe man to deal with, but no fire in his belly. He didn't have her pride, of course.

One day Valerie encountered Hartley in an Eric Street shop. They stood side by side at the perfumery counter for some minutes before Valerie realised that the woman in the enviable Persian lamb with sable facings was none other than her successful rival. Gertrude Hartley bowed coldly and moved away as Valerie sought her inhaler frantically. That woman had no right to a coat like that, it was a touch vulgar.

Before the year was out, the ancillary buildings of Thorpe Underwood Hall were again advertised in a leading regional estate agency's newspaper. The price asked was eighty thousand pounds. The advertisement appeared twice before it was dropped. The owner, it was rumoured, had got his price and kept the tennis court. Soon after, he put the Hall itself on the market and got a quarter of a million pounds. or so it was said.

Valerie railed, not at the London agency that had advised her ill and betrayed her trust, but at the local men, whom she claimed, had led her astray. Such was the power of Saville Row tweeds.

Valerie hated the penthouse, it was so cramped, and Daddy so got in the way. Really, there was scarcely room to breathe and entertaining was quite impossible.

Giving herself up to an afternoon on the bed with her diary, daydreams and oxygen tanks, Valerie vowed she would outlive Daddy.

There was a correct and chronological order for these things. Her disease she decided was in remission. It was a new, encouraging word. At the end of her days, she must occupy the centre stage. It was the only place she felt entirely at ease.

Choosing a new stage, once Walter paid up, would be fun. She began to toy with an attractive possibility. It hinged on the state of Denise Radcliffe's health. Valerie never thought of her as Lady Barwick. What a travesty of a marriage that must have been. The wretched woman had been sick for years.

Valerie's hopes of an early divorce and adequate settlement had been cruelly dashed by Mr Robertworth.

"I've looked into this closely," he said, "and I think your best plan is to go for a divorce by mutual consent after two years have elapsed since the day he left the matrimonial home. More discreet, eh?"

"But, Mr Robertworth, why? He deserted me ... I have evidence, witnesses ... and his dreadful behaviour towards me ... Everyone will tell you."

Why were people so beastly? All she wanted was to be left with enough to live on, and a little dignity. Clothes cost so much money now, and after all, people did expect certain standards from her. The girls, for one thing, and all the charity people. She was a kind of figure-head, wasn't she? One had to set an example in life. One couldn't just give up.

Putting down the handbag and gloves she had gathered onto her lap, Valerie continued. "My marriage was never consummated, you know," she glanced at the lawyer speculatively. "We never slept together, what about an annulment? He failed me completely, you see."

"Unless you are in haste to be married again," Mr Robertworth replied with some asperity, "1 see no merit in the procedure. Obtaining the proof would be distasteful and er, difficult. Financially, there would be no advantage. A settlement of any kind is unlikely in either case. You wish me to try for an annulment?"

"No," Valerie said quickly. There were too many people, she remembered, whom she had allowed to think differently about the realities of her marriage. "1 shall just have to be content with whatever you can get for me, and what he leaves me, of course."

Mr Robertworth jerked his head up in sudden alarm. Valerie, as he called his client privately, was an exasperating woman. She brought most of her troubles on herself and then shut her eyes to the probable consequences, and yet she was enchanting, like one of those cats that never learn that not every pot of cream is destined for her dish.

Her wide, hyacinth eyes never lost that look of confident expectation, of reproach when the cream was denied her. It ought not to be hard to disappoint her. But somehow, it was.

"Mrs Lancaster-Hey," the lawyer spoke gently. "Your husband's solicitors mentioned in passing that Colonel Lancaster-Hey changed his will some considerable time ago. You are no longer a beneficiary. It would hardly be reasonable, in the circumstances, for us to expect it. I'm so sorry."

Valerie exploded. She spoke of her rights, of treachery and double dealing, of the way her husband had been stolen from her by a jealous woman. All her life, she said, she had been the object of envy. Was it her fault that she was good looking, good company and successful with men? She had always been generous to those less fortunate than herself. What a fool she had been to let her heart rule her head. She had been tricked, robbed, badly advised. Valerie was beside herself.

"I have been an exemplary wife; I give, and I give. I think only of others and what is best for them. All I have ever asked is a little kindness … some understanding."

"Calm yourself, my dear Mrs Lancaster-Hey, I entreat you."

"Never, never call me by that name again. I shall be known as Lady Valerie Barwick … as I have never, in truth ceased to be. That is my name, I was married to Richard for nearly twenty years. Hey was just an appalling aberration, a tragic mistake. We were never man and wife, I tell you."

Valerie had an asthma attack and Mr Robertworth was obliged to call for his secretary to assist Mrs Lancaster-Hey.

****

For thirty minutes, Valerie treated Richard to a vivid account of the iniquities of Walter Lancaster-Hey. Richard gave her only half his attention. He had heard about the break-up of her most recent marriage, of course. Recently, his head gamekeeper had reported seeing Valerie's old Rolls, the one he had given her, in Thimbleby village.

262

There had been other sightings. Fortunately, Denise knew nothing about it. She had always said that Valerie haunted the place.

Utter bloody rubbish. Women and their imaginations.

Richard was tired of women. He was tired of life. He felt old and ill.

At night, he woke sometimes to a flickering cine reel of his life rushing through his head. A frame would suddenly freeze, showing him in painful detail, a portrait of himself. Crashing his head from side to side on the pillow didn't do any good. The demons were inescapable. Only whiskey faded them out. Richard kept a bottle on the table by his bed.

There had been no comfort in Denise's body in a long while. It was if that had never been. She lay now, or what was left of her, in a hospital bed, her skull bald from chemotherapy. White, as if it were already naked bone with a few wisps of faded red hair clinging here and there.

Nothing in his life had been good. It was all waste and lust. If only he had had a son to live for. Denise had not made him happy in the end. She had wanted everything that Valerie had got from him. Richard refused to give it. Indeed, he could not. Ready money was short now. They sat together in the evenings, drinking to take the edge off their mutual disappointment. It was a kind of companionship. Thimbleby slid into total neglect. Rooms were closed; the furniture sheeted up, the servants left, paid off or resigned because of Denise's temper.

The Barwicks had few visitors, though Robert sometimes came to shoot at his stepfather's invitation. He was glad to see the boy. No complaints and an admirable eye for a high bird. Robert who had had so little was grateful for what he got. A day on the moor among the people he remembered and a brace or two to take home. Robert had proved the best of the lot. Richard felt the stirrings of regret. It could have been different.

Perhaps, Richard reflected over recent weeks, he had done wrong not to adopt Robert. It would have meant someone to carry on at Thimbleby. Provide an income for himself and the girls, but that was all over. The old place would have to go, there wasn't enough working capital left. Death duties would wipe Thimbleby out.

"Oh darling, is it nearly over?"

"Pretty well, the old girl's going to snuff it, she's got a month perhaps six weeks, maybe. There's nothing more they can do. She wants me to take her to Guernsey."

Valerie paid close attention. Her path it seemed would soon be clear. Dear Thimbleby. How they all missed her there.

Richard was soon done with the topic of Denise's health. It was not, he said, the object of his call.

"I rang you to see about my will. I've been cogitating lately."

Valerie licked her lips. It was so obvious, wasn't it, that Richard had been thinking along the same lines as herself. They never should have parted, and now, there would be a second chance.

"Oh Richard, darling. You know I'll come just as soon as ..."

"Let me finish, Val," Richard interjected. He was nearly seventy now and found it difficult to concentrate on more than one thing at a time. "It's Robert, he's very badly off, poor lad and he's ..."

"You're going to adopt him, at last," Valerie shrieked delightedly. "Oh darling, how absolutely thrilled he'll be! We shall all be so happy and together again."

"No, no. Val, please just listen, please. There's nothing left here for Robert now. The estate's not viable anymore, it's my fault."

Richard rambled for some time about the mistaken judgements of the past. He stumbled through the events of his marriage to Valerie and his stepson's boyhood, rarely finishing a sentence or completing a thought.

Eroded by a lifetime's alcohol abuse, Richard's brain could no longer easily convert ideas to speech.

"I'm sorry, I'm sorry, Val," he said. "I know I don't make much sense these days ... I'm a sick, stupid old man. All I'm trying to say is that something must be done for Robert."

264

There was a pause in which Valerie began to speak again.

"Oh, shut up, Val! You don't know what it's like. What was I saying then? Oh God, my mind."

"About Robert ..."

"Yes, yes, thanks. I'm going to leave everything I have to the girls. And then, if you leave everything you have to Robert, that'll be fair, won't it? You've got a bob or two, haven't you Val? You must have taken that Hey character for something when you married him and that house; you'll have made a packet on it, won't you?"

"Darling, couldn't we meet, to talk things over. I should love to see you again. I think you need me now more than you ever have before. Shall I come to you at Thimbleby, my darling?

Richard agreed, after some demur, to a meeting in the near future, but no, Thimbleby was no good. Yes, Denise was in hospital, but it couldn't be until after the Guernsey trip anyway. He would have to engage two nurses. He felt ill himself, plagued by a duodenal ulcer, it was his own bloody fault. Valerie would get him well again, she said. Richard laughed and said it was all too late for that. He must go he was due to visit Denise. He would be in touch later; they must talk about Robert. He'd had a lousy deal.

Feeling better than she had for years, Valerie threw herself into a programme of self-improvement. She booked a course of facials, massages and the new aromatherapy at Brian Leslie's Princess Square salon. Shoes, frocks and lingerie, some new things were essential.

It was amazing what you could find in Harrogate once you really knew the shops. No need to go to London, there probably wouldn't be time. Richard would need her by his side at a moment's notice

For three weeks, Valerie viewed the telephone as both friend and foe. At any time, it might summon her to Guernsey and final fulfilment of her thwarted destiny. If only Denise could last long enough to ensure that Valerie was ready. She still had not found quite the right gloves to go with her new cream barathea. For this reunion, everything must be perfect. An investment in the future.

Richard has asked me to marry him again, Valerie wrote in her diary. Divorce was not possible for us. Our love has survived everything. Once the turquoise ink dried upon the page, the words took on the character of eternal verity in Valerie's mind. It could not matter, after all, which one of them had said these things. All that mattered was the truth.

****

Richard too, wrote. He began a letter in a hotel room in St Peter Port whilst Denise slept. In it, he made certain confessions to Valerie about the way in which he had disposed of Dennis Dangan's rival suit all those years ago. He had gained Valerie's consent to marry him under false pretences. Perhaps, because of that, they had never actually been married, he couldn't say. He had not thought of it for years but now, it was on his conscience. Their married life, from start to finish had been a bad joke. He accepted the lion's share of the blame. It was ironic, wasn't it, that one never understood how short life was until one had thrown it away?

Valerie might choose to forgive him or not. It was Robert he felt guilty about. Dangan would have made the boy a better stepfather than he had been, and it was because of this, that since their last telephone conversation, Richard had rethought the matter of his will.

The thought died with Richard. The chambermaid found his stiffened body slumped over the smudged, incomplete letter in the morning. He had knocked a tumbler of whiskey and water over the page, which was almost indecipherable. In the muffled hue and cry that followed, the letter was stuffed into the dead baronet's writing case and packed with his other effects. A complete inventory, the hotel manager instructed his staff, must be taken, nothing was to be discarded. That was the correct procedure. Nor must anything remain in the room.

The handsome gold Rolex dress watch that Richard had purchased the previous day for Robert, ended up in the manager's pocket and stayed there.

266

It was the same with his gold Parker pen, only the hall porter got that.

Eventually, Denise was told. She herself would have to be moved to a hospital on the island. The nurses had quarrelled about it. One proposed a double dose of morphine for her Ladyship. After all, they had been employed to relieve pain and make sure Lady Barwick enjoyed her last holiday with her husband. The holiday was over. The patients might as well leave together, but the other nurse, an Irish catholic, disagreed violently. Euthanasia was a sin.

"I just hope the old bugger left me enough to live on," was Denise's first reaction on hearing the news. Both nurses looked shocked, they had been trained to cope with tears.

Ashamed of their patient, themselves and each other, the nurses turned away from Denise's accusing gaze. Both understood now, that these two arrogant, angry old people had loved one another in their grudging, speechless way.

An ambulance came to collect Denise from the hotel. She wouldn't put on her red wig for the short journey to the hospital but clutched it to her breast like a cat.

"Bloody thing. Richard got it for me. I only wore it for him."

It was Robert who broke the news to his mother. It came to him through one of his half-sisters. Richard Barwick had died on Guernsey of a massive cerebral haemorrhage. Doctors said it was an easy way to go, just a bad headache, and then, most probably, nothing.

Valerie raged at fate. Another door had closed.

Grief for Richard, the greatest of all her loves, as Valerie unblushingly termed him, impelled the purchase of black clothes once the first agonising wave of disappointment had passed over. Like a monarch ordering court mourning, Valerie announced to her family that she would wear black for three months. It would give her something to do.

Only Robert asked what had happened to Denise. Where was she? And was she alive or dead? Nobody seemed to know.

267

"How could you mention that woman's name to me at a time like this, Robert?" moaned Valerie, trying on a new black hat. "You always were an insensitive boy as far as I'm concerned."

They laid Sir Richard Barwick 3rd Bt. to rest in his family's vault in the Barwick Mausoleum in Sunderland. Valerie was not present at her ex-husband's obsequies. Bobby dissuaded her from attending the funeral.

"Don't be a fool, Val. You'll get no welcome there. You and he were at loggerheads most of your married life."

"We were to have been married again as soon as that woman died. He cried and said I was the only real Lady Barwick, and now …" Valerie's eyes filled with emotion at her own oratory. "I am widowed."

CHAPTER NINETEEN

Phillip Bradburn combed a lightly pomaded lock into place. His luxuriant hairline, with its slight widow's peak, still showed no signs of receding, thank God.

Phillip took his appearance very seriously. After all, it was, you might say, his living. Only Phillip would never have said such a thing or even allowed himself to think it. Phillip lived on his tiny naval pension augmented with whatever he could pick up on the way. A stock market tip here, a legacy from a friend there.

In strictly practical terms, Phillip's friendships had outperformed anything he'd purchased in the way of stocks and shares over recent years. He enjoyed the company of women and when they died, they never failed to show their gratitude for all the devoted care and advice that he gave them. And then, sadly, since, as he always said on these occasions, life must go on, he forced himself to go out and make new friends. Fortunately, the supply of prospects had not yet dried up.

All Phillip had ever found necessary to establish his credentials was a good address, his was a bedsit in Knightsbridge, a first-rate wardrobe, a perfectly engraved visiting card and his own imposing presence.

In fact, Phillip had been born Arnold Davies in a pleasant enough part of South Ruislip. His father had been a hardworking GP and his mother, the pretty receptionist whom Dr Davies had later married. It was her mother who had been an Esterházy and a remote connection of that exclusive clan of naturalised Austro-Hungarians, a grandee who had settled in Britain after the First World War.

Among Mrs Davies's possessions was a faded photograph of a moustachioed officer in an operetta uniform, littered with ribands and orders. Great Uncle Phillip, she had called him. All she knew about this decorative gentleman, who wore his cavalry gaiters with such an air, was that he had once been some kind of equerry to the ill-fated Prince Dennis. For the youthful Arnold, it had been enough.

Dr Davies died suddenly when Arnold was seventeen. His widow moved from Ruislip to a pleasant flat in Hove with sea views. Arnold enrolled at the Royal Naval College, Dartmouth, under the name of Phillip Bradburn. The problem of his next of kin's name was quickly got over. His mother, Arnold (now Phillip) said, had married twice and been widowed twice. At that stage of Phillip's infant career, nobody bothered to check, Esterházy, it was reckoned, was promising officer material. Already, he had a decided air of command.

Phillip was saving himself for something better. He deserved, he sincerely felt, an heiress. Or failing that, a young lady with a name, which like his own, was plangent with the echo of lost palaces and ghostly hunting horns sounding in forgotten forests. No girl in either category was to be found.

One day at Chatham, Phillip's Admiral told him that he had, with some regret, recommended him for a post in naval intelligence. Talents such as his, the Admiral said with a sigh, should not be wholly absorbed in sherry pouring and poodle faking, valuable though his services in that sphere had been. Phillip caught onto the picture of himself as a cloak and dagger man with enthusiasm. He would be based in London. He could belong to a Club, be the boulevardier he had always at heart, longed to be. This was at last, work truly fit for an aristocrat.

Before Phillip's attachment to the intelligence arm of the service, there would be some formalities to complete. The Admiral could conceive of no possible difficulty there. With a name (albeit fictional and substitutional) like Esterházy, itself a metaphor for honour, loyalty, and strong monarchist principle, the vetting procedure would be mere routine.

Phillip was subjected to a series of embarrassing interviews with stone-faced Admiralty men. The positive vetting team had conducted the most pedestrian of enquiries and immediately encountered a startling discrepancy regarding the name and precise origins of Lieutenant Esterházy. Had he anything to say?

Phillip said a good deal. He had wished to honour his maternal grandmother's memory; he refrained from mentioning that he had never met her. His relationship with his doctor father had been difficult. They had not shared the same values. The change of name had been a personal choice.

The Navy men and their civilian cohorts grunted. Esterházy was a silver-tongued customer. Apparently, his German was good, and he had more than a smattering of Russian. That tended to authenticate his revised autobiography. Modestly, Phillip assured his judges that his mother had spoken in both these tongues to him, from his cradle up, but only when they had been alone.

Phillip's interrogation, for that is what it was, was prolonged. The final upshot was that he was invited to resign his commission quietly and carry out some of the surveillance duties with which he would otherwise have been charged, as a civilian. A salary would accompany the appointment, but no pension, or only that which his previous service had already earned him. Furthermore, should he ever run into any trouble in the pursuance of his intelligence gathering, the Navy would not own him as theirs. No protection, no rescue.

Having no funds, and therefore no choice, Phillip accepted what was offered him. He rented a room on the Cromwell Road and toiled during the day over intercepted signals in a Whitehall basement. Although his mother had never spoken a word to him in either language, his German and his Russian were adequate. He had worked hard at both when at school and bought Linguaphone records with his pocket money. It had been part of his planned future persona.

Phillip Esterházy was proposed and elected to the Travellers Club.

The annual subscription was steep, but Phillip looked on it as an investment for his old age. Membership gave him a respectable address in London and when his mother died, he was able to buy the fifty-year lease on the minute Chelsea flat. So now he had two unexceptionable addresses on his card.

Cultivating friendships made at the Club, Phillip found himself invited about. He was that rare commodity, a presentable spare man who could play a rubber of bridge without making a fool of himself ... or his partner.

From dinner parties he graduated to country-house parties where it was soon found that he played a passable game of tennis, too. In well-appointed, well-staffed houses up and down the country Phillip met the sort of woman he had always hankered after. True, they were usually divorced or widowed by now, and the ones available to him were invariably older than Phillip and prevented by the rigidity of family trusts from marrying again. But that was all to the good. He became the constant companion of one wealthy dowager, was pictured with her in the *Tatler* and at her subsequent funeral was feted as chief mourner. The lady left him fifteen thousand pounds.

Tonight, Priscilla Prescott had pressed him to escort Lady Valerie Barwick. Phillip sincerely hoped the exercise would prove worthwhile. A suite, (it had to be a suite), at Birmingham's monstrous Hotel Europa cost an alarming amount of money. The occasion, the annual dinner dance of some animal charity in which this Lady Barwick interested herself, was, Priscilla had said, the ideal opportunity for them to meet, or might have been. Phillip understood the signal perfectly. He wrote a cheque to cover a lifetime subscription to the charity in exchange for the introduction.

Time spent in reconnaissance, as the Navy had taught Phillip, is never wasted. His preliminary researches were most thorough. Recently, Lady Barwick had acquired and restored an impressive Edwardian country house.

She was quoted as saying that the refurbishment, structural and decorative had cost far more than she had anticipated but she could not regret saving this architectural rarity for the nation. Apparently, her health, which had suffered in the stuffy confines of a penthouse flat was improving already. There was a photograph. Lady Barwick looked very appealing; it was all most suitable.

****

On the floor above, Valerie was putting the finishing touches to her own toilet. She was excited.

It was a pity that she had confided in Robert. He had been against Sharow Cross from the start, but it was her life and they were her jewels. The girls wouldn't mind if they knew, Valerie persuaded herself. They had good, generous husbands of their own. They would have no need to inherit anything from her. No, Rozanne, Sandra and Victoria would never begrudge their mother a little pleasure in the closing years of her life.

The acquisition of Sharow Cross had been part reaction to Richard's death, part resentment of her father's perpetual nearness. The penthouse was really far too small for the two of them. It had never been intended as more than a pied-à-terre after the sale of Thorpe Underwood Hall.

Sharow Cross still had its superb wrought iron gates at either end of the carriage sweep. They were sufficient to daunt the encroachment of unwanted neighbours. In spite of its echoing reception chambers, Valerie insisted the house was manageable. There was a splendid staff flat, now occupied by Leonard who had come with a sheaf of references including one boasting a Royal signature. He had negotiated a very comfortable salary for himself on the strength of it, but that too, Valerie pointed out to Robert, was an investment. Leonard's experience and high standards would enable him to run the place alone, helped only by a couple of dailies.

Brushing heliotrope shadows over her eyelids, Valerie thought of Mr Esterházy. Terribly handsome, Priscilla said. He hadn't worked for many years apparently. There must be some money then, and what a name! Valerie couldn't find him in the Almanac de Goethe, but then they had probably stopped recording the English offshoots long ago. In reality, this mysterious friend of Priscilla's might be a prince, or a count at least. Nothing, in fact, Valerie convinced herself was more certain.

Phillip fell head over heels for Valerie. He quickly revealed a lifelong fascination with turn-of-the-century domestic architecture. A week of swotting in the British Museum Reading Room had provided him with an impressive quantity of information on the subject. She invited him up to Sharow Cross for the weekend before the evening was over.

Phillip was relieved, no doubt he could engineer an extension of the invitation. He had spent the whole of his next week's budget for food and incidentals on the suite and vintage champagne. Lady Barwick, Priscilla had told him, was a connoisseur. His tailor's bill for the new dinner jacket would have to be paid out of his precious little nest egg. Naturally, there were always expenses. Good friends did not come cheaply.

As a house guest, Phillip fulfilled the most exacting criteria. Collected from York Station in the cream Rolls by Leonard. (Phillip did not run a car), and arriving behind an enormous bouquet of gardenias, Phillip had already discovered how many servants his hostess kept.

These details, together with other nuggets had been finessed from Leonard with such sleight of hand, that the butler did not notice himself giving his mistress's secrets away. No, Lady Barwick kept no chauffeur now. Yes, there was a part-time gardener. No, Leonard was pleased to complain into Phillip's sympathetic ear, he had no parlourmaid to understudy his duties. The rough work of the house was done by dailies. Extra staff for entertaining and so forth, were hired as required.

Her Ladyship's old father, Leonard further volunteered, was a card. Not a bit of trouble either and played a demon hand of dominoes when he felt up to it. His heart was giving a spot of bother though. The old gentleman had been in and out of hospital lately. Not surprising at his age. And then, of course, her Ladyship wasn't what you'd call a well woman herself. Mind, she didn't give into it. Oh no, not her Ladyship. Always on the go she was. She ought to take things a lot easier than she did.

It was all moderately satisfactory, Phillip thought. A most comfortable set up. As regards his own behaviour, the situation called for a modicum of cosy helpfulness combined with well-timed grandeur. Accordingly, Phillip carried his own and Valerie's empty coffee cups back from the morning room to the kitchen, a gratifyingly long march ... but did nothing clumsy like offering to help set the table for dinner.

Phillip spun elegantly on his heels, looking wherever his attention was directed, placing and removing his pince nez with a refined flick of his large white hand. Concerning Valerie's references to cost, he made no comment, substituting instead some knowledgeable allusion to similar restoration projects in houses of national renown where, he managed to hint, he was a frequent and valued guest.

Upstairs in his hostess's bedroom, Phillip had no time to conduct more than the swiftest appraisal. He saw the oxygen tanks beside Valerie's bed and opening the dressing table drawer where he had been told he would find her inhaler, he saw a number of plush and leather jewel cases. Some were empty, their original contents in a safe somewhere in the house no doubt. Others contained wonderful things. There was money here, enough at any rate.

By now, past experience dictated, he should have been urged to stay on into the middle of the week. Valerie had said nothing. Eventually, Phillip rose from his armchair by the fire and begged his hostess's permission to retire in the courtliest fashion. He had, he said, to leave by the earliest train tomorrow.

An engagement in London prompted this abrupt departure. He hoped it was not inconvenient to the household.

Valerie was pleased but not moved to entreat Phillip to stay longer. She wanted time to think. He had not responded well to her hints about money. It was early days, of course, but then, mature people of the world like themselves did not mess about.

Rising herself, Valerie made a gracious speech about the pleasure Phillip's visit had given her. The Rolls, she said, would be at his disposal at eight o'clock in the morning. In view of that, they would have coffee and rolls together in the glassed-in veranda at half past seven. It was delightful there on midsummer mornings. They exchanged a light, brushing kiss.

Shocked at the coolness of his dismissal, Phillip went cursing up to bed. He never rose before nine as a rule. Valerie was no push over. Taking leave of Valerie in the morning, Phillip betrayed none of his resentment at going. He clicked his heels like the Prussian officers he had seen in so many films and stooped gracefully to reverence Valerie's fingertips with the touch of his lips. What diamonds! Why didn't she sell some of those instead of trying to batten on an elderly bachelor?

Finally, before taking his seat in the car, he turned and embraced her, squeezing her body briefly but passionately. He saw her pupils dilate a little. An unmistakeable sign, Phillip felt his speedy return to Sharow Cross, as something more than a weekend guest, was guaranteed.

In less than a year, a mutually-agreeable fiction had been established. Valerie could not do without the moral and emotional support of her beloved friend. For his part, Phillip was exhausted by all the travelling his growing intimacy with the household at Sharow Cross involved. The cost was crippling too, although this was not admitted.

Valerie was too cute for that, she had never previously married for love and she was too old to start now. Did she love Phillip? Not exactly, not in that way.

He was too poor, she had discovered, to start the pulses racing, but he was an ornament to Valerie's life at Sharow Cross. Phillip could be trusted in any company and he was a good listener, which was becoming increasingly important to her. Valerie had reached that stage of life when the need to unfold her entire history at frequent intervals, dwelling one day on a particular incident, and the next on another, was imperative.

They had talked, she and Phillip, of writing her memoirs. It was Phillip's own suggestion. And there he had struck a seam of pure gold. Valerie's vanity was the key. She had been known and loved by so many important people, Phillip flattered. Very important people. She herself was important. A significant bystander in life's most glittering courts. Who, Phillip enquired, was better equipped to chronicle the deeds and sayings of those titans whose confidence she had enjoyed?

Phillip had proposed himself in the role of resident editor and agent. He would deal with any correspondence from potential publishers; it would save the expense of a secretary. The competition for the manuscript would obviously be keen and as Phillip had so charmingly expressed it, Valerie's mind must be protected from all sordid contact with commercial negotiations during her task of creation.

Robert was more than satisfied. They all liked Phillip. Whenever he was at Sharow Cross, Valerie was happy, energetic and occupied. He would be a great addition in himself, and the incremental two thousand pounds per annum which he offered should keep the wolf from the door.

Privately, Phillip had been of the opinion that his informal services as editor and secretary should have been more than sufficient recompense for his keep. However, Valerie had been delicately adamant. She needed money, and if Phillip could produce nothing in the way of a lump sum, income would have to do instead. There was need.

Already, the Rolls was sometimes hired out for weddings. All very discreet, of course. The car would collect Phillip from the station on Friday evenings and then, whenever the hire company Valerie dealt with had a requirement for an extra wedding car on Saturday mornings, a man would come and collect it, leaving an old banger in its place for Valerie's use.

It was not what Phillip expected, not what he had a right to expect after all the loyalty he'd shown, but half a loaf was better than no bread. What was more, he'd had a very good proposal for the sub-letting of his bedsit. A junior diplomat attached to the Swedish legation. Sixty-five pounds a week for a year and unimpeachable guarantees over wear and tear. The Swedish Embassy would redecorate at the end of the tenancy. It wasn't to be missed. Phillip would be well in profit on forty pounds a week.

Content with their bargain, Phillip moved up to Yorkshire. He never told Valerie that he had let his flat, which would have compromised his dignity. A gentleman without a permanent residence of his own was in an invidious position. When he had to go down to London, he would stay at the Club. There would be a saving there too. He could allow his membership to lapse and take out country membership at reduced subscription.

****

Old Bobby's heart finally gave out. Attempts at resuscitation in a local hospital failed, somewhat to Valerie's relief. She and Robert were with him at the last. Bobby faced his end with the practical composure that had marked all his dealings in life and made him a popular man. His affairs were in order and his small estate, mainly in unit trusts, was left to Valerie. His last words to her were spoken out of pure affection, for once.

"Now then, Val, you've been a good daughter to me. Make sure you're a good mother to your son," he added gnomically. "And think on, yon Esterházy's a grand fellow and I'm glad you've met your match at last, but he'll take some watching, mind, don't you give an inch. What's Robert's is Robert's."

So, saying, Bobby closed his eyes majestically and fell into a sleep from which he did not plan to wake.

Valerie burst into a flood of inartistic tears. They were the most authentic she had ever shed other than those wept over the demise of a dog.

What could Daddy have meant about Phillip? They had always seemed such good friends.

Robert drove his mother back to Sharow Cross, also preoccupied with his grandfather's last utterance. The dear old chap had been confused. It was a wicked thing to have said about Phillip, whatever it was supposed to mean. But then, Bobby couldn't be held responsible.

Valerie had actually forgotten that Phillip knew all about heraldry. He was so well up on the jargon, too. She could always depend upon him. He was so intelligent about these things. Of course, he was an Esterházy, which made it perfectly natural. It had been so strange of Daddy to distrust him, most odd.

Dearest Val, he calculated, should be good for twenty thousand pounds at least, and that would be a modest enough return on his time. How much time was an open question. Meanwhile, he was philosophic. A man could stretch his legs at Sharow Cross. To Phillip, the future looked bright.

****

A month after the funeral, Valerie raised the alarm in the small hours of the morning. She could get no breath. No one could figure out later how it was, that with no oxygen in her lungs, she could have summoned Phillip. He slept on the far side of the house and his suite, although it had a telephone, had no house facility on it. An oversight. Leonard, on the other hand, had only a house telephone in his quarters. Nonetheless, it was Phillip who called an ambulance and alerted Robert to his mother's plight.

By the time Robert arrived at the gates, a blue-flashing, siren-screaming ambulance was halted there. There was little evidence of panic in Esterházy's demeanour.

Robert, caught up in a whirlwind of confused emotions, did not notice, why should he? Phillip was always calm, that was why he was so good for his mother.

The ambulance shot forward and halted before the veranda entrance. Men with a stretcher spilled from the back. A light at the top of the house showed. Leonard.

"Where is she, guv?"

The stretcher team did not wait for Phillip's answer but shouldered their way through the doors and spotting the staircase, galloped ahead, shouting for directions. Leonard in a checked dressing gown met them at the head of the stairs.

"You her hubby?" one of the men asked. "Come on sport, get a move on. Where's your old lady?"

Stunned by the error, Leonard indicated his mistress's bedroom door. Gathering his wits, he thrust his way in front of the stretcher men, barring their way. There were howls of exasperation, Leonard was rudely shoved aside.

Scandalised that impious hands should be laid on her Ladyship's person, Leonard lifted her from the bed himself. She was all but naked. Her face was blue grey. The men snatched her from the butler and bundling her into a red blanket, careered down the stairs leaving the stretcher abandoned. There were oxygen tanks in the ambulance.

"Come on, sir, if you're coming. She's almost gone ...."

Leaping in beside his mother, Robert felt her hand. It was warm still.

By the time Valerie reached the Harrogate District Hospital, her vital signs were faint. They gave no clue to what may have happened. Emphysema was emphysema, a death warrant with a limited stay of execution built in.

But when Phillip took his place in the row of plastic chairs in the casualty ward corridors alongside Robert, an impish nurse waggling her hips provocatively at the handsome gigolo type, tumbled to it when she saw his brown eyes smoulder back at her.

They saved Valerie that time.

Valerie had taken to leaving a pair of gloves on a console table just outside her bedroom door. A signal that she was not to be disturbed.

She had heard the Queen did it. Phillip had heard the same story. True or not, the gloves marked the end of a certain experiment.

The memoir, which was still at an early stage of preparation, would now provide all the stimulation Valerie needed. It was the last act; she knew it even better than Phillip who waited for his reward in reasonable patience.

In the meantime, three meals a day not counting afternoon tea, a four-course dinner every night, excellent claret, his shirts done for him, endless hot water, as many clean towels as he could drop on the bathroom floor and fresh-laundered bed linen every week, gave a fellow much to be thankful for. Darling Val, he was going to hate losing her.

CHAPTER TWENTY

A junior editor at Methuen's listened to Phillip's lengthy telephone description of both author and manuscript. She said Valerie's autobiography sounded most interesting, and yes, every manuscript submitted was considered for publication, though this could take up to twelve weeks. Perhaps Mr Esterházy would care to send in an outline of Lady Barwick's material and just three completed chapters to begin with. It certainly sounded intriguing. If Methuen's wanted to take it any further, they would be in touch. No, the safety of the manuscript could not be guaranteed. Lady Barwick must keep a copy. After all, the girl softened her stricture, it might be worth money, mightn't it?

Neither Phillip, Robert, nor Valerie herself knew that the very-newly-promoted secretary to whom Phillip had spoken was merely honouring a time-honoured maxim of the publishing trade. Never be too impatient with a trying author. He or she might become the best seller that gets published in years to come by a rival house. Unlikely, but just possible. The politeness of the publishing world was a matter of enlightened self-interest.

Valerie certainly found it harder than she had ever imagined. What to put in and what to leave out. How to arrange the material coherently. What points needed explanation, and which needed none, and her spelling. At first, she looked up every other word in a dictionary laboriously. But it was too slow, and she gave the dictionary up on Phillip's advice.

Phillip was quite invaluable. He knew how to caress a faltering ego and keep discouragement at bay. Equally important, he knew when to keep his mouth shut.

Reading with surprise that Valerie had been presented at court, although she was herself divorced at the time, and the second wife of her husband, Barwick, he repressed the question that rose to his lips. Had the way been smoothed with money? Was it conceivable that a corrupt courtier's palm had felt the touch of coin?

Curious as he was. Phillip said nothing. He and Valerie were two of a kind. Their minds could have been cast from the same mould. For both of them, truth was what you chose or stated it to be. A lie was not a lie until it was exposed. There were no bribes, only expenses.

Two desks stood in the library now, tucked into each of the two window embrasures. Author and editor were seated there and at work by half past ten every morning. Phillip cleaned through the previous day's grosser errors while Valerie hacked gamely through the rank growth of her memory. The rate of progress varied.

At each exasperated sigh, the dogs on the hearth rug looked up sympathetically. A Great Dane and a black Pekingese just like at Thimbleby, even the same names. Leonard tip-toed in from time to time, to mend the fire, with cups of coffee or to take the dogs for a walk. Her ladyship's fragile concentration was not to be disturbed. On a bad day, Valerie was heartily glad when luncheon was announced at fifteen minutes past one. Writing, even about oneself she remarked guilessly, was gruelling work.

In the household books. Valerie saw no sign of the surplus cash she had expected Phillip's rent to generate. It was difficult to understand where it was all going.

There were hidden costs. The electricity and gas bills, even allowing for an increase in charges, were up by a third. Phillip slept with his window healthily open but liked his room warm. He kept his gas fire on low all night, a fact of which Valerie was unaware. Phillip, always so exquisitely clean, took a hot shower in the morning and a bath before changing for dinner. Quite often, he had another just before bed. It helped him to sleep. And meanwhile, the washing machine in the back kitchen churned relentlessly.

Never mind, Valerie thought as she closed the books. It wouldn't last so very much longer. Just until the memoir was finished. There had been two night-time rushes to the hospital since the first one. Each time she had fought back, co-operating with whatever they wanted to do for her. Machinery, injections, drips ... determination. But it was nearly over. The money had run out.

****

Valerie's partially-completed memoir was seen by a number of publishers before it was mentioned in passing to Cyril Connolly. This Lady Barwick, he was told, might be able to assist him with his researches into the unsolved Earl of Erroll murder ... the Delves Broughton affair.

Cyril wanted to write a book about it, but the trail was growing cold. So many of those old Kenya hands were dead, in the last stages of senile dementia, or simply unwilling to talk. Approaches to Lady Delamere, formerly Diana Delves Broughton, had so far been politely rebuffed. She was now the richest woman in Kenya and seemingly, as unreachable as the stars, but somebody, somewhere, must know something.

Lady Barwick, if the space she had allotted to the subject in her otherwise unreadable screed was anything to go by, might supply some missing links in Cyril's chain. Why did he not go up and see her? True, her account was guarded and rather confusing, but she wrote as someone having inside knowledge. She hinted fairly strongly at membership of the Happy Valley crowd ... They had secrets those people. Perhaps Cyril could shake something loose.

Proposing himself for a visit to Sharow Cross, Connolly took a leaf out of Disraeli's book: "We authors, ma'am ..." That gentlemen had been accustomed to flatter Queen Victoria during his prime ministerial chats with the diary-scribbling monarch. Valerie responded well to considerate treatment of the same sort.

Reading Cyril's initial letter of approach, she felt herself to be in the thick of things again. Evidently, her manuscript was causing quite a stir in the publishing world. She was being taken seriously at the highest level.

Phillip shared the illusion. He was practically co-author of the book. He preened himself, and as such expected a share in the explosion of glory, which was poised to burst around Valerie's head, or so he thought. A substantial offer for the manuscript seemed daily more likely. No doubt Valerie would treat her editor fairly. Mr Connolly must certainly come; he advised Valerie who needed no urging. They must begin to think of making personal contacts in the publishing world. It was all part of being successful. Moreover, Phillip privately judged, Cyril Connolly would see that without his own scholarship, Valerie's story could never have been told. Soon the whole of London would know it. Phillip might accept some book-review work, he thought. Moderately well paid and not too taxing.

In a state of high excitement, Valerie replied at once to Cyril Connolly's letter. She would be delighted to see him. He must stay, of course. Her doors were always open to writers, musicians, artists and theatre people. All her life she had maintained the closest contacts with the arts. As for Cyril's charmingly diffident suggestion that she might fear his plundering her own material, Valerie reposed complete confidence in his professional probity. As a writer herself, she was very much aware of copyright law, but she went on, she was also an historian, and before petty personal considerations of profit, the truth must be served.

The meeting, when it happened, gave as much enjoyment to both parties as each had anticipated. Although lavishly entertained, Cyril was starved of information. Valerie talked at large and at length of her years in Kenya, but every loaded question of Cyril's was detonated in a puff of smoke.

Obfuscation, confusion, stonewalling, Valerie addressed every question with a frank, open countenance while her lips shaped evasions. Who did she think had murdered Lord Erroll? She had her own ideas. No, she couldn't say more. Had she actually been present in the Muthaiga Club on the night of the murder? Yes, she had already said so, hadn't she, surely, she had been.

And had she gone on to the Claremont Club later with Joss and Diana? Yes ... No. She couldn't quite remember now. Not at this distance. She would try to recall ... Yes! That was right. She had gone but her husband, Roddy had gone home.

It was the exact opposite of what had actually happened. But Cyril was not to know that. He made a note.

Valerie was happiest to answer questions about the people she knew. Especially the deceased. Times, places and dates. Connolly noted, seemed to make her restive. Nor would she state with any exactitude the intimacy of her relationship with the dramatis personae involved. Of course, she knew June Carberry. Everyone did. She was charming ... if a touch fat in those days, poor girl. And as for Diana Delves Broughton herself, Valerie knew her, naturally. Always marvellously well dressed ... her pearls were worth a fortune.

It was, Cyril decided, quite hopeless. Whatever Lady Barwick knew, she intended keeping it to herself. Either that or she was simply incapable of sticking to the point. An undisciplined mind. Returning to London the following day he looked over his notes and decided that Valerie knew absolutely nothing of value. It was even possible that her friendship with the significant players amounted to nothing more than a nodding acquaintance.

Later he had cause to revise that opinion somewhat.

Cyril Connolly went first, bequeathing his Erroll murder notebooks to James Fox. When his book, *White Mischief*, based on Cyril's researches came out, Lady Barwick was mentioned not at all. The contribution she had made concerning the night of the murder was puzzlingly attributed to somebody else and was all upside down. Even so, it was in direct contradiction to what Valerie wrote in her own memoir.

As for the rest, Cyril had never made any note of it. It was unsound, unsafe; lethal in fact. While Valerie and her son lived, that line of enquiry was blocked. James Fox knew nothing of Lady Barwick's input and Conolly, of course, was stone dead. Valerie was torn between relief and disappointment.

Valerie lived to see James Fox become a star author. She showed her copy of *White Mischief* to each of her increasingly-rare visitors. It was odd, wasn't it, she suddenly rapped out to one caller, that the murder weapon had never been found? And then for a moment she seemed disorientated before retreating into general effusions. The whole Happy Valley crowd were so much in vogue now ... *Echoes From My Heart* was the logical follow up. The public were hungry for any titbits they could get about people such as they had been. Forty years ago, now. Gods and goddesses gambolling in Elysian fields.

The memoir was finished. Altogether, it had taken the best part of two years. The costs had run into many hundreds of pounds. It was typed, retyped, amended, typed again to take account of various publishers' comments and finally the master copy was bound.

Valerie turned its pages in wonder every day. It had become more real to her than her own flesh and bones. The book, work of her hands and mind, was invested with the vitality she was losing hour by hour. They would never bury her now. The book would do her living for her in the future. The fact of physical death was reduced to an administrative detail. The sooner it was over and done with the better. It would be, she told herself, inconvenient if anything happened now. That would spoil the book. Make it untidy ... the goatskin covered boards were coffin bottom and lid. Valerie, all that she was and had wished to be, lay neatly arranged between the two.

****

In the last days, Valerie moved about the house slowly, clutching an inhaler. Every few minutes she put it to her face. She mounted the staircase by degrees. A few steps ... a rest ... inhalation ... and then she continued. She would allow no one to help her, resenting any notice taken, or comment made on these agonising journeys.

Robert offered to carry his mother upstairs once and was irritably repulsed. Proposing a home stair lift, Robert was scorned by both Valerie and Phillip. It would ruin the look of the hall. This wasn't a nursing home.

"The day I can't walk up my own bloody stairs," Valerie rasped, "you'll be signing my death certificate."

Phillip took Robert on one side and urged him to desist from any further attempts to interfere. Arguments were bad for his mother. She felt her dignity was at stake and that surely, was the paramount consideration.

Valerie still dressed every day and dressed again for dinner. It exhausted her, but she would do it. Putting clothes on and taking them off was an unshirkable duty. People might call. She went to the hairdressers twice a week. She was driven to the tiny back-street salon in Ripon by Leonard in the Rolls. The place was cheap, the girls respectful and had the knack of washing Lady Barwick's hair while her head remained virtually upright. The air passages to the few cubic centimetres of lung she had left now, must be left clear, she explained. She always slept sitting up these days.

Phillip was away in London, reletting his flat when they took Valerie to hospital for the last time. It was inconceivable, he reasoned, that Robert would evict him from the house if Valerie died before the lease expired. He could make a little more profit and then decide what to do with Valerie's legacy when it came. Her lawyer had come up to see her last week. An encouraging sign, although she seemed to have left things rather late, her lease on life was about up. Walking through Knightsbridge, Phillip encouraged a lump in his throat to grow, he never thought of himself as a cynical man.

On the second day of Phillip's absence, Leonard took her Ladyship's breakfast tray into her as usual at nine o'clock. He stood at the foot of her bed for a second, willing his eyes to make normality return. Lady Barwick in her satin peignoir, hair brushed and shining, lipstick on, but she wasn't there. In Valerie's place a malicious caricature was slumped.

The face was engorged like that of a hanged man, blue eyes staring from her skull. Asphyxiation. Her hand groped feebly for the oxygen mask dangling out of reach.

Leonard was openly weeping when the ambulance came. Robert arrived at the Harrogate District Hospital within moments of Valerie. There was a man carrying an oxygen tank at a run beside the racing trolley on which she lay. Robert too, broke into a run. His mother's face was two-thirds covered by the oxygen mask, but her eyes were open. She closed them when she saw Robert with a paper in his hand.

"We can't sign that," the flustered registrar said. "Our job is to save life."

"You must sign it," Robert insisted. "Or I take my mother away."

"How? She'd never make it out of the front gates. We've got to do a tracheotomy."

"No! Sign it, or she goes."

The young doctor scanned the paper and hastily initialled it with a biro. It was the only way of keeping the patient. The document devised and signed by Valerie Barwick stated that she must receive no treatment. Nothing but ordinary nursing care. No drugs, no surgical intervention. It was on that basis alone that she would submit to suffocation in their hospital.

"And the ward sister must sign it."

"For God's sake man. who does this bloody woman think she is?"

"She's my mother," Robert said simply. "And she must have what she wants, she always has."

There was no more argument. They put Valerie in a side ward to complete the process of drowning at leisure. Couldn't she be moved to a private room, Robert begged. His mother would hate the idea of a public ward, but the hospital administration set its face against that. Enough trouble had been caused. Lady Barwick was too ill to be moved.

Her dignity was of minor significance to them. Defeated, Robert sat beside the bed in the bleak little cell and held his mother's hand. Speech was impossible, an oxygen mask was strapped to her face.

Her three daughters had arrived: Rozanne, Sandra and Victoria.

Robert was glad to see them and Valerie's dulling eyes were welcoming. Making a supreme effort, Valerie tried to remove the oxygen mask from her face. Uncertainly, Robert rose to help her. She smiled at him. That immobilising smile of hers which froze everything caught in its beam like a security floodlight.

"You'll be so rich, my darling …"

Her voice trailed away. She took her final breath and seemed to sleep.

It was a week after the funeral when the postman delivered a registered letter to Sharow Cross. Leonard had taken the letter. Robert opened it in the freezing-cold library. Its content was depressing.

Apparently, Valerie had taken a thirty-thousand-pound loan from the bank using the house as security. She was behind with the interest repayments. The bank was threatening foreclosure. She had not left enough cash to pay for her own funeral.

Robert's laughter could be heard echoing through the house. After the will was read, Robert opened his mother's jewel safe to distribute the contents to his half-sisters, explaining that most of the pieces are only copies of items Valerie was forced to sell. Incredulous at first, his sisters later discover that this was true.

EPILOGUE

Valerie's will expressed a desire that her body be laid beside that of her 'one true husband', Sir Richard Barwick, in the family's Barwick mausoleum, in Sunderland. Accordingly, Robert approached the surviving members of the Barwick clan. His mother's request was denied. The mausoleum was full, they said. Privately and amongst themselves, they wondered why Mrs Walter Lancaster-Hey should imagine she had any rights over Barwick property. What breath-taking effrontery.

So, Valerie was interred in the Skelton vault beside her father's remains. The struggle to escape her roots, therefore, resulted in very graphic failure.

Her funeral was well attended. Many who came had no cause to remember Valerie with love but burying her was an act that seemed to require the force of numbers. It was as if death itself was but one more catastrophe she might easily overcome.

Valerie's children co-opted the services of a noteworthy clergyman to read the funeral oration in Ripon Cathedral. Canon Ford, who freelanced in these matters, was provided with a range of nattering facts from which to compose a portrait. The resulting pulpit performance caused a tremor of irritation in the pews. Who had this selfless paragon been, an ex-brother-in-law of Valerie's asked ... this woman, who through a lifetime of sorrow and sickness, had put her outstanding gifts of charm, breeding, influence, intelligence and worldly goods at the service of others? Had Valerie written the panegyric herself?

After the final, impersonal blessing, Valerie's polished mahogany coffin was loaded back into a shiny hearse and driven to the neglected, windswept cemetery in Sheffield with its commanding views.

Robert followed in weary procession with his half-sisters. Leonard went back to Sharow Cross to oversee preparations for the reception that would follow the interment. He would be ready with champagne when the first wave of hungry hunters rolled up. 'Mourners,' Robert corrected absently.

Phillip received nothing under Valerie's will. He was not even appointed her literary executor. Accepting his disappointment with professional calm, Phillip continued to reside at Sharow Cross with Robert and Leonard, until the house was eventually sold. Then he went to live in Cyprus in a rented apartment overlooking Kyrenla harbour.

She was his equal, a worthy opponent. Their score was love all.

Lady Pricilla Prescott died in London leaving a surprisingly tidy little estate. She had done very well out of introducing her friends to each other. She'd always felt guilty about Valerie's marriage to Walter Hey, but he'd offered a worthwhile 'charitable contribution' and Valerie had been warned. Phillip Bradburn (Esterházy), on the other hand had more than made up for things. He had been a complete success.

The purchaser of Sharow Cross converted it back into a nursing home. Leonard stayed on, cringing to the desecrating sound of saw and electric drill and took care of the dogs.

Diana, Lady Delamere, sometime Lady Broughton died in London a few years after Valerie. On her deathbed she admitted shooting the Earl of Erroll herself. Broughton changed his mind about giving Diana an income if she should ever marry anyone else. Erroll would not marry Diana without the money, so naturally she killed him. The insult was not to be borne.

The gun she used was one she found lying beside Roddy Ward's unconscious body in his wife's car on the Ngong Road. Diana had brought her own for the job, but Roddy's had seemed a better idea at the time. Poor, pathetic oaf. And, after all, they'd all get out of it somehow. Presumably little Valerie Ward had managed things quite cleverly, because they never did find the murder weapon. Diana disliked Valerie and had no idea what happened to her. There, dignity had cancelled out jealousy.

Robert too, died in April of 2017, leaving the entire manuscript in his will to his youngest half-sister Victoria. The title had been changed to *Hard Bargains*.

At the end of her memoir the question hangs in the air: what exactly did Valerie live for?

An obituary in *The Times* tells the world she lived for wild animals. One is left to reflect that perhaps she was one of them: a beautiful survivor until other predators came to fight over her bones.

END

Acknowledgments:

Huge thanks to Andy Gibney and Caroline Snelling and the team at 3P Publishing for all their help, support and guidance. I could not have done it without you!

Thank you to Debi Noone for initially helping me editing and proof-reading the book, amending the text accordingly and to Melissa who re-typed the entire book into a digital format.

To my two beautiful children Georgina and Ben for supporting me through the process and may they enjoy reading about their Grandma's incredible life story.

And finally, to all my friends for their words of encouragement in making this book possible.

Victoria Barwick (daughter of Valerie Barwick)